THE DRAWINGS OF
PAUL AND THOMAS SANDBY
AT WINDSOR CASTLE

PHAIDON PRESS

TWO LADIES SEATED UNDER A TREE

(Cat. No. 280)

THE DRAWINGS
OF
PAUL AND THOMAS
SANDBY
IN THE COLLECTION OF
HIS MAJESTY THE KING
AT WINDSOR CASTLE

BY

A. P. OPPÉ

MCMXLVII

OXFORD & LONDON

THE PHAIDON PRESS LTD

The reproductions in this Volume are from a new set
of photographs taken by Alfred Carlebach, F.R.P.S.

1947
MADE IN GREAT BRITAIN
PRINTED AT THE BAYNARD PRESS · LONDON

PREFACE

*T*HE DRAWINGS BY PAUL AND THOMAS SANDBY *in the Royal Library are to some extent familiar to the public through the exhibition of a selection at the entrance to the State Apartments, and they have been freely lent to represent the artists at exhibitions of British Art at home and abroad. Several were reproduced in colour to illustrate the 'History of Windsor Castle', by St. John Hope, and these plates, with some others, were issued separately as the 'Windsor Castle Series'. They have, however, in common with Paul Sandby's work generally, never been studied, William Sandby's book, published in 1892, being confined to biographical matter and quotation of references to the artists by previous writers.*

A summary list of the drawings at Windsor Castle is appended by William Sandby to his book. Reference to this and to the earlier Loan Exhibitions is only made when their mention of an identifiable drawing provides the first indication of its presence in the collection. A list of the landscape drawings, with descriptions and measurements, was drawn up before 1915 by Miss Heaton Smith, then an Assistant in the Royal Library, and a similar list, both of the landscape and figure studies, was made, independently, by Mr. A. C. Sewter, to whom this catalogue was entrusted until he joined the army. For the landscape drawings, especially those of Windsor, the order is that of the inventory, which was carefully prepared by the Royal Librarian on a topographic principle. Similar treatment was not found possible for the figure studies, largely because the arrangement of several, sometimes as many as nine, on the same mount fails to accord with either chronology, subject or material. No order, however, can be anything but a series of compromises, and it is hoped that the headings of the groups and the index will facilitate reference.

Grateful acknowledgment is due to H.R.H. The Princess Royal, the Duke of Buccleuch, the Hon. Sir Richard Molyneux and Capt. Bruce Ingram for permission to photograph and reproduce their drawings, to Sir Robert Witt, Capt. Brinsley Ford, Mr. I. A. Williams and many others for information and opportunity to study their collections, to Miss Clayton, late of the Victoria and Albert Museum, and to Dr. Westcott of the Science Museum for assistance in describing costumes and vehicles, and to the officials, past and present, of the British, Victoria and Albert, London and Soane Museums for special facilities to overcome, as far as possible, the limitations caused by the war and the succeeding period—limitations but for which this work would never have been undertaken. Mr. L. Goldscheider has given himself great trouble in preparing the presentation of complicated material. Above all I am indebted to the Royal Librarian and the staff of the Royal Library. Sir Owen Morshead has discussed every material point with infinite patience, and, indeed, enthusiasm, even when the investigation has led to the abandonment of a cherished legend. Mr. F. E. Parsons has kindly set me right on topographical details, and in one or two instances Mr. F. W. Barry's memory has supplied deficiencies in the documentation of individual drawings. Miss Scott-Elliot has given me, both before and after her appointment to the Royal Library, invaluable assistance in every way and at every stage of the compilation of this catalogue.

A. P. O.

TABLE OF CONTENTS

INTRODUCTION . . . . *Page* 1

CATALOGUE:

   I. Windsor: the Castle 19

   II. Windsor Great Park and vicinity 33

   III. The Duke of Cumberland's Campaigns . . 46

   IV. Richmond, Kew and London 48

   V. Miscellaneous designs and views 54

   VI. Subject and caricature drawings 56

   VII. Early figure studies and groups 57

   VIII. Interiors at Sandpit Gate and Windsor characters . 63

   IX. Women: full watercolour 65

   X. Women: red chalk 66

   XI. Man: red chalk 67

   XII. Women and children: pen, pencil and wash . . 67

   XIII. Men 73

   XIV. The Great Lodge, its owner and occupants . . 78

   XV. Portrait sketches at print sales 83

CONCORDANCE OF NUMBERS 86

PLATES

     LANDSCAPES: NOS. 1–72

     FIGURE STUDIES: NOS. 73–141

     COACHES, HORSES AND DOGS: NOS. 142–156

INDEX

INTRODUCTION

I

THE BROTHERS PAUL AND THOMAS SANDBY are the only artists whose drawings have been consistently acquired for the Royal Collection from the dates of their death. They owe this distinction to a long association with Windsor. The elder, Thomas, lived in the Park for a great part of his long life and was there employed in the lay-out of the Park, Forest and Virginia Water, and in various buildings for the Ranger, William Duke of Cumberland, and his successors. Paul, the younger, was a frequent visitor to, and perhaps collaborated with, his brother, and while there showed himself so close a student of the Forest that his son could speak of it in a memoir[1] written shortly after his death as, with Scotland and Wales, one of the great influences on his life and perhaps the chief of these. It is therefore fitting that the collection of their work in the Royal Library should be the finest in existence.

The collection owes more than a foundation to George IV when he was Prince of Wales at Carlton House. A complete series of Messrs. Colnaghi's invoices from 1799 to 1812 is preserved in the Royal Archives. Several drawings, mainly of military or Windsor subjects, 'by Sandby' which are mentioned in those of the earliest years most probably derived from the sale in July, 1799, of Thomas Sandby's property after his death in the previous year, and the fact that the sale was of his possessions and not of his 'remaining works' would account for the non-committal omission of a Christian name in the invoices. Besides the titles, the prices marked on the back and the pencilled inscriptions on the mounts in a handwriting which is clearly that of the firm identify several of the drawings with certainty as those entered in the invoices. Much more extensive purchases were made after Paul Sandby's death at the first sale, on May 2, 1811, and following days, of his remaining works. The lots bought for the Prince Regent at this sale by Colnaghi, either in their own name or under the name 'Shepperd', which was used for no other purpose, are not only marked in catalogues preserved in the Royal Library, but are also brought together in duplicate lists bound up with the catalogues and repeated in a general invoice from the firm, with the addition of the commission charged and interest. In several cases pencilled lot numbers still remain on the mounts of the drawings and identify them with certainty as those marked and priced in the catalogues and lists.

The watercolour landscapes bought at the sale of 1811 were 48 in number, about half being views of Windsor and the remainder mostly of London, including several of the Encampments of 1780. Five lots were returned, presumably because they were not connected with the Royal interests, but some of the drawings contained in them were bought separately later. A few cannot now be identified safely, but the bulk of the purchases remains intact and includes most of the large and most decorative watercolours by Paul Sandby in the Royal Collection. In addition, a series of twelve pencil sheets of Windsor views was bought in one lot and a volume containing 'ninety figures, mostly in the dresses of the middle of the last century', the only figure-studies included in this sale.

Sporadic purchases seem to have been made between 1812 and the end of the century, but as no register was kept it is not possible to date single acquisitions with any certainty. It is not even recorded when the 'Cumberland Papers', which included some drawings and prints, entered the Royal Library. The plan of Culloden and a large watercolour of a camp (No. 158), both by Thomas Sandby, were among these, and it is most probable that the long watercolours by him of Windsor Park and Forest (Nos. 111-115), dating from 1752, come from the same source and are

---

[1] *Monthly Magazine*. June 1st, 1811. p. 437, *reprinted Burlington Magazine*. LXXX. June 1946, p. 143.

five of the six recorded in eighteenth century guide-books as then hanging on the walls of Cumberland Lodge. By far the most important of later accessions occurred in 1876 when sixty-seven views by Paul Sandby of Windsor and Eton, which were collected by Sir Joseph Banks, were sold at Christies' by Sir W. Knatchbull, to whom they had descended. At this sale the then Royal Librarian, Richard (afterwards Sir Richard) Holmes, bought twelve in his own name; and since these do not cover the list of drawings from the Banks Collection stated to be in the Royal Library by William Sandby, who bought some lots at this sale for his own collection, it is probable that other drawings were acquired after the sale from the dealers (principally Hogarth) who had secured them. A few further lots were bought at this sale by William Seabrook, then Inspector of the Castle, after whose son-in-law's death some sixty years later they were acquired for the Royal Library, while still other drawings which can be traced to the Banks collection have been added during recent years by the present Librarian. In all, some twenty-three can be identified with complete or approximate certainty as deriving from this collection. Most of them have distinctive inscriptions on the backs of the mounts in a uniform handwriting which is probably Paul Sandby's own, while the mounts themselves are of an early type and quite different from those of the 1811 sale. A few have special labels which are found also with drawings from the Banks sale in other collections. Sir Joseph Banks' Collection was already celebrated in Sandby's lifetime and since it belongs to an earlier and more careful period than the drawings which were left unsold in Sandby's studio at his death, and was not framed but was preserved from the light in portfolios until the sale in 1876, it shows the artist at his best and the drawings from it have come to be regarded as more representative both of the artist and of the Windsor Collection even than those bought for the Prince Regent.

Another important accession was the purchase in 1930 at a nominal figure from Sir Francis Dyke Acland of the figure studies bought by Sir Thomas Dyke Acland in two[1] out of some twenty books included in the third sale of Paul Sandby's works on April 16-18, 1817. If William Sandby is correct the volume of ninety figure studies bought for the Prince Regent in 1811 had already been swollen to contain a hundred and thirty-four by 1892. Conceivably an addition may have been made in 1817, when the Earl of Yarmouth, who frequently acted for the Prince in such matters, bought four books, two of which were of the same type as those bought by Sir T. D. Acland. Of this, however, there is no evidence, nor, since all the drawings have been removed from their volumes and uniformly mounted in one series, is it possible now to distinguish between those which derive directly from the 1811 sale, and those which come from the later sale through Sir Thomas Dyke Acland or otherwise, except that in some cases mention by William Sandby in his book of 1892 shows that the drawing does not come from the Acland collection, and in a few cases a particular drawing is remembered as coming from that source. It is particularly unfortunate that the evidence of mounts and inscriptions, which has been so happily preserved for so many of the landscape drawings, is wanting in these, for in the vast majority of cases there is now no indication whence the descriptions were obtained which are now written on the modern mounts. In the comparatively few exceptions the names are written on the drawings themselves and apparently are in Paul Sandby's own hand. These are by no means reliable and perhaps always much later than the drawings. The rest are so often manifestly incorrect that it would have been an advantage to know what, if any, authority lies behind them. It is worthy of note that no inscriptions other than those occasionally on the face of the drawings themselves seem ever to have accompanied the collections of studies in the Soane,

---

[1] It is not clear whether the single volume purchased from Sir F. D. Acland incorporated both the books (lots 39 and 44) bought by his ancestor. For lot 44 see *infra* on No. 416; the other book does not seem to remain at Killerton where, by the kindness of Sir Richard and Lady Acland, I have searched for it in vain.

FIG. I. PORTRAIT OF PAUL SANDBY, C. 1760. BY FRANCIS COTES. (TATE GALLERY, LONDON)

the British, and the Victoria and Albert Museums. Since the volume purchased in 1811 contained the only figure studies included in the sale of that year, it is possible that it consisted of specially selected drawings to which Sandby himself or his son had affixed inscriptions. The market value of association was already recognized at that date.

II

IT WILL COME to many as a surprise and a disappointment that none of the drawings by the Sandbys in the Royal Collection can be traced back to George III, and that the best known and the most representative of the views of the Castle were only acquired in 1876, a whole century after they were executed. It is indeed possible, since there still remain several drawings of which the history cannot be ascertained, that some may yet be found to have been acquired by, or for, the King. Against this, however, is the fact that while the old inventories of the Library mention a volume of Paul Sandby's aquatints which remains there with its old press-mark and was probably formed about 1785, there is no trace in them or elsewhere of any drawings by either of the brothers. Nor were any included in the collection of Queen Charlotte which was sold in 1819. Her preference was for Gainsborough, twenty-two of whose compositions were in her sale together with some landscape drawings by other artists. The King's collection contained very few English drawings of any kind. With his patronage of West on a large scale, he aimed at encouraging English painters to higher objects, both in his and the artists' eyes, than topographic landscape. Moreover he was more interested in the re-conditioning of the Castle as a place of residence than in the record, however picturesque, of the untidy, to say the least, state into which it had fallen. Thomas Sandby certainly received marks of royal favour, if not as a draughtsman, but the tales of Paul Sandby's direct commissions from the King, lessons to the Queen and the princesses, and even lodgings in the Castle, are not corroborated by anything in the Royal collection except for some doubtful evidence of lessons given on one day to the infant princes[1]. Nor are they contained in any of the early notices or obituary memoirs, or in Angelo's gossiping account of the Royal instructors. They first appear in confessedly ill-informed articles some twenty or thirty years after the artist's death whence they were collected by William Sandby, and thus passed into common currency. Some notes, as far as possible from contemporary and confirmed sources, showing the brothers' relations with the Court and Windsor will serve to explain the comparative lateness of the appearance of their works in the Royal Collection.

The two brothers are said to have come to London from Nottingham in 1742, when Thomas was aged 21 and Paul 17. The elder was already a competent topographical draughtsman with a special bent for perspective. In London he entered the Drawing Office of the Tower, on the books of which he remained until nearly the end of his life, continuing to draw a salary of three shillings, later 3s. 6d., *per diem*, and, concurrently, a half-pay allowance of £91 5s. per annum 'on the old establish-ment'. No doubt through this employment he became attached to the Commander-in-Chief, William Duke of Cumberland, and, as his drawings show, he accompanied the Duke in his cam-paigns in Scotland and the Netherlands. According to W. Sandby he was already with the Duke at Dettingen (1743), and Anthony Pasquin says that he signalised himself by being the first to bring from Fort William the news of the Pretender's landing in 1745. In the next year the Duke became Ranger of Windsor Forest and began at his own expense the formation of Virginia Water and other works in Windsor Great Park, partly, it is said, to give employment to the men who had served under him. It is not clear from what date and in what capacity Thomas Sandby became associated with this work. It has been assumed, apparently from Anthony Pasquin[2], that the Duke appointed him Deputy Ranger immediately upon his own appointment. There is no doubt but

---

[1] cf. on cat. No. 79.   [2] *Lives of the Royal Academicians* (1794), p. 141. His wording is very loose.

FIGS. 2-3. PORTRAITS OF PAUL SANDBY (1789) AND THOMAS SANDBY (1792). BY SIR WILLIAM BEECHEY. (NATIONAL PORTRAIT GALLERY, LONDON)

that he was known as Deputy Ranger, and his residence as the Deputy Ranger's Lodge, towards the end of his life, but as the office appears not to have been official it is not recorded, as are other similar posts, in contemporary calendars. In these and in other official contexts he is invariably described as Draughtsman to the Duke, and he did not hold even this post until 1750. In its account of the Duke's household the *Court and City Register* of 1750 explicitly describes the post as vacant, but in the next year assigns Thomas Sandby to it at a salary of £100. In 1764 Mr. (Andrew) Ford, who had been the Duke's Clerk of the Stables and from 1750 his Steward at Windsor, died and was succeeded by Thomas Sandby. If the inscription now placed under the portrait sketch of Ford in the Royal Collection (No. 213) is correct in calling him the Deputy Ranger, the two offices may have been combined and this would fix the date of Thomas Sandby's appointment as December, 1764. Unfortunately, even if as is probable the main part of the inscription derives from Paul Sandby, the detail regarding the Deputy Rangership cannot be accepted as reliable, and from the death of William Duke of Cumberland, in 1765, and the appointment of Prince Henry Frederick as his successor, the statement in the *Court and City Register* of the ducal household is given in a different form and all relevant information is wanting.

Thomas Sandby's second wife, Elizabeth Venables, whom he married in 1753, was appointed Sempstress and Laundress to the Duke at a salary of £300 per annum in 1757, and held the post until 1760. This may have been a London appointment, for her predecessor had been the wife of the Duke's house-steward, and though Sandby must have spent a great part of his time at Windsor and his eldest child was born at the end of 1758 at Cranbourne, he is now known[1] to have had a

[1]Much fresh information regarding the movements of the Sandbys in London, in connection with their invitation to an evening meeting for figure drawing at Poultney Street in 1753 (cf. *infra* p.13) will shortly be published in an article by E. H. Ramsden in the *Burlington Magazine*, to whom I am much indebted for its early communication.

considerable house in Poultney Street in 1752 and 1753, and according to William Sandby all his remaining children were born in London, most of them in Great Marlborough Street, where he lived from 1761 to 1765. From that date his address is uniformly given as Windsor Great Park, and it is possible that the permanent change of residence may have followed his succession to Ford and the assumption of the Rangership by Henry Frederick Duke of Cumberland. In any case he was still more heavily engaged on works in the Park. The restoration of Virginia Water after a great flood in 1768 seems to have taken many years, and it was not till about 1780 that Sandby's stone bridge, which replaced the wooden bridge (pl. 120), was spoken of as being under erection.

Association with the Dukes of Cumberland was by no means tantamount to Royal favour. During the whole period from 1757 to his death, when he was principally occupied with Windsor, William Duke of Cumberland was prominently in opposition. His successor was brought into even greater disfavour by his marriage with Anne Horton in 1766. In 1771 he was actually banished the Court, and with him the Duke of Gloucester, for whose wife the Countess of Waldegrave, the cause of his disgrace, Thomas Sandby built or enlarged a house on St. Leonard's Hill. As if to mark the connection, Thomas Sandby chose as godparents for his two youngest children the Duke of Cumberland himself, his Duchess and the Countess of Waldegrave. This was, however, in 1770 and 1773, some years before George III took up his residence at Windsor; nor is it likely that the unacceptability of the two Royal Dukes at the Court extended to so comparatively humble a follower as their Steward. At any rate, in 1777, Thomas Sandby, who had been appointed Professor of Architecture in the Royal Academy, became one of the two architects on the Board of Works, which was then a part of the Royal Household, and he was promoted Master Carpenter in 1780. He lost the office shortly afterwards when the Board was remodelled, but it was perhaps in this capacity that he designed or supervised the erection of a new reredos in St. George's Chapel, which was projected in 1782, though payments were only made from 1785 to 1787. This is the only work recorded as having been executed for the King by him at Windsor, and if he submitted the designs which are now in the Royal Library for an extension of the Queen Elizabeth Gallery (Nos. 66-68) and for a booth on Ascot race-course (No. 148) they were not carried out. The King entrusted both new buildings and restorations to Chambers and Wyatt, not to him. On the other hand, he may well have been, with his friends Dr. Lind and Sir William Herschell, in the circle of Windsor residents, outside the Court, whom the King treated with his easy familiarity, though the tales told by W. Sandby of impromptu luncheon-parties at the Deputy Ranger's lodge accord badly with other accounts of Court etiquette at this date. It is certain, too, that he continued as Deputy Ranger when the King took the management of the Park into his own hands on the death, in 1791, of Henry Frederick, Duke of Cumberland and the appointment of Prince William of Gloucester as Ranger, for twice[1] in 1794 and always after his death in 1798, Sandby is spoken of with that title. Indeed, in the absence of previous references to the title it is conceivable that he only obtained it on the Duke's death. In his obituary notice in the *Gentleman's Magazine*, written, it is said, by Richard Cumberland, stress is laid upon his long services to the King and on his rectitude in not having turned his various offices to profit. The notice ends with a somewhat whining appeal for a Royal recompense to Thomas's numerous family. This was met, according to William Sandby, by a grant from the Royal Bounty of £100 a year to his second daughter Harriott, who had married in 1786 Thomas Paul, the son of Paul Sandby. She and her husband had lived with her father until his death, and the bounty may have been, at least in part, a compensation for the loss of that residence, against which the younger Sandby had unsuccessfully protested[2].

---

[1]Anthony Pasquin, *l.c.*: Farington, *Diary* (unpubd.) March 12th, 1794.   [2]Undated correspondence in the Whitley memoranda at the British Museum.

III

LIKE HIS ELDER brother, Paul Sandby is said to have entered the Drawing Office of the Tower soon after arriving in London, but unlike him he was not fortunate enough to hold a post which gave him a sinecure salary for the rest of his life. From 1746, when Thomas was with the Duke of Cumberland in the Low Countries, Paul was engaged under Colonel David Watson on the Survey of the Highlands, and he appears to have remained in Scotland for the next four or five years, practising, besides his military work, figure sketching and landscape drawing, and becoming proficient in etching with the assistance, as his son tells us, of an engraver Bell in Edinburgh. One of his larger Scottish views is inscribed 'P. Sandby delint et sculp, Windsor, Aug. 1751', and the same date with 'Old Windsor' is placed upon the drawing pinned on the wall of a room at Sandpit Gate at Windsor Great Park, which is shown in the sketch (No. 247) in this collection. This, and the publication in that year in London of his larger Scottish views, would seem to indicate that he had left Scotland, although one of his Scottish etchings of a figure subject contains the date 1752. In any case there are numerous indications that during the next few years he was frequently at Windsor where he lived with his brother. It is clear from a reminiscent remark in one of his later letters that he never had a house of his own in the country, whether at Windsor or elsewhere. Writing to his friend Gandon, the architect, towards the end of his life, and congratulating him on his hobby of planting, he speaks as though his only experience of that activity was that 'in the juvenile part of my life I put a few acorns in my brother's garden at Windsor and found great pleasure in viewing the opening buds'.

In London Paul Sandby was sufficiently prominent to become a protagonist in the movement about 1753 towards the formation of an Academy, the precursor of the Society of Artists, and eventually the Royal Academy. He signalised himself in this cause by a series of caricatures which were directed against Hogarth because of his hostility to this movement among the artists and constant denunciations of the Old Masters. The caricatures are also much concerned with the '*Analysis of Beauty*', which appeared in that year. Ten years later, when Sandby had gained fame among the *cognoscenti* by the exhibition at the newly formed Society of Artists of a large historical

FIG. 4. WINDSOR CASTLE FROM THE SOUTH. (THE DUKE OF BUCCLEUCH, DRUMLANRIG)

landscape illustrating Gray's ode *The Bard*, he produced another series of caricatures. These were, again, partly directed against Hogarth, but now he was denounced because of his acceptance of a pension from the Court as Serjeant Painter, and this was only an incidental feature in a general attack on the Earl of Bute, the favourite of the young King, and Augusta Princess of Wales, the King's mother. In one of these prints, the drawing for which has found its way into the Royal Library (No. 204), the Duke of Cumberland is called upon, with his nephew Edward Augustus, Duke of York, to repeat his victory of Culloden and drive the Scots faction from the field. Hogarth in person, and the Earl of Bute symbolically, are introduced into the plate. Were it possible to accept a statement in the *British Topography* of 1780, that Lord Bute bought more than a hundred of Paul Sandby's drawings of Windsor, the statesman might be supposed to have devised a simple method of reconciling an opponent, but there is no confirmation either at the time or now of any such collection, and the statement is probably due to a confusion of names.

Paul Sandby exhibited a view of Windsor for the first time at the fourth exhibition of the Society of Artists in 1763. He sent four in 1765 and two each in 1767 and 1768. The latter date occurs on the only signed drawing of early date in the Royal Collection (No. 60) and on other Windsor views elsewhere. Some of the subjects of his small series of Windsor Views, dated 1780, are stated on the prints themselves to have been drawn in 1769 and 1770, and one of the large 'North Terraces' in 1771. In 1774 he exhibited two views of the Terrace at the Academy, and in 1775 two stained drawings of the Castle, which, as the latter were accompanied by apparently similar views of Warwick Castle, may have been the subjects of his large aquatints of 1776. No further views of Windsor were exhibited until 1793. The years from about 1760 to 1771 may therefore be taken as the period of Sandby's principal artistic activity in and around the Castle itself. This was before the date when the King took up his residence there. The large aquatints were not dedicated to him but to the Duke of Montagu, the Governor of the Castle, who is expressly mentioned in the son's memoir as his father's patron. Seven drawings of the Castle and an imitation or copy by F. Powell, which are in the possession of the Duke of Buccleuch at Drumlanrig, were probably among the pictures which were expressly mentioned as being left on the Duke of Montagu's death to his daughter and heiress, the Duchess of Buccleuch. By the courtesy of the Duke two of them (Figs. 4 and 5) are reproduced here, partly because of this association and partly because they show views of the Castle which are not represented in the Royal Library. A pair of the 'North Terrace' are subsequent to the aquatints, but of the others which are uniform with those reproduced here, two are almost exact duplicates of drawings in the Royal Library which derive from the Banks Collection, and there are other indications that those drawings derive from the decade 1760-1770. The date 1752 constantly given to that collection (e.g., W. Sandby p. 215) is due to a misinterpretation of a loose statement in one of the earliest biographical notices[1]. At that date Sir Joseph Banks was only nine years old.

In 1778, when George III took up his residence at Windsor, an event occurred which was not likely to improve the feelings of the artist towards his sovereign. Sandby, who had been appointed ten years before drawing master at Woolwich, through the influence of the Duke of Grafton, obtained a promise, through the same patronage, of the reversion to the Surveyorship of the King's Pictures on the death of the occupant, George Knapton. According to Horace Walpole, who tells the story, both in one of his letters[2] and in his Journal, this post was not in the King's gift, though it was in the Royal Household, but the King, in his resentment against the Duke of Grafton, refused to ratify the Lord Chamberlain's appointment of Sandby and insisted that the post should be filled by Richard

---

[1]*European Magazine*. Aug. 1796, p. 75, followed by the obituary notice, *Gent's Mag.*, Dec. 1809, p. 1177.   [2]To Mason Jan. 17, 1778 (*ed.* Toynbee, x.177). *Last Journals* (1910), ii.113.

FIG. 5. WINDSOR CASTLE FROM THE SOUTH-EAST. (THE DUKE OF BUCCLEUCH, DRUMLANRIG)

Dalton, the Keeper of the Royal Medals and Drawings. The Surveyorship of the King's Pictures has no special reference to Windsor, nor does Walpole represent the King's action as due to hostility to Sandby, who, as a Royal Academician, was one among, in Walpole's phrase, 'his artists', but Sandby was scarcely likely to accept his disappointment philosophically. When the post again fell vacant, on Dalton's death in 1791, and Benjamin West was appointed his successor, Sandby again had hopes of obtaining it. Farington, in an unpublished passage, tells on November 30th, 1804, of an occasion when 'Sandby spoke with asperity of West having prevented his being appointed Inspector of Pictures'. He seems to relate this conversation as explaining to some extent the persistent animosity against West shown by Sandby throughout the troubles and intrigues of the Royal Academy during these years. Since West was out of favour with the King, the members who formed the opposition to him might be regarded as the King's party, and Sandby's adherence to it as evidence of some personal connection. But there is no indication throughout all Farington's full accounts of the negotiations that Sandby either claimed to have any special status with the King or was put forward, or appealed to, on any occasion for that reason. On the contrary, on one occasion[1] when during Wyatt's temporary presidency Sandby, as Deputy President (no doubt as senior member), went to Windsor with Yenn and Richards the Secretary on formal business, it was reported that the King signed the papers 'but did not, as when Mr. West went, enter into conversation'. There must have been other occasions when the King received Sandby as a member of the Council, and perhaps it was on one of these that he showed some insight into Sandby's character by remarking to him, as Sandby himself relates in a letter to Gandon, that he 'was never idle but could turn his hand to anything'. The remark may equally well have been made at some informal meeting with the artist and his brother, and if there is nothing to show that the King looked upon him with any special favour the words may be taken as evidence that their relations were at any rate friendly, and Sandby's quotation of them that at the end of his life he had ceased to feel any resentment.

[1]Farington, *Diary*, May 11th, 1806 (*ed.* Greig, iii. 227).

It is good to know also from Farington's unpublished Diary[1] that when West returned to the Chair at the Academy Sandby sought a reconciliation, both with him and with Farington himself. He called on West in January, 1807, to express his satisfaction at his being re-elected. 'I told 'em', said he, 'that nothing else would do'. Farington adds that West spoke prudently to him, telling him that they two were of the small number of original members remaining, and it would be for them to do whatever they could for the benefit of an institution which his Majesty had so much favoured. In December of the same year, Farington records[2] shaking hands with Sandby and having lively conversation with him for the first time in many years.

The absence of exhibited views of Windsor during the years following 1775 need not be taken as a sign that Paul Sandby no longer visited there, and, indeed, these must have been the years when J. T. Smith, who claims to have known both brothers well, says that he found them when he was a young man busily occupied with works in the Great Park. Moreover, it is to the years following 1770 that Paul Sandby's son attributes his father's best and most careful studies of trees which he associates with Windsor Park. From 1786 he had another reason for visiting Windsor, for his son then settled there with his wife in his father-in-law, Thomas Sandby's, house. It is perhaps to distinguish his own drawings from his son's that the sketches of the Wood-yard, which was near the Deputy Ranger's Lodge, are so consistently signed and dated in 1792. In the next year Sandby exhibited at the Royal Academy two views of the Wood-yard and another of the Great Park, and of his four subsequent Windsor views there, in 1802, 1806 and 1807, three were of the Park or Forest. The fourth (1802) was a view on the Terrace, but it was Sandby's constant habit to repeat subjects which had been sketched long before, and as his late dated drawings of the Terrace and other views show he did not even trouble to bring the features, such as young trees, up to date. Probably with the alterations in the Castle he hoped that his views of it would have an interest on antiquarian grounds. In general, his art had by this time become out of date and the account of his last years in Farington's unpublished Diary does not make happy reading. He records on July 26th, 1794, that when Sandby exhibited his drawings in the auction room where Sir Joshua Reynolds' works were to be sold, they were admired but did not sell. Three years later he is found complaining that his failing eyesight prevented him from executing small objects[3]. For long before his death he is said to have had no commissions nor pupils, and he was burdened by his family. He expended nearly £3,000 on his eldest son, who obtained a commission in the Army and died in 1793, and he gave £1 per week to his daughter, whose conduct, according to Farington in 1810, was so profligate that no one would support her application for assistance from the Royal Academy. With only £60 from the funds and a pension of £50 from Woolwich when his son succeeded him there as drawing master, he sought, in 1799, a reversion to the Librarianship of the Royal Academy for the sake of the salary, and in 1801 and again in 1808 he was reported to be likely to come upon that body for help. In fact, though Farington does not note it, he was granted[4], in 1808, a pension of £60 from the funds of the Royal Academy. In the next year he died, and if Farington shows him in his Diary to have been a factious and irritable opponent of himself and Benjamin West, and apparently with little influence in the Academy Councils, he left with others the memory of a good friend and a whimsical and kindly member of society.

---

[1]February 2nd, 1807.   [2]December 10th, 1807 (ed. Greig, iv. 234).   [3]April 4th, 1797. This may have contributed, with the high price of glass for drawings, as noted by Farington on January 13th, 1807, to Sandby devoting himself to oil-painting at that time. The further references to the Diary are to November 4th, 1793, December 4th and 6th, 1797, December 10th, 1799, July 11th, 1801, January 21st, 1808, July 18th, 1810, and October 31st, 1816.
[4]Whitley, *Art in England (1800-1820)*, p.139.

THOMAS SANDBY is a somewhat enigmatic figure. As an artist he probably preferred to be regarded as an amateur, at any rate from the time when he set up as an architect. It was in this capacity that he was appointed in 1759 on the committee of the newly formed Society of Artists—losing his seat in a year, no doubt because he only attended once—and his only exhibits with them were a design and a plan 'for a country seat for a nobleman' in 1767. He was also an architect member of the Royal Academy and their Professor of Architecture from its inception. Of his drawings exhibited there, which only numbered nine, all were of buildings; and three were designs or elevations and three others illustrations for his lectures. As a member of the more lucrative and respected profession he is designated as Esquire in the catalogue of the exhibition of 1767 and in other lists at a time when, before the establishment of the Royal Academy, painters were not entitled to that distinction. This, together with his importance as a general factotum to the Duke of Cumberland, no doubt justified him after the practice of the time in placing his name alone and without qualification on works which were partly executed with the help of merely professional hands, including his brother's.

Both in architecture and in drawing he was self-taught. Apart from his own acute observation and interest in perspective, this means that his sole instruction came through engravings. As a military draughtsman he would be exercised in both capacities, and his models were such elaborate and detailed prints as those of Leclerc, himself originally a military draughtsman, in which the foreground figures belong to the conventions of painting, the buildings are often almost an architect's elevation while the background passes insensibly from landscape to plan. The artistry consisted in the neatness and the amount of detail shown; in one of his drawings of this period in another collection, a Flemish villa seen from the front, everything, outline, ornaments, brickwork, foliage and foreground is treated with an elaboration of spidery penwork. The drawings in this collection, showing the Duke of Cumberland's campaigns in Scotland and the Netherlands, may properly be classed as landscapes, though their purpose was primarily to record the disposition of the troops in their encampments, the principal objects in their neighbourhood and the configuration of the surrounding country. The occurrence of foreground figures which were shared in common with his brother suggests that even at this date he made use of his brother's skill when the drawings came to be worked up, but the incidents in the middle distance and the delicacy with which the towns and churches in the background are drawn are no doubt Thomas Sandby's own.

The five large panoramas of Windsor in this collection, two dated in 1752 and probably executed for William Duke of Cumberland at the Ranger's Lodge, although not military, show the same laborious fidelity and want of picturesque intention except in details. In all but one, figures are entirely absent, as in early prints after his drawings, and in the exception they are by his brother. The vast expanses delineated and the lack of any prominent object as centre of interest give them a certain breadth, and time, which has robbed them of some original strength of colour, has given them an unity of tone. Some idea of their original colour may be obtained from the more finished of the drawings of the Great Lodge in this collection (No. 100) which was included in Paul Sandby's collection and thereby saved from the exposure and rough usage which seem to have been the inevitable consequence of Thomas Sandby's predilection for wide views on vast sheets of paper. In this drawing, though the limits of the architect's palette do not seem to have been exceeded, the dainty colouring sets off the precision, amounting to exquisiteness, of the ruled lines of the house which forms the central incident. In coloured copies of the engraved series to which this subject belongs, the strong black line of the engraving shows through bright colouring in gouache and perhaps also indicates the effect that was originally intended.

In some of the drawings and engravings of this series which were intended to show the improvements carried out for the Duke of Cumberland, the landscape gardener replaces the architect, and in the views from Somerset House Gardens where the assistance or example of Paul Sandby is to be presumed, the obvious imitation of Canaletto secured an element of picturesqueness. In other drawings such as those of Somerset House itself the architecture is paramount. As much as possible is shown of the buildings, which are often in full elevation, and they possess the attractiveness of sharp contour, precise line, flat wash, fine detail and strong shadow which marks the immensely skilled architectural drawings of the 18th century, and makes them on the whole more effective and pleasant decoration than the bulk of contemporary landscape. Constantly repeated details of cornice or brickwork, varying only with their perspective, have the effect of fine embroidery, as had in his landscapes the seemingly endless repetition of fine ruled lines in a fence, or the innumerable faint contours of the distant hills. There are no accidents nor dispositions of a purely picturesque type, but details such as scaffolding are worked out with clean rectangular precision and virtuosity of perspective. These qualities are summed up in Thomas Sandby's *magnum opus*, the series of drawings for an extension of Somerset House and a Bridge of Magnificence, of which one example exists in the Royal Library and several others at the British and Victoria and Albert Museums. Here the grandeur of the paper architect's imagination is joined to the painstaking labour of the ex-military draughtsman. We have his own word for it that the drawings were never intended to be carried out, but it would seem that in designing them the conceivability of construction was never overlooked. Extravagant and superhuman as these mighty vaults and terraces may be, they are never fantastic or theatrical as were the imaginary constructions of the Bibbiena or Piranesi. The decorative draughtsman as such never takes the lead. The halls and façades are imposing because they are heavy and pompous, while for embellishment they depend on the constant repetition of simple ornamental detail.

Two characteristics of Thomas Sandby, his inability to finish his drawings and his reliance on others for his figures, appear forcibly in the comparatively few drawings by him in the Royal collection, and are confirmed by documentary evidence. The frequency of unfinished repetitions with some parts fully elaborated and others left blank suggests either idleness or an amateurish diffidence which caused him to discontinue his work and then to repeat it on another sheet of paper without progressing beyond the point that he had reached before. The blank spaces were perhaps left to be supplied by his brother with figures, or if these were introduced by himself they are feebly and clumsily executed, showing, even where the originals are not forthcoming, that they are crudely copied. Their joint work on a drawing is attested by Paul Sandby's own inscription on the back of the view of Virginia Water (No. 120), and his inability to bring his drawings to completion is confessed by Thomas Sandby himself in one of his lectures. Even after delivering his lectures for twenty years he had to express his regret that he had not been able to complete all the drawings with which he wished to illustrate his Bridge of Magnificence. Both characteristics are proclaimed in a letter and notes by Horace Walpole. Writing to Mason on June 16th, 1781, Walpole, who was a friend of both brothers, says that he could never prevail on Thomas to finish his fine view of the gallery at Strawberry Hill. When it was exhibited at the Royal Academy in the following year Walpole noted in his catalogue[1] that the pictures had been put in by Paul Sandby, and the carpets, chairs and table by Edward Edwards.

It is, however, possible that this estimate of Thomas Sandby, formed from such remnants of his work as are now available, does not do him full justice. While in his work at Windsor he seems to

---

[1]Whitley. *Artists and Their Friends in England, 1700-1799.* ii.395.

have had recourse whenever possible to the ruler and compasses he himself advised his students to make drawings by the unaided eye, and there are many small pencil sketches by him of architecture which have all the daintiness of his finished work. He also spoke in his lectures of the value to an architect of figure drawing, and in 1753 Paul and others met at his house for that purpose. There are, too, larger drawings of architecture executed with considerable freedom. Indeed, if the attributions to Thomas Sandby in the extra-illustrated copy of Pennant's *London* bequeathed to the British Museum by Thomas Crowle could be accepted as authoritative, one drawing in that volume would place him on an altogether different plane. It would show him, when working freely by the eye, to have possessed a sense of massiveness and grandeur which he all but suppressed when he tidied up his sketches into finished productions. Unfortunately there is no indication to whom these attributions are due, and at least two of the best drawings in the volume, though attributed to Thomas Sandby, are shown by a print to be by Paul. Moreover, even the two vast drawings of Somerset House and its gardens, which would seem both in merits and defects to be eminently the work of Thomas, are attributed to Paul by J. T. Smith[1], who should have known, since he was intimate with the brothers, and not only had the volume under his charge at the British Museum but had actually contributed his own drawings to it when it was being formed by Crowle. The two brothers were constantly confused, and it would be natural to attribute all mainly architectural drawings to Thomas while those with landscapes and figures would be given to Paul; but it remains possible that it is not owing to a mere confusion of memory or in jotting down a conversation in a diary that Farington records[2] on March 29th, 1807, West as remarking 'that a style of drawing had been practised in this country such as had not been seen in any other, and that with Thomas Sandby it originated'. If the claims of the two brothers should ever become the playground of art critics as have those of other pairs, a little perverted ingenuity only would be needed to contend that the greater part of Paul Sandby's drawings of Windsor, including all the best, is really the unacknowledged work of his elder brother.

v

WHETHER SOME OF the most delicate detail in Thomas Sandby's finished landscapes is the work of Paul or, as is more probable, the elder led the way, and each spurred the other on in a common field, the earliest of the younger's drawings in the Royal collection, apart from portrait studies, shows that he soon acquired far the greater facility. The little drawing of the grounds of Heriot's Hospital, Edinburgh (No. 219) is only incidentally a landscape; the interest is mainly in the groups of figures which crowd the foreground and middle distance, and show an ease in their disposal and minuteness in execution which recall the gouache drawings of Blarenbergh. Paul Sandby produced more important landscapes, some of which he engraved and published on his return to London in 1751; and in at least one watercolour of Edinburgh, dated 1751, which made a brief appearance in the market in the darkest days of 1941, even greater crowds of neatly drawn figures had for their background the Rock and Castle of Edinburgh drawn with as much delicacy as the Heriot's Hospital, and coloured with the gay pinks and blues with which the distances are sweetened in the landscapes of both brothers.

During his stay in Scotland Paul Sandby devoted much attention to etching. Some of his small landscapes purport to have been etched on the spot in September, 1750. In these and in the landscape compositions of the next decade in London, he exercised himself in a microscopic minuteness of touch which surpassed even his brother's neatness in architectural detail. He also seems in his early years to have had some intention of qualifying as a figure and portrait draughtsman. Among

---

[1]*Book for a Rainy Day* (1845), p.287.   [2]*ed.* Greig, iv.106.

the portrait studies for which the Royal collection is outstanding, some must date from his very earliest days in Edinburgh. Clumsy and awkward, largely drawn in heavy black, they are the honest efforts of a more or less untaught beginner, but in their very woodenness they show a tendency, which is rare in English art and unfortunately was not maintained by Sandby, to see objects solidly in the round. At the same time they show a real interest in the lighting of the figure and surrounding objects, frequently that produced by artificial light. This study was continued in London, for a drawing[1] recently given to the London Museum shows Paul Sandby as painter, and Thomas as poet, inviting their friends to an evening meeting in Poultney Street for the study of *chiaroscuro* in drawing from one of their number posing as a model. This interest in lighting, now the gentle sunlight of an English summer, is still more evident in the altogether charming interiors of a house at Sandpit Gate (Nos. 245-250), where it is accompanied by complete ease in drawing and a simple elegance and homely truth of figure which, had they been sustained, would have placed Sandby in the forefront of English figure draughtsmen. The date, 1754, placed on one of them may be merely a retrospective approximation, but these drawings must date from this decade, as must the figure studies and groups used in the drawings of Somerset House Gardens and the engravings of Windsor Great Park (also dated 1754) either in Thomas Sandby's name or in Paul's own. In the drawings mainly in red or black chalk which seem to begin at the end of the period in Edinburgh, there is a preciosity of attitude which is due in part to the foppish artificiality of the moment, but also to the effort to give animation where the power of draughtsmanship by itself was not sufficient to give life. Where, however, colour is employed, its variety and richness and the delicacy of the contour and modelling are quite sufficient to give vitality. These qualities persist and even increase in the portrait-drawings which seem to date from the '60s. The few drawings on the same scale in the Royal collection which can be dated later than, say, 1775 by the costume or other indications, are more summary and careless, though some of the thumb-nail portraits dating from at least 1786 show that he could still work in his finer manner; and while they still show ease and fluency they have not the strength of draughtsmanship which would compensate for the loss of precision and elegance.

The exact counterpart of the finer portrait drawings is to be found in the best landscapes from the Banks Collection. They are not a uniform series, but vary considerably in size and degree of finish, and while most are in pure watercolour, several are in gouache. Farington in his Diary recorded (December 12, 1793) that accuracy of drawing seemed to be a principal recommendation to Sir Joseph, but while this virtue is certainly possessed by these drawings they also display much more. They show the same simple and faithful observation, patient delineation, tender colouring, and exquisite contour as the best among the portrait studies. However minute the detail, and frequently it is positively microscopic, the effect remains broad, and however neat and precise the contour it is never pronounced. The old description of Sandby's earlier landscape as being completely drawn with the pen and merely washed with colour, with the result that even if the tints disappeared the drawing would be quite intelligible, is no more true of these drawings than of many other contemporary works. The colouring, with its infinite gradations, is an essential part, in fact it is almost the whole, of the drawing. In the best of them the greys do not show as a uniform shadow tint, but are varied with blue and pink to accord with the general scheme. The soft lines merely define the contours and it is quite indifferent whether they are drawn with pen, pencil or brush. It is true that there is no naturalism in the later sense, that the tone is kept low and the effect at first sight somewhat flat and two-dimensional; in a word that the scheme is conventional. But naturalism is

[1] cf. note on p.5 *supra*. Possibly some of the figure studies Nos. 322 *et seq.* may have been drawn at these meetings.

no more demanded here than it would be in Hollar, from whom the convention is directly or indirectly descended, or from the seventeenth-century portrait miniatures of which these drawings are the perfect counterpart. As in them, there are no strong effects of light and shade, but the even illumination of mid-day; and, as in them, with their lack of strong *chiaroscuro* and of decorative design the chief virtue disappears when the colour fades. Photography or reproduction largely fails to convey their effect, and the damage suffered by exposure can be observed even in such of the Banks drawings in the Royal Library as were framed before they entered it. It is very noticeable in one of the drawings bought by Mr. Seagrave at the Banks sale, which, when purchased after his death, was ceded to Eton as a view of the College. After some 70 years of exposure it has become so drab a piece of mere interesting topography as to have raised doubts whether it is really by Paul Sandby. When, however, the drawings have been preserved from the light and retain their freshness as, it is hoped, will long continue to be their fortune at Windsor, the finest of them exhibit a consummate welding of intimate observation with complete mastery of a perfected convention. In such drawings as the 'View of the Store Tower from Castle Hill' (No. 19) or 'The Governor of the Poor Knights Tower' (No. 30), and, still more, in the extensive 'General View' (No. 37), and the 'View of the Seat near the Terrace' (No. 51) the limpid, even light and the tender colouring aptly suggest the cool atmosphere of the Thames Valley, and the somewhat haphazard disposition of the features with their casual and frequently amusing details is that of the great castle which has grown up during the centuries without conscious architectural design.

Two drawings which were used in gouaches of the Banks series, the 'Black Rod' (No. 40) and the large 'Devil's Tower' (No. 39), perhaps also the sepia drawing for the Henry VIII Gate (No. 27), show that at any rate in his preliminary sketches Sandby already worked in a large and free manner which is in complete contrast to the neat style of the Banks drawings. Developments from this manner appear to mark his second period. The change may have been partly due to his excursions into Wales about 1770, where a broader style fitted better with a wilder landscape, or to his experiments in aquatinting, about 1775, which helped him to achieve bolder effects of light and shade than he had obtained by engraving. Certainly, some of the earlier Welsh aquatints are much more powerful in effect than anything in drawing by him, at any rate in its present preservation. The new manner is to be seen in a generally looser and broader brushwork, and in a more liquid atmosphere under floating cloud, but principally in a new treatment of trees. His son dates his finest studies of trees to this decade, and though he is referring more particularly to increased care in drawing with the pencil the structure of trunks and branches, this was accompanied by looser brushwork and broader repetition of tints in the foliage, which gave it mass and amplitude as well as light. In general the movement was for naturalism. As his son says, 'he aimed at giving his drawings the appearance of nature as seen in a camera obscura with truth in the reflected lights, clearness in shadows and aerial tint and keeping in the distances and skies.'

The change can be observed in the drawings of Windsor in the Royal Library (e.g. Nos. 22 and 84) of which earlier examples in the Banks series exist elsewhere. Necessarily the grafting of a new manner on drawings which were conceived in another convention produces an unsatisfactory result, though with a larger scale there is sometimes a more dramatic effect and, to the end, as in some of the drawings of the North Terrace looking West, there remain happy vestiges such as the distant view over the Thames Valley which persist from the early inspiration. For fresh subjects in the new manner Sandby turned from the Castle to the Forest. Drawings of these are naturally fewer in the Royal Library, for their topographic reference is so slight that, as in the cases of Nos. 86 and 87, they might equally well be entitled 'Forest' or 'Woodland Scenes' just as his more heroic Welsh views tend to merge into compositions after the manner of Marco Ricci or Richard Wilson. In a later example, No. 97, though inscribed by Sandby himself 'Windsor Forest', and in the enormous undescribed gouache, No. 149, the landscape background merely sets off Sandby's at once distressingly faithful and fantastically exaggerated representation of contorted trunks and branches. Here he recalls on one hand the engravings of scenes from Tasso which he had produced in collaboration with a mysterious J. Collins and the harlequin engraver Ned Rooker, and anticipates on the other the early work of Cornelius Varley and Samuel Palmer. He was not always so romantic. In a simpler style the trunks and foliage of the View from Bishopsgate (No. 86) provide a massive frame for the distant Castle, which is as far removed from the theatre as from the thin and stiff fringe of trees through which are seen many of the buildings of his early drawings. In another large view of Bishopsgate (No. 106) and in the Woodyard (No. 96), dated 1792, light and air are introduced as the principal feature. The raw material for such drawings is to be found in the sketches of the Woodyard from different points of view (Nos. 91-94) and in the still more casual notes of the same place and of Hyde Park (Nos. 95 and 185(a)) in which there are so few features and so little effect that the artist's intention in making the sketch is scarcely revealed. In his representations of actual scenes as opposed to his ideal compositions, Sandby looked upon everything, buildings, trees, animals or men, as of equal interest, and if he did not succeed in his later period as he had in his earlier and as did the painters of the next generation, in casting them into truly pictorial form, the fault lies in an interest which was too lively to be selective and not in any lack of regard for, or appreciation of, nature.

With the looser and more naturalistic treatment of landscape and buildings there came more emphasis on, and vigour in, the figures. This is in accordance with the whole trend of fashion and of painting in the period and comparable to Gainsborough's abandonment of delicious manikins for more fluent and florid forms. Of the two puppets who fit so completely into the diaphanous dream world of the 'View of the seat near the Terrace' (No. 51), the lady persists into the aquatint of the North Terrace looking West, but she is overwhelmed there by the coarser, almost caricatured figures which replace the equally dainty personages of the Banks version of that view (Fig. 6). These in their turn give way to more active but also more awkward and lumpy groups in later versions of the same scene. It is noticeable that in the effort to give life to the less attractive companion subject, the North Terrace looking East, the figures are invariably made more grotesque and exaggerated in their antics. Sandby's monochrome drawings of the Town Gate (No. 27) and 5th of November (No. 36) show that he had a quite adequate power of sketching human figures in action, but when elaborated the attempt to give them vigour only makes them appear more wooden. This is in part the consequence of his method of tracing, reversing and combining independent sketches and then introducing them into his landscapes. They are not fused into the scene; at best they are as casually dotted about it as are the trees or houses. Even so they were from the first markedly superior to those of the topographic prints or drawings by his predecessors; and in the drawings of the Encampments in Hyde Park, where the landscape is summarily and perfunctorily treated with very little topographic interest, and still more in the prints of the same subjects, in which the figures and incidents occupy nearly the whole scene, they are so successful that these subjects have been singled out by no less a critic than Laurence Binyon as perhaps Sandby's chief claim to consideration.

In these drawings of the Hyde Park Encampments Sandby has often been claimed to have opened the way to Rowlandson, as, it may be added, he did also in his colouring and landscape. In his aquatints of Wales, as has also been duly recognized, he gave more than a hint for Turner's 'Liber'. His would-be heroic compositions, by means of which he at one time gave hope that he would become an English Claude, mark the end rather than the beginning of an epoch, but both his acceptance of nature in its simplicity and his delight in her more fantastic appearances led the way to the artists of the next generation. Indeed, with a range embracing heroic composition on one hand and political squib on the other, and a scale reaching from stage scenery at Wynnstay and wall painting at Drakelow to microscopic etchings and trade cards, there is scarcely a direction in which Sandby's influence was not felt. Whether or not he was himself the initiator, he was certainly the prolific vehicle of dissemination. As such he was surpassed and replaced even during his lifetime. Farington wrote[1] of him in 1811, 'I could not but sensibly feel the great difference between his works and those of artists who now practise in water colours. His drawings so divided in parts, so scattered in effect—detail prevailing over general effect'. This is a long way from Gainsborough's praise of him, in a letter to Lord Hardwicke[2], as the 'only man of genius', who has painted 'real views from Nature in this country.' The next period found him wanting in poetry, meaning, perhaps, that he lacked the vignette-like elegance and facile prettiness which marked the 'Keepsake' age. No doubt, too, his earlier work had faded or had been swamped by late and careless repetitions and jaded impressions of his prints. But he was by no means the only English artist whose younger and more conscientious work, in a convention which he insensibly adapted while he was mastering it, is more satisfactory than his later, more facile and more showy adventures; and because of his very simplicity of vision and naïf, slightly whimsical interest in details of life, light and form, the best of his drawings of Windsor and its Castle, and his intimate studies of his friends and neighbours, have a sure place, if not among the most imposing, at any rate among the most genuine and charming, achievements of English art.

---

[1] May 2nd, 1811 (*ed.* Greig, vi. 266).   [2] Whitley, *Thomas Gainsborough* (1915), p. 358. Undated, about 1762.

CATALOGUE

I. WINDSOR: THE CASTLE

1. The North Terrace, looking West, showing the West end of Queen Elizabeth's Gallery, Winchester Tower, the Canons' houses, Clewer church and the Thames Valley to the hills beyond Maidenhead.

Pencil, with border, 16.75 × 23.25 cm. (6⅝ × 9⅛ in.) *No. 14523.*

Inscribed in pencil, below, 'Windsor Terrace, W. 1777'. The same arrangement, also abbreviated at the top, but with different figures (see on No. 242), as on the gouache from the Banks Collection (1876 Sale, lot 12) belonging to the Hon. Sir Richard Molyneux (Fig. 6).

One of a series of 12 (now 13) small pencil drawings of favourite Windsor subjects, uniform in size and manner and mounted alike on sheets of grey paper. The numerals 3-20/12 in pencil which still remain on the mount of No. 17 identify them with certainty as Lot 20 on the 3rd day of the first Paul Sandby Sale at Christie's, May 2nd-4th, 1811, 'Twelve sketches in pencil fixed, views of Windsor Castle in 1777', Bt. Colnaghi (for the Prince of Wales), £5 7s. 6d.

Each of the drawings is inscribed at the foot with the subject, in a small pencil hand which occurs also on several other of Paul Sandby's drawings and studies and may be accepted as his own. Several of them have also the date 1777 at the end of the inscription, but as such inscriptions on other studies are evidently retrospective, this cannot safely be taken as indicating the date of their execution. Much less can they be regarded as the original pencil drawings 'made on the spot' from which the many enlargements and repetitions of the subjects were derived. A comparison

FIG. 6. THE NORTH TERRACE LOOKING WEST. (HON. SIR RICHARD MOLYNEUX)

of No. 23 with the corresponding watercolour drawing is enough to prove this. Moreover the drawing of the architecture is mechanical and insensitive, the ruler has been used as much as possible, and has even left its traces between windows, both horizontally and vertically, when they are in the same alignment. The figures, on the other hand, are freely drawn and, as a rule, the lines of the buildings, etc., can be discerned through them. Probably the group forms the first stage towards a projected series of small repetitions of Windsor views which was never carried out. Two of them are identical, including the figures, with outline etchings of approximately the same size which formed part of a small Windsor set of 1780, some from drawings of 1769. These are most commonly found with colouring by hand and were reissued as aquatints by T. Palser, 1812. The architecture may be partly the preparatory work of assistants.

A puzzling feature of these drawings is the pencil mark approximating to a capital 'F' which is found, with the inscriptions, on two of them, this and No. 17. This mark occurs on other drawings, mostly in pencil or chalk, in this and other collections, most frequently among the studies by the Sandbys in the Soane and the Victoria and Albert Museums. Since this set of twelve passed direct from Paul Sandby's family to the Prince Regent's collection, the presence of the mark on some of them proves that it is connected with Sandby; and, except perhaps for two drawings among those acquired by the Victoria and Albert Museum in 1901, every drawing bearing this mark that I have so far seen is either certainly his work or his brother's, or, if anonymous or otherwise attributed, may be confidently given to one or other of them (cf. on No. 272). A large and indisputable 'F' on the grey mount of No. 17 seems to show that although the small mark on the drawings themselves is sometimes so ambiguous that it might be taken for an E as cryptic as that of Delphi, or for a combination of T with F signifying Thomas fecit, or of P with l, as occasionally in Paul Sandby's signature, it is really the sixth letter of the alphabet, whatever that may indicate. It is identical, too, with the 'F' of 'F.A.S.', where both occur on a portrait sketch of Francis Grose, belonging to Mr. I. A. Williams, whether that drawing is by Sandby or another. A plausible explanation that it refers to the 'fixed' of the auction description is strongly supported by its constant use on the pencil drawings only in the volume of Thomas Sandby's small studies in the Soane Museum but elsewhere does not fit either its merely occasional occurrence or the medium of some drawings.

2. The same, with some different figures; sunset sky.

Pencil and watercolour, 31.5 × 43 cm. (12⅜ × 16⅞ in.) *No. 14524.*

Reprod. *Connoisseur*, XCII, p. 6.

Paul Sandby exhibited a 'View on the North Side of the Terrace at Windsor' at the Spring Gardens exhibition, 1766 (No. 146); 'The Terrace of Windsor Looking Westward', at the R.A., 1774 (No. 259), and 'A View on Windsor Terrace' at the R.A., 1802 (No. 601). Two 'high finished tinted drawings' of the subject, both 'looking West', were bought by 'Shepperd' for George IV as Prince of Wales at the P. Sandby sale in 1811 (first day, Lot 88, £2 10s., and Lot 96 £3 3s.) which might be this, No. 3 or No. 4, since all three have the mount of this sale; but there appears to be a recent dealer's cypher at the back of the mount of this.

While, except for one group of figures, this drawing is identical with the preceding, one of the two promenaders in the foreground is wearing the Windsor uniform which was only introduced in 1778 (cf. O. F. Morshead, *Connoisseur*, May, 1935,) and the boy with the large dog has a costume of still later date. Compared with the early drawings, the workmanship of this is deliberately loose and free and there is no pen outline, but there is still care and precision in the details of figure and distance.

3. The same; from within the embrasure of the terrace, slightly farther to the East, showing the arch leading to the courtyard.

Pencil and pen and watercolour, with gouache. Two figures unfinished, 36.5 × 53.5 cm. (14⅜ × 21⅛ in.) *No. 14527.*
PLATE 2

The mount lettered 'A View from Windsor Terrace looking Westward'.

Perhaps Lot 88 or 96 on the First Day of the 1811 Sale (see on No. 2).

Exhib. R.A. (British Art), 1934, No. 593 (909). Reprod. *Souvenir*, p. 78. *Windsor Castle Series* A.

Topographically intermediate between the last two drawings and Nos. 4 and 5, etc., this shows more of the castle than the former and the promenade of the terrace is at an angle; in the latter the angle is still steeper and more of the castle and embrasure is shown. In date it would appear to be as late as No. 5, for most of the figures are the same; or even later, since two women in the mid distance who are common to both, appear here only as a shadowy beginning in white body colour. On the other hand, the action of the woman with the children in the right foreground in this drawing shows less variation than does No. 5 from a prototype which is also used in No. 161. The drawing and colouring are careless, but the detail is lively, both in figures and landscape. There is much pencil work, and the houses in the town below are outlined with pen.

4. The same from a point still more to the East, showing more of the embrasure.

Watercolour with touches of gouache in the figures, 34.75 × 53 cm. (13⅝ × 20⅞ in.) *No. 14525.*

Perhaps Lot 88 or 96 on the first day of the 1811 Sale (see on No. 2).

The same landscape as in the aquatint of Sept. 1st, 1776 (initialled and dated 1771), the following drawing and the gouache dated 1800 at the Victoria and Albert Museum (D. 1832-1904), but with fewer figures. A seat which in the two latter is against the castle wall is transposed to the parapet, right, where, by an afterthought, it is occupied by a solitary officer. Earlier examples are in the collection of H.R.H. the Princess Royal (Borenius 429, 14¾ × 21 in., pendant dated 1768) and at the Victoria and Albert Museum (P. 7, 1945. 18¼ × 24¼ in., damaged and restored)

5. The same, with more figures, sunset sky.

Gouache, 62.5 × 86.9 cm. (24⅝ × 34¼ in.) *No. 14526.*

Exhib. Burlington F. A. Club, 1871, No. 228a.

No. 809 in the Inventory of Pictures in the Lord Chamberlain's Department, and there stated to have been removed from a stretcher and remounted in the Royal Library 28th July, 1870. It may therefore be identified safely with Lot 70 on the third day of the Paul Sandby sale, 1811: 'A large highly finished view of Windsor Castle from the North Terrace, looking West, painted in body colour on canvas, framed and glazed'. Bt. 'Shepperd', for the Prince of Wales, £31 10s. od.

Though the view is different from No. 3 and almost identical with No. 4, the aquatint of 1776, etc., the figures remain much the same as in the former. The two ladies on the extreme right of No. 3 are omitted, and the action of the remaining group in that corner is more scattered and lively. The awkward file of soldiers to the left of No. 3 is omitted and a seat, much as in the example of 1800 at the Victoria and Albert Museum, still more awkwardly introduced in their place. Another boy with a dog is brought in and the raven of the aquatint of 1776 makes a surprising reappearance in much the same position. Costume and execution are alike late, scarcely before 1800. Several of the figures are clearly superimposed.

7. The North Terrace, looking East.

Pencil, 16.25 × 23.5 cm. (6⅜ × 9¼ in.) *No. 14529.*
PLATE 3
Inscribed in pencil, below, 'Star Chamber Wr Castle 1777'. (See on No. 1.)
Reprod. St. John Hope, *Windsor Castle* 1913, pl. CXXII.
The use of the ruler is most conspicuous in this drawing. The figures, superimposed on the drawing as usual, are lively and careful; those in miniature engaged on the scaffolding being especially noticeable. The scaffolding cannot be connected with James Wyatt's replacement of the Wren windows by Gothic, for that work was not begun before 1800 (Hope, *op. cit.*, p. 348).

FIG. 7. THE NORTH TERRACE LOOKING EAST. (H.R.H. THE PRINCESS ROYAL)

6. The same, the West end only, showing Winchester Tower and Canons' houses, with a view of the Thames valley. Two pairs of figures.

Pen and watercolour, traces of pencil, 15.4 × 19.1 cm. (6 × 7½ in.)
PLATE 4 *No. 14528.*

Bought locally, May 6, 1925, with Nos. 61 and 72.

Miniature manner, moderately neat, lines ruled, the architecture precise and the figures superimposed. Perhaps from a series of small drawings such as No. 14 and No. 82.

A still smaller version is at the British Museum (L.B. 18 [a]) in pencil on green prepared paper, the figures the same, but the view from a slightly different angle.

8. After Paul Sandby.
The same from further West, showing the West end of Queen Elizabeth's Gallery with the lantern window.

Watercolour, 25.9 × 45 cm. (11⅝ × 17¾ in.) *No. 14530.*
Paul Sandby exhibited 'The Terrace of Windsor looking Eastward' at the Royal Academy, 1774 (No. 260), and published an aquatint of the subject on Sept. 1st, 1776. The present drawing is a copy of poor quality from the latter with some careless omissions, of which the principal is that of a dog in the foreground. Without the dog, the gesture of the child is meaningless. The version in the British Museum (L.B. 12) is almost equally indifferent. Better examples are in the collections of H.R.H. the Princess Royal (Fig. 7. Cf. Borenius, *Cat.* 430, 14¾ × 21 in., dated 1768) and of the

Duke of Buccleuch ($19\frac{5}{8}\times23\frac{3}{4}$ in. pendant dated 1778). A reduced version or copy, 12.1 × 17.5 cm., possibly by M. A. Rooker for an intended engraving (cf. on No. 116) is on p. 34 of the album 'Drawings of Windsor Castle' in the Royal Library.

9. After Paul Sandby.

The same abbreviated.

Pen and watercolour over slight pencil, 13.5 × 20.2 cm. ($5\frac{1}{4}\times$ 8 in.) *No. 14532.*

A copy or a concoction, both landscape and figures imperfectly understood.

10. The same, 1803, from the West end of the Terrace; the Round Tower visible on the right above the trees.

Gouache, 38.8 × 53.3 cm. ($15\frac{1}{4}\times21$ in.) *No. 14531.*

Signed: P. Sandby, R.A., 1803.   W. Sandby, p. 215.
A more comprehensive view than the preceding, some of the costume brought up to date.

11. The West approach to the Norman Gate; the Magazine Tower on the left, the Deputy Governor's House and Garden and the mound of the Round Tower to the right.

Pencil, 16.5 × 23.7 cm. ($6\frac{1}{2}\times9\frac{3}{8}$ in.) *No. 14533.*

Inscribed: 'Windsor. End of Picture Gallery, etc., 1777'.
The date apparently in another hand (see on No. 1).
Identical with the etching 'View taken from the Guardroom at Windsor', undated, but apparently forming part of the small Windsor series of 1780.

12. The same, from nearer the gate.

Pencil and watercolour. Touches of gouache in the figure. A border left around the drawing. 23.5 × 34.7 cm. ($9\frac{1}{4}\times13\frac{3}{4}$in.)
PLATE 5
                                                        No. 14534.

Inscribed in pencil at the back of the mount in (?) the artist's hand, 'West Entrance (into) the Great Court'.

According to W. Sandby, p. 215 from the Banks Collection, in which case it was probably Lot 5, 'West Entrance to the Great Court'. Bt. Hogarth, £2 15s.

Reprod. St. John Hope: *op. cit.* pl. L. (colour). *Windsor Castle Series B.*

The architecture, some of which is drawn with the ruler, is careful: the foliage, formalised on the left, and apparently unfinished on the right, is careless. The figure of a woman with a wooden leg, carrying a basket, has evidently been added as an afterthought.

13. The same, with the Deputy Governor's house from the Moat Garden.

Pencil and watercolour, some gouache in the figure, within black border, 37.2 × 51 cm. ($14\frac{5}{8}\times20\frac{3}{4}$ in.) *No. 14535.*
PLATE 6

Without inscription, but possibly Banks Sale, 1876, Lot 20, 'View of the Housekeeper's Apartments and Garden', bt. Seabrook, £4 10s. William Seabrook was Inspector of Windsor Castle, 1862-83, and may have transferred this drawing to the Royal Library, but, as is shown by the V.R. mark and mention by W. Sandby (p. 215), it was not among those bought from his family in 1925 (see on Nos.

61 and 72). Another example with different figures and foreground is in the collection of H.R.H. the Princess Royal at Harewood (Borenius, No. 427).

Darker and heavier than the generality of the Banks drawings, but with the same precision of detail and careful drawing of the figure and dog.

The apartments of the Housekeeper at Windsor Castle were in the circular tower on the right of the Norman Gate. They now form the kitchen of the residence known as Norman Tower at the foot of the Round Tower. They were described by Lady Mary Coke in a letter of Oct. 26th, 1764, to Lady Strafford (*Letters and Journals* [1889], Vol. 1, p. 16), when the post of Housekeeper was vacant on the death of Mrs. Handysyde, as 'one of the prettiest apartments I ever saw'. The appointment was held from 1764 to 1800 by Lady Mary Churchill, for whom see on No. 290.

14. View through the Norman Gate, looking West towards Winchester Tower.

Pen and watercolour, 17.5 × 23.5 cm. ($6\frac{7}{8}\times9\frac{1}{4}$ in.) *No. 14536.*
PLATE 16

Inscribed at the back of the mount in pencil, 'Gate Way under the Library Windsor P. (or T.) Sandby', apparently in an old hand; and again in pen, reading 'P. Sandby'. An erased inscription apparently reading 'By Thos Sandby' on the face of the mount and the dealer's number and cypher price for a pair on the back of this and No. 82 identify them as two drawings purchased in 1910 from Messrs. Leggatt.

Almost identical with the etching in the small Windsor Series 'Under Queen Elizabeth's Picture Gallery', by Paul Sandby, 1780, but without the figures. 'Library' in the old inscription must be a prophetic error for 'gallery'. There was no library in the Queen Elizabeth's Gallery till about 1835.

15. The Round Tower, North-east View, from within the Entrance to the Great Court.

Pencil, 16.3 × 23.7 cm. ($6\frac{3}{8}\times9\frac{3}{8}$ in.) *No. 14537.*

Inscribed: 'From the Lower Court. Windsor Castle, 1777'. (See on No. 1.) The careless error in the description is highly suggestive of Paul Sandby himself.

16. The King's Gate and Entrance to the South Terrace, showing the moat and the bridge connecting the King's or Rubbish Gate with Castle Hill. Seen from the East just within the Home Park.

Pen, pencil and watercolour, with gilt border, 19.7 × 26.7 cm. ($7\frac{3}{4}\times10\frac{1}{2}$ in.) *No. 14538.*
PLATE 8

Inscribed on the back of the mount in pencil in the (?) artist's hand, 'Windsor. View of, etc.', as given above.

Banks Sale, 1876, Lot 10, bt. Holmes, £4 15s.

Reprod.: St. John Hope: *op. cit.* pl. xxv
Windsor Castle Series B (both in colour).

This and the following 8 drawings show the South side of the Castle and Castle Hill as they were before the erection in 1778 of Queen's Lodge, as a residence for George III, opposite the South Terrace. This involved the destruction of part of the South Terrace, the filling in of the moat and, in order to give the Lodge a view of the Round Tower, the lowering of the curtain wall between the Edward III and Henry III Towers. The whole of this part of the Castle was rehandled by Wyatville when he formed the St. George's and George IV Gates and closed the old Rubbish Gate.

Queen's Lodge, the Town (Queen Elizabeth's) Gate and the houses on Castle Hill were all demolished. The smaller gate into the Park was also removed, but Castle Hill remained a thoroughfare, being continued across the Home Park by a public footway. (T. E. Harwood, *Windsor, Old and New*, 1929, p. 94.)

The views are arranged in the order of a descent down Castle Hill from East to West.

17. The (old) South Entrance, showing the Moat Bridge and Rubbish Gate as in the preceding drawing but from the West.

Pencil, 16.5 × 23.5 cm. (6½ × 9¼ in.) No. 14539.
PLATE 7

With the auctioneer's Lot number and, separately, a large 'F' on the grey paper mount (see on No. 1).

Inscribed 'South Entrance to Windsor Castle 1777.'

The horse-kicking incident recurs in No. 172, one of the Encampments in Hyde Park, 1780, and appears to derive from a sketch, in pencil and brown wash, in an album at the British Museum (L.B. 138, No. 72.)

18. The Store [now Henry III's] Tower, from the top of Castle Hill.

Pencil, 16.2 × 12 cm. (6⅜ × 4¾ in.) No. 14540.
PLATE 9

Inscribed, within the drawing, 'Windsor' (see on No. 1).

Originally with No. 46 on one sheet, having on the reverse a slight sketch of No. 46 extended by a wall on the right.

The carpet-beating incident connects this with the preceding drawing and may be based on a rapid pen-over-pencil note in the Victoria and Albert Museum (D. 157-1901) showing several figures engaged in this task.

19. The same, extended leftwards to include the Governor of the Military Knights' Tower and nearer buildings on Castle Hill; a water cart and a chairmender with a girl and other figures in the foreground.

Pencil, pen and watercolour with touches of Chinese white, within toned margin, 22.3 × 36 cm. (8¾ × 14⅛ in.) No. 14541.
PLATE 11

Banks Collection. Lot 6. 'View of the Store Tower from Castle Hill'. Bt. Holmes, £4.

Reprod. St. John Hope, *Windsor Castle* pl. VI (colour). *Windsor Castle, Series B.*

One of the most delicately drawn and tinted of the 'Banks' series, the figures fresher and less *découpées* than is frequently the case. The ruler has been much used, especially in the foreground building to the left; tiny touches of body colour in the foreground add considerably to the effect of light.

20. The Devil's [Maids of Honour] Tower from the Clerk of the Works' Office. A coach in centre, driving towards the castle, stopped by a beggar woman with a child.

Pen and watercolour over slight pencil, with black border, the mount apparently modern and without inscription, 26.1 × 35.4 cm. (10¼ × 2⅛ in.) No. 14568.
PLATE 12

Banks, Lot 16, title as given. Bt. Holmes, £5.

The figure of a soldier is from No. 378 but with his musket in his left arm. A very similar drawing of a coach from behind in No. 392.

It is not clear whence the title was obtained. The Clerk of the Works' house is shown on James Wyatt's plan of 1810 to the South of Castle Hill but with no direct access to it.

21. The entrance to the Castle from the Town [Queen Elizabeth's] Gate, looking eastwards up Castle Hill.

Pencil, 16.5 × 23.7 cm. (6½ × 9⅜ in.) No. 14542.

Inscribed 'Windsor' within the drawing and 'Entrance from the Town Gate' in the border. The 'F' mark curiously duplicated (see on No. 1).

An earlier version from the Banks collection (Sale 1876, Lot 38) in the possession of the Hon. Sir Richard Molyneux has an additional figure of a man with a wheelbarrow in the foreground.

The name 'Town Gate' was applied both to Queen Elizabeth's Gate on Castle Hill and to the entrance to the Lower Ward of the Castle (Henry VIII Gate).

22. The same.

Pencil and watercolour, 30.5 × 45.5 cm. (12 × 17⅞ in.). No. 14543.
PLATE 14

Inscribed on the back of the mount in a later hand 'Entrance to Windsor Castle from the Town Gate 1770, His late Majesty's improvement'.

Almost identical with the preceding but very slightly curtailed on either side, the cart omitted and figures added on the right. Retaining much of the lightness and transparency of the Banks drawings and some of their sparkle but without their precision of line and detail, this drawing marks an intermediate stage between them and the looser picturesque type. The view is taken from an elevation, perhaps from over the gate itself, its shadow forming the foreground.

Presumably 'before' or 'taken before' has been omitted from the title in front of 'His late Majesty's' in copying an inscription of George IV's time. There had been no 'improvement' to the castle by 1770, the date supposed by the writer. The phrase 'taken before His Majesty's alterations' is used in describing six Windsor aquatints by Sandby in the 1812 Sale catalogue and Lot 28 on the third day of the 1817 Sale was 'A book, a large collection of views of the Castle and St. George's Chapel at Windsor, taken before His Majesty's improvements'. For George III's improvements see on No. 16.

23. View through the Town [Queen Elizabeth's] Gate, looking Westwards down Castle Hill; Henry VIII Gateway and Salisbury Tower on the right.

Pencil, 16.5 × 24 cm. (6½ × 9½ in.) No. 14544.

Inscribed 'Town Gate Wr. Castle 1777', the date apparently added later (see on No. 1).

The sketch for the horse and cart in this and No. 24 is No. 406. There both horse and driver are at rest. In No. 24 the horse is trotting quietly; here it is straining uphill and the driver whipping it on. This improvement alone indicates that this is the later drawing.

24. The same.

Pen and watercolour over slight pencil, within border, 31.7×46.7 cm. (12½×18⅜ in.) *No. 14546.*

PLATE 13

Inscribed in pencil on the back of the mount in the (?) artist's hand 'Windsor. View of the Town through the Gateway, from the Castle Hill', a date 1768 with a query added later.

Banks. Lot 23. Bt. Holmes, £14 14s. Banks label transferred to the back of the modern mount.

Exhib. Royal Academy (British Art) 1934, 591 (806), pl. CXLIX.

Reprod. as above, Harwood, *op. cit.,* p. 200, and *Connoisseur* XCII (1933) frontispiece, *Windsor Castle Series A* (both in colour).

Identical with the preceding but with considerable additions on either side and more subsidiary figures. The detail, seen through the Gateway, of the utmost delicacy.

A 'Town Gate of Windsor' was exhibited by Paul Sandby at Spring Gardens in 1768 (No. 277). Hence, probably, the date placed on this drawing and on No. 406.

25. Henry VIII Gateway from Castle Hill, with houses to left and Salisbury Tower beyond.

Pencil, pen and watercolour, some gouache, 30.5×40 cm. (12×15¾ in.) *No. 14547.*

PLATE 15

Inscribed at the back of the mount in pencil in the (?) artist's hand, 'Windsor. View of the Town Gate'.

Banks. Lot 26. Bt. Holmes, £10 10s. Banks label transferred to the modern mount.

Reprod. St. John Hope, *op. cit.,* pl. XXII, *Windsor Castle Series A.* Harwood, *op. cit.,* p. 106.

The cart, two horses and barrels, sketched from different angles, appear in several other drawings. Here they are added as an afterthought. The other principal figures are carefully but rather heavily drawn and loaded with gouache and this, especially as the red of the 'Sandpit Gate' drawing (No. 245) is employed in the brick wall on the left, makes a strong contrast with the dainty detail of the background. The castle wall is also somewhat more coloured than usual; the sky has few clouds. The ruler is freely used.

26. Henry VIII Gateway from without, showing the West end of St. George's Chapel and part of the Horseshoe Cloister.

Pencil, pen and watercolour, 33.7×46 cm. (13¼×18⅛ in.)

PLATE 19   *No. 14548.*

Erased inscription on mount 'Town Gate Windsor Castle'.

Exhib. International, 1862, No. 818.

Reprod. *Windsor Castle Series A.*

Similar to the etching, 'View of St. George's Chapel and the Town Gate of Windsor Castle', by Walker and Angus after Paul Sandby, Jan. 1st, 1780 (*150 Select Views,* No. 4), but with more foreground, more on the left and less on the right, and different figures except the knife-grinder. In both, the figures are overcrowded and somewhat lifeless. The strong outline of the figures recalls the large aquatints of the Encampments of 1780. The costumes of the ladies and the carriage suggest the same date or later, and this is confirmed by the free and somewhat careless drawing and colour.

Paul Sandby's first exhibit of a subject from Windsor, at Spring Gardens, in 1763, was 'A Gateway in Windsor Castle' (No. 113).

27. Henry VIII Gateway from just within the Lower Ward, the debtor's window on the right.

Pen and brown wash, some indications of pencil, 24×29 cm. (9½×11⅜ in.) *No. 14549.*

PLATE 17

Inscribed in pencil on the drawing in the (?) artist's hand, 'Town Gate Windsor Castle'.

Apparently a rough sketch for the next drawing; fresh and vigorous, it removes any doubt whether other monochromes as, for example, Nos. 40 and 44 are rightly claimed for Paul Sandby. A figure of a child on the ground, extreme left, is in pencil only.

28. The same, with more detail and more to the right.

Pen and watercolour over slight pencil, touches of gouache, 28.5×36 cm. (11¼×14⅛ in.) *No. 14550.*

PLATE 18

The horse and rider are identical with figures in No. 54 and in the aquatint of Shrewsbury Old Bridge 1778. The revellers occur in the preceding drawing.

A placard fixed on the wall, right, is inscribed in minute characters, 'Pray Remember the Poor Confin'd Debtors'. The Debtors' Prison was removed between 1790 and 1805, cf. Tighe and Davis, *Annals of Windsor,* 1858, ii. 555.

The architecture of the houses seen through the arch, while still delicate, has not the precision of other drawings of the same type. The figures are superimposed.

29. Henry VIII Gateway and the Chancellor of the Garter's Tower from the Lower Ward. Evening light.

Pencil and watercolour, a little pen. 22.5×34.5 cm. (8⅞×13⅝ in.) *No. 14551.*

PLATE 20

Inscribed in pencil at the back of the mount, in the (?) artist's hand 'Windsor. The Town Gate and Chancellor of the Garter's Tower from the Lower Court'.

Banks. Lot 15. Bt. Holmes, £5.

Reprod. St. John Hope, *op. cit.,* pl. XXIII. *Windsor Castle Series B.*

A somewhat more careless and unfinished work than the others of the Banks series, considerably more pencil work being retained. The figures, a groom with two horses, clearly superimposed, with slight pencil indications, in pen and wash over colour. Some of the watercolour washes are insensitive and rough. Some lines are ruled. The similar character of the mounts suggests that this was intended as a companion to No. 32.

30. The Governor of the Poor Knights' Tower and the Garter Chamber; the corner of St. George's Chapel in the right foreground.

Pencil, pen and watercolour with black border, 23.7×33.7 cm. (9⅜×13¼ in.) *No. 14552.*

PLATE 21

Inscribed in pencil at the back of the mount in the (?) artist's hand 'Windsor. View of, etc.', as given.

Banks. Lot 19. Bt. Holmes, £7 7s.

Reprod. St. John Hope, *op. cit.,* pl. XIII. *Windsor Castle Series A.*

One of the most finished and delicate of the series, the details precise and sparkling, the washes loose and transparent. The principal figures are dark and strong and carefully drawn, spaces having been left for them from the first.

The row of 13 houses, divided by a tower, was converted and built as lodgings for 'Poor Knights' in 1557/8. The tower, originally the Belfry of St. George's Chapel, became the residence of the Governor of the Poor (or Military) Knights. The houses and tower have been much restored and altered since Sandby's time; in particular, the range of windows appearing in the drawing below the parapet has been removed, and the brick garden wall with gate posts, etc., was replaced by a stone wall in 1840. Hope, *op. cit.*, ii. 532-3.

31. The West end of St. George's Chapel and the entrance to the Singing Men's [Horseshoe] Cloister, from the bottom of the Lower Ward: the Curfew Tower behind.

Pen and watercolour, slight pencil, a border left around the drawing, 24 × 32.2 cm. (9½ × 12⅝ in.) *No. 14553.*
PLATE 22

Inscribed at the back of the mount in the (?) artist' hand, in pencil, 'View of Part of St. George's Chapel from Henry VIII's Gate with the Entrance to the Singing Men's Cloister'.

According to W. Sandby, p. 215, from the Banks Collection and, if so, Lot 14, title as inscribed, but with 'Town Gate' for 'Henry VIII's Gate'. Bt. Hogarth, £4. A version in the collection of H.R.H. the Princess Royal (Borenius, *Cat.* No. 428, 14¾ × 21 in., dated 1768).

The Gothic tracery and the railings are detailed with the utmost minuteness; the washes light and transparent, the railings left white. Some use of the ruler with pen. The figures are noticeably added as afterthoughts over pen and even colour.

One of Paul Sandby's exhibits at Spring Gardens, 1765 (No. 232), was 'Entrance into the Singing Men's Cloister and the West End of H.M. Chapel of St. George in Windsor Castle'.

The two male figures in the foreground appear to be Poor Knights in the purple mantles with a St. George's Cross on a shield on the left shoulder worn by them until 1833 (cf. E. H. Fellowes, *The Military Knights of Windsor*, 1945, p. xlviii).

32. A similar view, but from nearer, and showing the North end of Crane's Building on the left. Morning light.

Pen and watercolour over pencil, 23 × 32.5 cm. (9 × 12¾ in.).
PLATE 23   *No. 14554.*

Inscribed in pencil, at the back of the mount, in the (?) artist's hand, 'Windsor. View of the Apartments of poor Knights on the Lower Foundation and entrance to the Singing Men's Cloister.'

From the Banks Collection, according to W. Sandby. If so, Lot 7, title as inscribed. Bt. Hogarth, £2.

Reprod. St. John Hope, *op. cit.*, pl. XXIX.

Apparently a companion to No. 29; the figures not superimposed.

Crane's Building, shown on the left of the drawing, was erected in 1657-8 for the accommodation of five poor knights in addition to the original thirteen, and was demolished in 1863 for the present guard-room. The entrance to the Horseshoe Cloister (originally the Vicar's lodgings), shown on the right, which dated from the 15th century was remodelled under Sir Gilbert Scott in 1870. (St. J. Hope, *op. cit.*, 531 and 520.)

33. Julius Cæsar's [Curfew] Tower and the Singing Men's [Horseshoe] Cloister. Stonemasons in the foreground.

Pen and watercolour over pencil, the mount gilt next to the drawing, 34.5 × 50.7 cm. (13⅝ × 20 in.) *No. 14555.*
PLATE 24

Inscribed on the back of the mount, in pencil in the (?) artist's hand, 'Windsor. View of Julius Cæsar's Tower from the West end of St. George's Chappel (*sic*)'.

Banks. Lot 40. Bt. Holmes, £17 17s.

Reprod. St. John Hope, *op. cit.*, pl. XCI.

The strength of the shadows is especially noticeable; it has compelled the abandonment of figures sketched in pencil upon the shadowed doorway under a lamp and of those in one of the foreground windows. A seated stonecutter in a similar position, but without the shelter, occurs in a drawing at the British Museum, L.B. 109, and in an aquatint of Jan. 1st, 1776 (Eton from Crown Corner), with the shelter separately; also in a study at the Victoria and Albert Museum (D 167-1901).

The miniature drama visible through an open garden door, a master scolding a maid who is washing linen, and the dog begging in the corner from a boy with a bun are characteristic of Paul Sandby.

The Curfew Tower, originally known as the Clewer Tower, one of three built in 1227-30, has been the Belfry of St. George's Chapel since about 1475. The old bell-cage and dome seen in the drawing remain enclosed in the additions of 1863 (Hope, *op. cit.*, ii. 525). The building on the right, probably the old vicar's hall, has been used as the Chapter Library from about 1693. The wall across the cloister, separating private gardens from a public thoroughfare, dated from the Restoration. It was swept away in the remodelling of the Horseshoe Cloister in 1870, when the library also was reconstructed. (Hope, *op. cit.*, ii., 520 *et seq.*)

34. The Lower Ward, looking East, from half-way up; the Portico of the Guard-room towards the left. Henry III's and Round Towers to right.

Pencil, 17 × 24 cm. (6⅞ × 9⅝ in.) *No. 14556.*

Inscribed 'Lower Court Windsor Castle' (see on No. 1).

Since Sandby's date the Round or Great Tower was raised to twice its height by Wyatville, perhaps the most spectacular of George IV's 'improvements'. For the guard-room, cf. on No. 37.

35. The same, slightly extended on each side, with more figures.

Pen, within border, 18.8 × 26.5 cm. (7⅜ × 10½ in.) *No. 14557.*

A close copy, possibly not by Paul Sandby, of the preceding, or a common original.

36. The same, a nocturne with a bonfire and festivities.

Pen and watercolour, nearly monochrome in blue-grey, 29 × 45.75 cm. (11⅜ × 18 in.) *No. 14558.*

Acquired March 16th, 1932.

Used for the aquatint of Sept. 1st, 1776, 'Windsor Castle from the Lower Court on the 5th November', with alterations in the figures including another position and somewhat more movement for the figure of a ratcatcher with his box, the sketch of which is No. 239.

A 'View of Windsor on a Rejoicing Night' was exhibited by P. Sandby at Spring Gardens in 1768 (No. 145). The title fits equally well with No. 60, etc.

37. A General View Westward from the base of the curtain of the Round Tower.

Pencil, pen and watercolour within black border; washed mount composed of strips, 28.5×61 cm. (11¼×24 in.) *No. 14559.*
PLATE 25

Inscribed in pencil on the back of the mount in (?) the artist's hand 'Windsor' and the title as given. 'Coffie and Tea' in microscopic letters above the door of the inn.

Banks. Lot 45. Bt. Holmes, £31 10s.

Reprod. St. John Hope, *op. cit.,* pl. 30; Harwood, *op. cit.,* p. 82. *Windsor Castle Series A.*

The masterpiece in Paul Sandby's best series, in perfect preservation except for a slight tear, almost invisible, in the centre. A Hollar-like panorama, showing the whole extent of the Middle and Lower Wards, the buildings of the town and the surrounding country with villages and churches, it combines the utmost delicacy of a miniature with breadth and simplicity of colour and atmospheric truth. The exhibition of this drawing at Burlington House in 1934 (No. 592) and of the similar but less detailed No. 51 at Amsterdam in 1936 did much to restore Sandby to the position that he had held in his lifetime.

The guard-room of the seventeenth century, immediately in front of the Chapel to the East, and the building adjoining it which was a public house (called 'The Royal Standard') were cleared away by Wyatville and replaced by the Lord Chamberlain's upper stores (Hope, *op. cit.,* 540-1).

38. The Quadrangle, the interior from the East end, looking towards the Round Tower.

Pencil, pen and watercolour, possibly not quite finished, 30.0×52.3 cm. (11¾×20⅝ in.) *No. 14560.*
PLATE 26

Inscribed in pencil on the back of the mount in the (?) artist's hand, 'Windsor. View of the Royal Court'. This title repeated on the label of the Banks collection now transferred to the new mount.

Acquired Christies' June 19th, 1936, Lot 76, with No. 52. Presumably Banks, 1876, Lot 49, 'View of the Royal Court', which was bought for 16 guineas by Lord Stair, who also bought No. 52 q.v.

The figures early and neat; some are superimposed, one is touched with Chinese white. The detail throughout is in almost excessive miniature, and in order, perhaps, to preserve it, the colour is kept down to little more than grey monochrome.

Of special topographic interest in showing the interior of the Upper Ward with the Rubbish Gate, etc., before the Gothicising of the windows and the removal of the statue of Charles II from the centre to the west side by Wyatville in 1827.

39. The Maids of Honour Tower from the Black Rod.

Pen and watercolour, torn and mended towards the foot, 58.5×46 cm. (23×18⅛ in.) *No. 14561.*
PLATE I

Inscribed in pencil in a recent hand on the back of the mount, 'Part of Windsor Castle from the Black Rod 1767'. Probably with No. 191, Lot 26, on the first day of the 1811 Sale, 'Two views of Windsor Castle and Charlton, on cartridge paper', bought by Colnaghi (for the Prince of Wales) for 1 guinea.

An unrecorded engraving of about the same size (52.6× 37.7 cm.) without lettering but presumably by Paul Sandby,

is at the British Museum. It is almost identical with the drawing except for the figures which, though different, are similar in style and treatment.

Although this drawing or a common prototype was used for part of a drawing (see on No. 42) in the Banks Collection, its monumental character places it in complete contrast with that series and, indeed, with the generality of Sandby's drawings. It was perhaps drawn direct from nature and owed its concentration and simplicity to a single, powerful visual impression and not to any topographic purpose. In this it is akin to the drawings in monochrome, Nos. 40 and 44, but Sandby had still to learn, perhaps from, or in connection with, his experiments in aquatint to invest his subject with an effect of atmosphere or lighting. There is a conscious interest in the design of the foreground which formed an essential part of the scene; but while Sandby had not at his command the complicated processes necessary for the completion of a watercolour on this scale, he had too much virtuosity to be satisfied with a simplicity which, even had he used gouache, would have come near to baldness. This has now been mellowed with age, but it was, no doubt, the reason for the drawing's Cinderella-like appearance at the sale of 1811 and its comparative neglect to this day. It is noticeable, too, that the engraving was apparently not published. Sandby preferred, as did his contemporaries and succeeding generations, more comprehensive and gently discursive vistas. When he introduced into his earlier schemes the greater vigour shown in this and in its companion, No. 191, he sacrificed their dainty but artificial charm, but he led the way to development in the art of watercolour which he himself was unable to bring to perfection.

The alterations in this part of the Castle (cf. on No. 16) are thus described in Knight's *Windsor Guide* of 1783, p. 99:—

'The apartments belonging to the Usher of the Black Rod, together with some offices which were greatly out of repair, have lately been taken down to enlarge the space between the castle and the Queen's lodge, and to open a view towards the keep or round tower; other improvements are now carrying on which when completed will render this a most delightful spot'. An unfinished sketch in the Royal Library, No. 14564, showing these buildings in course of demolition, hitherto tentatively attributed to Paul Sandby, may now be assigned with certainty to Dr. John Fisher (1748-1825, tutor to the Duke of Kent 1780-1785, and later Bishop of Salisbury).

40. The Henry III and Round Towers from the Black Rod, a man in the centre hammering the wheel of an overturned barrow.

Pen and grey wash over slight pencil, on very thin paper, 24.5×35 cm. (9⅝×13¾ in.) *No. 14562.*

Inscribed in ink by the artist on the drawing 'Black Rod, Windsor Castle', and numbered at the top (?) 179. Words in pencil which can be read as 'black, mould, pug' (i.e. the binding used in brickwork), 'brick' in the doorway, right; and on the parapet above the cottage 'brick'.

Similar in technique to No. 44, which is numbered '14' at the top. Loose and free in penwork and light in its washes, evidently the sketch on the spot utilised in the following drawing and in the outline etching 'Windsor Castle from the Black Rod' in the small Windsor Series of 1780, in which the man hammering a wheelbarrow is retained. The portico of the Guard-room (see on No. 37) is just visible to the right of the Henry III Tower.

41. The same, enlarged and with different figures.

Gouache, 37 × 47.5 cm. (14½ × 18¾ in.) *No. 14563*.

Banks, Lot 28, 'Windsor from the Black Rod'. Bt. Holmes, £6 6s. od. The title inscribed as on the other Banks drawings in pencil on the back of the mount.

The wheelbarrow and the man hammering of No. 40 are omitted, a cottager and woman introduced sitting at the door of the cottage, and a boy with a cat in his arms and a dog against a wall, right.

Early, smooth and dry, detailed gouache, producing the same effect of clear cool light, precise detail and contrast of dark red brick against grey stone, as the watercolour drawings of this (Banks) series.

42. The Round Tower, Royal Court and Devil's [Maids of Honour] Tower from the Black Rod, morning light.

Pencil and watercolour, a little gouache, 28 × 43.5 cm. (11 × 17⅛ in.) *No. 14565*.

PLATE 29

The mount lettered 'View from the Black Rod of the Round Tower, Royal Court and Devil's Tower, etc., in Winds[or] Castle'.

Presumably Lot 89 on the first day of the 1811 sale, same title. Bt. 'Shepperd' (for the Prince of Wales), £2 10s. od.

Totally different though its effect, the right half of this drawing is a repetition of No. 39. The scaffolding on the Round Tower itself is the same as in the following two drawings; but while here further scaffolding is in course of erection against the curtain, in No. 43 it is already in position. This does not indicate the date of the actual drawings, merely of the sketches on which they are based. A replica, one of two drawings with the same title in the Banks collection, in gouache and with different figures and more on the right, is in the National Gallery, Melbourne (reproduced *Studio* Winter Number, 1922-23, pl. 1); it was Lot 22 at the Banks sale (bt. Weston, £6; Anderdon-Weston sale, Sotheby's, Feb. 16th, 1922, Lot 85, bt. Daniell, £35, illustrated in catalogue). The other Banks example, Lot 43, was bought in.

The curtain of the Round Tower was said to be in a bad state in 1749 and 1752, but nothing was then done (Tighe and Davis, *Annals of Windsor*, 1858, ii. 526). The date of the repairs under George III is not known.

43. The Round, Winchester and Store Towers from the Black Rod, evening light.

Pencil and watercolour, a little gouache, 28 × 43.5 cm. (11 × 17⅛ in.) *No. 14566*.

PLATE 28

The mount lettered 'View of the Round, Winchester and Store Towers in Windsor Castle'.

Presumably Lot 93 on the first day, 1811 Sale, 'one high finished tinted drawing' title as on mount. Bt. 'Shepperd' for the Prince of Wales, £2 5s.

Companion drawing to the preceding, the scaffolding erected both on the Tower (as in the next drawing) and on the curtain. The Round Tower itself almost as in No. 44 but from farther away.

44. The Round Tower from the Black Rod.

Grey wash, damaged and repaired, 25 × 32.2 cm. (9⅞ × 12⅝ in.)

PLATE 39 *No 14567*.

Inscribed in ink on the drawing 'Round Tower, Windsor Castle', and numbered at the top '14'.

See on No. 40.

45. An unidentified tower.

Pencil, 8.2 × 6.5 cm. (3¼ × 2½ in.) *No. 14569*.

Inscribed in pencil 'Windsor Castle'.

With a similar pencil inscription but not included among the 12 pencil drawings bought at the 1811 sale (see No. 1).

46. The North Side of St. George's Chapel, looking West, with Denton's Commons.

Pencil, 16.2 × 12 cm. (6⅜ × 4¾ in.) *No. 14570*.

PLATE 10

Inscribed 'Windsor' in pencil. (Cf. on Nos. 1 and 18.)

Denton's Commons, seen on the right, was founded in 1519 by James Denton, a canon, as a hall for the Chantry priests and choristers who had previously been obliged to take their meals in the town. It was later used for various purposes and was demolished in 1859. Hope, *op. cit.*, ii. 515.

47. The Hundred Steps.

Pencil, 16.5 × 24 cm. (6½ × 9½ in.) *No. 14571*.

Inscribed in pencil 'The Hundred Steps. Windsor Castle 1777'. (See on No. 1.)

Identical with the etching 'Windsor Hundred Steps', apparently forming part of the small Windsor Series of 1780.

48. The same, showing Winchester Tower.

Pencil and watercolour, paper joined horizontally towards the top, the join smeared with body colour, 30.2 × 44 cm. (11⅞ × 17⅜ in.) *No. 14572*.

The mount lettered 'View of the Hundred Steps at Windsor'.

Probably Lot 95 on the first day of the 1811 sale, 'a high finished tinted drawing, View of the Old Hundred Steps, Windsor Castle'. Bt. 'Shepperd', for the Prince of Wales, £3 7s.

Reprod. St. John Hope, *op. cit.*, frontispiece in colour. *Windsor Castle Series B.*

The view slightly wider on either side than in the proceding and the figures, which are different, coarse and careless. The drawing and colouring are late in character, loose and picturesque throughout.

49. The same.

Gouache, 43.9 × 58.5 cm. (17¼ × 23 in.) *No. 14573*.

PLATE 36

With No. 5 included in the Inventory of Pictures in the Lord Chamberlain's Department (No. 810) and removed from a stretcher and remounted in the Royal Library in 1870. It can therefore be identified with Lot 79 on the first day of the Paul Sandby Sale 1811, 'A View of the Old Hundred Steps at Windsor Castle, on panel'. Bt. 'Shepperd', for the Prince of Wales, £3 17s.

A careless drawing, later than the preceding, with more and livelier figures, differently disposed, and slightly more foreground. The trees to the right are rather fuller than in the preceding, that to the left more scanty; but in general the size and shape of the trees so far as shown remain as they were in the pencil drawing bearing a date of some twenty years earlier.

The Inventory of Pictures specifies the stables as those of the equerries.

50. Winchester Tower and part of the Hundred Steps.

Pen and watercolour, over slight pencil, within coloured border, 16.0×21.2 cm. (6¼×8⅜ in.) *No. 14574.*

PLATE 37

Inscribed on the back of the mount in pencil in the (?) artist's hand, 'Windsor. View of the', etc., as given above.

According to W. Sandby, p. 215, from the Banks Collection and, if so, Lot 2, same title, Bt. Hogarth, £2 2s.

Shows a highly conscious virtuosity in the composition and the elongated figures are posed in twisted, somewhat affected attitudes such as are common in Sandby's early studies, but are less often found in the landscapes. They may show the influence of Gainsborough or a common, momentary fashion.

51. 'View of the Seat near the Terrace and a View of the adjacent Country'.

Pencil and watercolour, the figures in body colour, and touches of white in the building and rails. Elaborate mount built up of strips, 27.7×57.1 cm. (10⅞×22½ in.) *No. 14575.*

PLATE 31

Inscribed in pencil on the back of the mount in the (?) artist's hand, 'Windsor', etc., as given. Banks Lot 56. Bt. Holmes, £6 6s.

Exhibited, Amsterdam 1936, No. 231, with reprod.

Lit. and reprod., *Burlington Magazine*, Nov. 1944.

A preliminary pencil drawing for the two figures (coloured; a gardener with a roller on the reverse) is in the collection of Mr. I. A. Williams. It is of the same size, but since the rail is higher and there is no upright post, the position of the man's legs is different, and the forearms and hands are hidden. A replica in reverse and based on an offset, together with the figure of an eavesdropper, also on an offset, is at the British Museum in an album (L.B. 138, No. 103). The two figures occur in an attitude modified to suit a more public situation in the aquatint 'Windsor terrace looking West' of Sept. 1st, 1776, and with somewhat more 'abandon' in the 'North Terrace looking East' at Harewood (see on No. 8).

To be compared with No. 37. Also in perfect preservation, this drawing exhibits the breadth, the clear lighting, and the subtle gradations of distance and detail which Sandby could achieve by his delicacy of pencil work and carefully chosen flat washes. The usual interest of architectural variety is here replaced by a pretty incident and the simplest of structural forms.

The summer house on the right, which appears also in No, 59, used to stand in the Home Park, just east of the Castle. in prolongation of the North Terrace. The engine-house, Baylis House, Slough and Stoke Place can be discerned in the distance.

52. Windsor Home Park. View to the East from a point at the top of the slopes, near the summer house shown in the preceding drawing. Two horses and a herd of deer in the foreground. Minute figures in the middle distance.

Watercolour on pencil, and pen, 27.8×57 cm. (11×22½ in.)

PLATE 30   *No. 14576.*

A larger version (17½×31⅜ in.), with additional figures, is in the possession of the Duke of Buccleuch (see Introd. p. 8).

The statement, without authority quoted, that this drawing came from the Banks Collection is corroborated by the label of that collection with 'Windsor. View from the End of the North Terrace looking towards London', which is now affixed to the modern mount, and by the old mount, composed of strips which is similar to that of the preceding drawing. Lot 54 of the Banks Sale, 1876, with this title, was bought by Lord Stair (12 guineas), as was No. 38, and the two together formed Lot 76 at Christies on June 19th, 1936, when they were bought for the Royal Library. Though it is now somewhat browned by exposure, it retains the same effective combination of great breadth in the distance and exquisiteness of detail. The touch in the foliage is miniature, some figures in the middle distance are so small as to be all but invisible, and the herd of deer on the edge of the slope have been left in pencil and barely touched with colour. In these drawings Paul Sandby set out to surpass his brother precisely in those technical methods which he, perhaps, learnt from him.

53. The Comet of 1783 as seen from the east angle of the North Terrace.

Watercolour, 28×49.5 cm. (11×19½ in.) *No. 14577.*

PLATE 32

From the collection of William Esdaile, with his mark on the mount and inscribed by him on the back of the mount 'EIE/W.E.P. 93. The representation of a fiery meteor which pass'd over London abt 9 Oclock in the evening of 18th August 1783/Taken from Windsor Terrace. P. Sandby'. It is not specified in the catalogue of his sale in June 1840.

An aquatint of the subject with improvements in the figures and grouping was published in October 1783 by Paul, after Thomas, Sandby. Of two drawings bequeathed to the British Museum (L.B. T. Sandby 27 (19 and 20)) by William Sandby, both show the same architectural setting as here and in the print, but one (L.B. 19) has the landscape only and the lighting from the right, the other (L.B.20) has the figures arranged as in the print. William Sandby, who did not know this drawing, attributed the former to Paul, the latter to Thomas. Probably, as the landscape is further elaborated and the figures better drawn and grouped, both are by Paul in preparation for the print, while this, *pace* William Esdaile, who is generally correct, may be by Thomas; or, since he is said to be represented as witnessing the occurrence in company with Dr. Cavallo, who wrote an account of it, Dr. J. Lind, Dr. Lockman and two ladies, he may have been credited with the authorship merely because he furnished the material, description or sketch on which the drawings and print were based. The whole duration of the meteor was less than a half-minute.

Dr. James Lind (1736-1812, physician to the Royal Household and familiar to readers of Fanny Burney's *Diary*) and Tiberius Cavallo (1749-1809, natural philosopher) made, with the daughters of the former, the silhouettes in a volume, recently acquired by the Royal Library from his descendants, which contains the portrait of Thomas Sandby reproduced at the end of this book. The single initial L. affixed to it indicates Dr. Lind himself as the artist.

54. The Secretary of State's [Victoria] Tower and the Tennis Court, from the Little Park.

Pen and watercolour over slight pencil, 16.5×23 cm. (6½×9⅛ in.)

PLATE 27   *No. 14578.*

The title in pencil on the back of the modern mount: 'S.E. corner with the Secretary of State's Tower and the Tennis Court, from the Home Park'.

According to W. Sandby, p. 215, from the Banks Collection. If so, perhaps Lot 3 with title as given. Bt. Hogarth, 18s.

The horse and rider occur also in Nos. 28 and 55 and in the aquatint of Shrewsbury, Old Bridge.

In the neat flat manner of the copper plate engravings; the figures superimposed.

Showing beyond the tower the end of the old Queen's Lodge (see on No. 16) and the Tennis Court which was built for Charles II.

55. The same.

Gouache, with black and gold border, 40 × 52 cm. ($15\frac{3}{4} \times 20\frac{1}{2}$ in.) *No. 14579.*

PLATE 27

Inscribed in pencil at the back in a modern hand 'S.E. Corner of Windsor Castle, 1772'.

Almost identical with the preceding, the drawing equally tight and the foliage spotty, but the poses of the figures slightly modified, and the trees brought nearer to the centre. The lighting is entirely altered and the sky more dramatic. The gouache is, however, used drily as in Nos. 41, 57 and 60, and without any of the picturesque looseness of later drawings.

56. The North East angle of the Castle from the foot of the Slopes.

Watercolour, largely gouache, the architecture in pen, 33.2 × 49.7 cm. ($13\frac{1}{8} \times 19\frac{5}{8}$ in.) *No. 14580.*

Inscribed in pencil on the mount, partly cut into, 'Windsor Castle from the little park'.

Effective but somewhat abnormal with its restless lines, broken lights, and summary handling of the foliage.

57. The North East angle of the Castle from the Home Park; a thunderstorm, lightning and a frightened horse.

Pen and gouache, 38.5 × 48.5 cm. ($15\frac{1}{8} \times 19\frac{1}{8}$ in.) *No. 14581.*

Inscribed in pencil on the back in a modern hand 'N. Side of Windsor Castle from the Home Park'.

Possibly Lot 91, first day, 1811 sale, 'The North Side of Windsor Castle, a storm' (bt. 'Shepperd', for the Prince of Wales, £2 7s.), but that was catalogued as 'a high finished tinted drawing'.

Exhibited International 1862, No. 825.

The early type of gouache drawing in dry greys and green with carefully drawn details and spotted foliage. Remarkable for the dramatic contrast of the solid building with the atmospheric disturbance.

58. The North front of the Castle from the Maestricht Pond in the Little Park.

Pencil and watercolour, the paper joined, 30.7 × 70 cm. ($12\frac{1}{8} \times 27\frac{5}{8}$ in.) *No. 14582.*

PLATE 34

Purchased and presented by H.M. Queen Mary, March 6th, 1930.

The modern mount has, pasted at the back, the elaborate label of the Banks Collection, reading 'Windsor. View of the Castle', etc., as given. Probably Lot 51 in the Banks Sale, 1876, same title. Bt. Weston, $8\frac{1}{2}$ guineas; Anderdon Weston sale: Sotheby, 16.2.22, Lot 118, and 27.6.22, Lot 48, £14 10s.)

The study used for the old horse at foot left is No. 384; the summer house visible on the crest of the hill is that shown from nearby in No. 51, and again in No. 59. Somewhat faded, probably through exposure, the drawing has not the transparency and sharpness characteristic of the well preserved examples of the Banks Collection, but it has their delicacy and lightness.

Views of 'Windsor Castle from the Little Park' were exhibited by P. Sandby at Spring Gardens in 1765 (No. 235) and 1767 (No. 273). A larger ($17\frac{1}{8} \times 31\frac{1}{2}$ in.) but otherwise almost identical version is in the possession of the Duke of Buccleuch (see Introd. p. 8).

Traces of the pond are said to be still visible in wet weather in the Little Park to the North-east of the Castle where, according to tradition, gardens were laid out on the lines of the troops at the investment of Maestricht. There may also have been some memory of the mimic representation of the taking of that city staged, below the Castle, for Charles II in 1674 and witnessed by both Evelyn and Pepys.

59. North East view of the Castle from the Lower [Home] Park.

Pencil, pen and watercolour, the paper joined, 31 × 70.5 cm. ($12\frac{1}{4} \times 27\frac{3}{8}$ in.) *No. 14583.*

PLATE 35

Bt. Christies. Dec. 22nd, 1920 (Lot 9, 'Windsor Castle from the Little Park', $12\frac{1}{4} \times 27\frac{3}{4}$in).

A note on the back of the mount, 'Drawn for Sir Joseph Banks', is corroborated by the character of the mount and by the inscription on the back, 'Windsor', etc., as given, in the (?) artist's hand as in the drawings from that collection. If so, Lot 52, reading N.E. for S.E. (Bt. Blane, 5 guineas).

Of precisely the same dimensions and rather more faded from exposure, it may have served as a companion to No. 58, though they reached the Royal Library from different sources. The pencil hatching in the trees is unusual and with other features suggests that the drawing is hurried and not quite finished. On the other hand, the horseman in the foreground is very neatly outlined with the pen.

The summer house of No. 51 reappears on the sky line of this drawing to the left of the Castle.

60. View of the Castle from Datchet Lane on a Rejoicing Night, 1768, showing the Park Wall and the King's Engine House to right, and the river bank at the foot with revellers returning, left. Nocturne with fireworks and illuminations.

Gouache, touched with gold, 30.7 × 45.7 cm. ($12\frac{1}{8} \times 18$ in.)

PLATE 38 *No. 14584.*

Signed in gold P. Sandby 1768. Not listed by W. Sandby.

This is the only signed and dated landscape by Paul Sandby before 1792 in the whole collection.

61. The same, extended on left and shortened on right, the Castle a little more distant.

Watercolour and gouache, a little gold, the black and gold border part of the drawing, 23.75 × 35.25 cm. ($9\frac{3}{8} \times 13\frac{7}{8}$ in.) *No. 14585.*

Purchased locally May 6th, 1925, as from the family of William Seabrook, Inspector of Windsor Castle, 1862-83. The mount and the pencil inscription on the back of it, 'Windsor, View of the Castle taken on a rejoicing night from the King's Engine House', are those of the Banks Collection. This may therefore be Lot 9 of the 1876 sale, same title. Bt. Seabrook, £1 10s. (cf. on No. 72).

Inferior to the preceding, if the topography has been made slightly more plausible.

62. Attributed to Paul Sandby.

The North front of the Castle from the Thames; the King's Engine House and the Wooden Bridge to the right, Datchet Lane and Park wall to the left, the river at foot.

Watercolour, almost monochrome in grey, much faded, 30.5 × 45.7 cm. (12 × 18 in.) *No. 14586.*

Inscribed on mount, above, in pencil and in an ornamental 'Colnaghi' hand, precisely as on Nos. 80 and 198, 'Windsor Castle by Sandby'.

The left hand portion possibly from the same sketch as the preceding two drawings.

Unusual and more like the work of Marlow than Sandby. Both landscape and figures are entirely in brush and grey, with little pencil, no pen, and mere touches of colour, brown and yellow.

63. North View of the Castle from the Eton bank, 1801, the Wooden Bridge and King's Engine House to left. The Royal Barge on the river in the centre. Trees to right on near bank. Sunset.

Gouache, 52.1 × 78.1 cm. (20½ × 30¾ in.) *No. 14588.*

Signed, P. Sandby 1801.

No. 1088, with a photograph taken in 1872, in the Inventory of Pictures in the Lord Chamberlain's Department and there stated to be on a canvas and stretcher. There was already then affixed to the canvas at the back a fragment of a letter relating that the drawing was purchased for 'What was then deemed a handsome sum' by the writer's grand-father 'more than 30 years ago'. There was then, also, another label reading 'Lot 85. One'.

A similar but still larger gouache, signed and dated 1794, was bequeathed by W. Sandby to the Royal Academy. Both are from the same drawing as the following, from which derive also probably Nos. 74 and 75 and a drawing by de Cort in the Royal Library (14587) formerly regarded as by Sandby.

64. The same.

Pen and grey wash, over slight sanguine, on tracing paper, torn and laid down, 31 × 46.5 cm. (12¼ × 18¼ in.) *No. 14617.*

Apparently a stage towards the aquatint 'Windsor from Eton' of Jan. 1st, 1777, which is of the same dimensions, but further completed and with several variations, e.g. in the action of the dog on the boat. The landscape back-ground and the right foreground served also, with an alteration in the position of the two horses, for the gouache of 24 years later, No. 63, even the young tree to the right not outgrowing its protective fencing.

65. The Castle from the back of the fields at Eton; a row of trees in the foreground.

Watercolour, 48.3 × 71.7 cm. (19 × 28¼ in.) *No. 14589.*

Probably Lot 73, 1811 Sale, second day, 'View of Windsor from the Playfields at Eton, tinted drawing'. Bt. 'Shepperd', for the Prince of Wales, £4 4s.

The loosely washed trees and architecture and the absence of figures suggest that the drawing is unfinished; but perhaps for that reason it is remarkably successful in its rendering of atmosphere.

The 'Banks' version of the subject, from a nearer viewpoint (Sale 1876, Lot 41), was bequeathed by William Sandby to the Victoria and Albert Museum (D. 1833-1904).

66, 67 and 68. Thomas Sandby.

Unfulfilled projects for a picture gallery proposed to be added in prolongation of Queen Elizabeth's Gallery (now the Royal Library) at the West end of the North Terrace.

66. Design for a picture gallery on Windsor Terrace.

Pencil, pen and watercolour, 16.7 × 28.5 cm. (6⅝ × 11¼ in.) *No. 14591.*

Inscribed in pencil 'T. Sandby invt', and with title as given. Probably the 'Design for a Picture Gallery on Windsor Terrace by Sandby' bought by the Prince of Wales from Colnaghi for 18s. on June 22nd, 1811 (Archives invoice 27639). Inscribed and mounted in a similar manner to Nos. 148, q.v., 188 and 189.

The lines of the elevation are drawn with ruler and compass as is customary in T. Sandby's designs, but the picturesque treatment of the sky, background and foreground, and the figures in pencil and watercolour, which are, as usual, superimposed over the pen lines, suggest the hand of his brother or nephew.

67. The North Front of the Castle; general view from below.

Pen and watercolour, 14.6 × 33.5 cm. (5¾ × 13¼ in.) *No. 14590.*

Inscribed in pencil 'Drawing by .. Sanby' [*sic*] (the corner injured).

68. The same with the projected picture gallery (marked A in pencil).

Watercolour, unfinished, 17 × 38 cm. (6¾ × 15 in.) *No. 14592.*

The proposed addition differs considerably from the careful elevation (No. 66) and would appear to be more extensive. The tiled house at the foot, right, reappears in No. 70.

69. The North front of the Castle from Datchet Lane near Romney Lock; on the left the Castle above the Park wall and the lane; river and trees on right.

Pencil and watercolour, 30.5 × 45.5 cm. (12 × 17⅞ in.)
PLATE 33   *No. 14599.*

Lettered in pencil on mount, 'Windsor from Datchet Road'. Probably Lot 94, 1811 Sale, first day, 'A high finished tinted drawing. Windsor from Datchet Rd.' Bt. 'Shep-perd' for the Prince of Wales, £2 4s.

A later version, with massive foliage and picturesque trees, atmospheric feeling and disproportionate figures, of the etching 'Windsor from Datchet Lane' in the small series of Windsor views of 1780, from a drawing of 1769. Another version, with effects of illuminations and bonfires at night similar to those of Nos. 60 and 61, was at Walker's Galleries in October, 1934.

70. The Castle from a point east of Isherwood's Brewery, with the houses of Datchet Lane to the right; sunset effect.

Pencil, pen and watercolour, 21.7 × 43.5 cm. (8½ × 17⅛ in.)
PLATE 41   *No. 14594.*

The inscription on the mount, 'Part of Windsor from Datchet Lane 1770', is recent or has been rehandled. The minute but rather mechanical penwork in the architecture and trees conflicts with the summary atmosphere colouring which is especially happy in the houses on the right. The figures are lightly drawn without outlines. The mount is watermarked 1798.

71. From Isherwood's Brew-house, Datchet Lane.

Pencil and watercolour, a strip added at the top, 29.5×40.7 cm. (11⅝×16 in.) *No. 14595.*

Lettered in pencil on the mount 'Windsor Castle from a Brew-house Yard in Datchet Lane' with a date, 1770, added later, and 'By Sandby' in the ornamental 'Colnaghi' hand.

Exhibited International, 1862, No. 854.

Inferior version of the following drawings. This and No. 72 are almost identical, except in size and the foreground figures, with the etching 'Windsor from Isherwood's Brewhouse in Datchet Lane, 1780', in the small Windsor set. One of P. Sandby's exhibits at Spring Gardens in 1765 was 'Windsor Castle from the Gateway of a Brewhouse Yard, Datchet Lane' (No. 234). A rudimentary note of the subject, akin to drawings dated 1750, is in the British Museum (L.B.5).

72. The same, from a slightly different angle.

Pen, watercolour and gouache, 37.2×54 cm. (14⅝×21¼ in.) *No. 14596.*

Inscribed at back 'View of the Castle from the Gateway of the Brewer's Yard in Datchet Lane' in pencil in the (?) artist's hand.

Purchased locally May 6th, 1925, as from the family of William Seabrook (cf. on No. 61). Probably, therefore, Banks, Lot 24, title as inscribed. Bt. Seabrook, £4 15s.

No girl in doorway nor the near carts and horses. The Round Tower has scaffolding. An early, hard and clean gouache.

73. The same, from slightly further back.

Pencil and pen, watercolour and gouache, 55.2×80 cm. (21¾×31½ in.) *No. 14597.*
PLATE 40

Signed 'P. Sandby' at foot right. Attached is a strip of paper cut from the mount or taken from an old frame bearing 'View of Windsor Castle from Mr. Isherwood [*sic*] Brewhouse in Datchet Lane' in ink, in P. Sandby's writing, and, in pencil, 2 - D (? second day) and a collector's mark, Lugt 2836, unidentified.

Some figures are identical with those in No. 71, others nearly so. The child in the doorway and the brewer talking to his man added as an afterthought.

74. The Castle from the Back Fields at Eton; showing the North and West fronts of the Castle from the Eton shore.

Pencil, pen and watercolour with gouache figures, joined to right, 37×92.2 cm. (14⅝×36¼ in.) *No. 14599.*

Exhibited, Paris (*Peinture Anglaise*), 1938, No. 229.

Because of the present discoloured and faded appearance and the intentional emphasis of the gouache figures in the foreground, the delicate drawing and colour of the background are not at once apparent. In all probability this is an early watercolour drawing left unfinished, the whole foreground with its figures being added at a later date and in a different manner.
The original sketch was not far removed from Nos. 63 and 64; the barge to the left occurs in a similar position in the aquatint of Jan. 1st, 1776, 'Eton College from Crown Corner'.

75. The same, somewhat extended to the right and curtailed to the left, and with different incidents in the foreground.

Pencil and gouache, mounted on canvas, 39.5×97 cm. (15½×38¼ in.) *No. 14598.*
PLATE 42

Bought May 1919 at Christies, with a note (written at the back) that it had belonged to 'Rt. Hon. J. W. Lowther, and had been exhibited as 'Windsor Castle from the Eton Shore, about 1755'.

76. Windsor Bridge from Datchet Lane, 1798. The Bridge in the central middle distance, the river and houses of Eton to the right. On the extreme left the West corner of St. George's above the houses of Datchet Lane. Sunset sky.

Gouache with border at foot, injured on left side, perhaps in removal from canvas, 33.5×61.5 cm. (13¼×24¼ in.) *No. 14600.*

Signed P. Sandby 1798.

Probably Lot 68, third day, Sale 1811, 'View of Windsor Bridge, high finished, body colour framed and glazed'. Bt. 'Shepperd,' for the Prince of Wales, 6½ guineas.

Transferred from St. James's Palace 1886.

A version at the British Museum (L.B. 109) in watercolour with some different figures (reproduced Harwood, *op. cit.*, p. 8, Finberg; *English Watercolour Painters*, n.d. facing p. 22). Loose construction and handling, picturesque and atmospheric effect.

77. Windsor Bridge. Seen from upstream; the engine house visible between the piers.

Pencil, 16.5×23.7 cm. (6½×9⅜ in.) *No. 14601.*

Inscribed 'Windsor Bridge 1777'. (See on No. 1.)

Buildings and several of the figures identical with the right-hand portion of a drawing at the Victoria and Albert Museum (201-1894) which is attributed to Paul or Thomas Sandby, but is a copy from the former.

78. Thomas Sandby.

Windsor from the Goswells.

Pencil and pen, grey wash with some touches of colour. On four sheets joined together, 12.5×58.2 cm. (4⅞×22⅞ in.) *No. 14602.*

Inscribed in pencil below (same hand as No. 1, etc., and with the short s of Gossels before the long as in No. 118), 'Windsor from the Gossels drawn in a camera T.S.' (the initials perhaps an addition) and in ink on the back of the drawing, under the mount, 'Windsor drawn in a Camera by T. Sandby'.

The indications in pencil are slight, the penwork hard, careful and mechanical.

A large Camera Obscura formed the last lot on the first day of the T. Sandby sale July 18th, 1799.

79. Windsor Castle from the West.

Gouache, the paper fixed on panel, 31×46 cm. (12¼×18⅛ in.) *No. 14603.*

Inscribed on the back of the panel 'Windsor Castle from the West. Paul Sandby R.A. 1802'; also at the back the label of Messrs. Colnaghi and an auction indication, apparently July 3/72 [N]o 56 or 50.

Derives from No. 78, curtailed on the right and with trees introduced into the left foreground.

A gouache copy of a similar view, inscribed on the back 'His Royal Highness Prince Ernest Augustus. December 8th 1780. Aged 9 years and a half. A View of Windsor Town and Castle', is in the Royal Library together with views of St. Leonard's Hill and of 'A Farm near Windsor', identically inscribed as the work respectively of H.R.H. Prince Augustus Frederick, aged seven years and three quarters, and H.R.H. Prince Adolphus Frederick, aged six years and three quarters. These three drawings are now in the portfolio devoted by Queen Charlotte to the drawings of the Princes and Princesses together with a smaller but still more competent gouache inscribed in another hand 'Painted by Prince Ernest and given by him to the P. of Wales 1771'. It is not improbable that all four have found their way to this portfolio recently as their most appropriate resting place and do not form part of its original contents, while the inscription on the smaller gouache, which credits its authorship and gift either to a German Prince or to a child of one year, throws some doubt on the authenticity of all. It need hardly be said that in each case the workmanship is far beyond the capacity even of Princes of the ages stated. Such as they are, however, the three drawings of 1780, which obviously derive from Sandby, are the only indications that he may on one day at least in 1780 have given a drawing lesson to the younger members of the Royal family.

80. The Castle from the Brocas.

Pencil, pen and watercolour, dulled from exposure, 21.7 × 43.8 cm. ($8\frac{1}{2} \times 17\frac{1}{4}$ in.) *No. 14604.*

Inscribed above 'Windsor Castle by Sandby' in the same 'Colnaghi' hand as Nos. 62 and 198.

Partly pupil's work, the architecture skilful and delicate, the foliage perfunctory and unintelligent. The figures are coarse and the children strikingly adult in appearance and unlike Sandby's usual figures.

A larger and in every way superior version ($17\frac{1}{8} \times 31\frac{3}{8}$ in.) is in the possession of the Duke of Buccleuch, forming with the drawings referred to on Nos. 52 and 58 and those reproduced, *supra*, as Figs. 3 and 4, a series probably executed for the Duke of Montagu (see Introd. p. 8).

81. South-East View of Windsor from the Spital Hill.

Pencil, pen and watercolour, 21.6 × 43.5 cm. ($8\frac{1}{2} \times 17\frac{1}{8}$ in.) *No. 14605*

Inscribed at the back, under the mount, 'Windsor. View of the Castle and Town from the Spital Hill', and, in pencil in a large 'Colnaghi' hand, on the mount below the drawing, 'Windsor Castle. Paul Sandby'.

Shows the buildings which were removed when Queen's Lodge was built in 1778 (demolished 1825). Perhaps a companion to the preceding, it is similarly mounted, but the pupil's work, if any, occurs only in the somewhat acrid colouring. The fine penwork in the tree, right, recalls No. 70, where, however, it is absent entirely from the tree in a similar position.

82. The Castle from the Long Walk, showing the houses removed for Queen's Lodge.

Pencil and watercolour, 15.4 × 20.4 cm. (6 × 8 in.) *No. 14606.*
PLATE 43

Inscribed on the back of the mount in an apparently old hand 'Windsor' (pen) and 'P. (or T.) Sandby' (pencil), and on the mount below the drawing, erased, 'By Paul Sandby'. Companion to, and bought with No. 14, q.v.

Careful neat miniature manner.

The view from the same point and with the same details (other than the figures) forms the background of the oil painting in the Royal Collection referred to on No. 388 (Fig. 19). The Seventeenth Century house and 'Nell Gwynn's House' to the south of it were altered and enlarged from 1778 to 1782 as the Queen's Lodge and the Lower Lodge respectively. St. John Hope, *op. cit.*, p. 347. It was there that George III took up his residence, until 1804, when he moved into the North wing of the castle, ground floor, the present Royal Library.

83. The Town and Castle from the lower end of Sheet Street looking north.

Pencil, 16.5 × 24 cm. ($6\frac{1}{2} \times 9\frac{1}{2}$ in.) *No. 14607.*

Inscribed below in pencil: 'Windsor Castle from Sheet Street 1777'. (See on No. 1.)

Of two earlier versions of this subject both belonging to the Hon. Sir Richard Molyneux and both from the Banks Collection (Sale 1876, Lots 30 and 36), one is identical with this and No. 84, with the coach of the latter but different figures in the foreground. The other is from a slightly different point of view and with morning light.

84. The same, slightly extended to the right and with a coach and different figures in the foreground. Afternoon light.

Pencil and watercolour, 30.8 × 46 cm. ($12\frac{1}{8} \times 18\frac{1}{8}$ in.) *No. 14608.*
PLATE 44

The mount lettered 'View from the Lower End of Sheet Street of Windsor Town and Castle', and inscribed in pencil, at left 'The scite [*sic*] of the New Barrack' and, at right, 'about the year 1775' (the second 7 over 8 erased). An almost illegible inscription apparently to much the same effect, also in pencil, on the drawing itself, at the foot.

Reprod. Harwood, *op. cit.*, p. 148.

A loose and rather careless drawing, about 1780-1790, with light colour and transparent washes. The feathery foliage of the tree to the left is a legacy from an earlier drawing such as is mentioned on No. 83.

The Barracks in Sheet Street were erected in 1795 (Harwood, *op. cit.*, p. 127).

85. Attributed to Paul or Thomas Sandby.

South-east aspect of the Castle from the Great Park.

Pencil and watercolour, much faded and discoloured, 35.3 × 59 cm. (about 4 cm. added on the right) ($13\frac{7}{8} \times 23\frac{1}{4}$ in.) *No. 14609.*

Inscribed in a large 'Colnaghi' hand in pencil across the sky, 'View of Windsor', and in pen over pencil on back, 'Windsor Park'. Possibly 'A Sketch of Windsor Park by Paul Sandby' bought by the Prince of Wales from Colnaghi on July 16th, 1810, for 10s. 6d. (Archives invoice 27546).

Hitherto attributed to Thomas Sandby, but probably not by either of the brothers.

86. Windsor Castle from Bishopsgate looking North; view through beeches over forest and an enclosure with sheds, from behind which smoke ascends; a keeper on horseback with two hounds, left centre, a wood-gatherer to right.

Watercolour and gouache, somewhat faded, 48 × 68 cm. ($18\frac{7}{8} \times 26\frac{3}{4}$ in.) *No. 14610.*
PLATE 46

Shows the influence of J. R. Cozens, who may have visited Windsor when his father taught drawing to the young Princes, and certainly made drawings of the Park and Castle.

The title of a drawing by Paul Sandby in a sale of his son's collection at Stanley's Rooms on Nov. 14th, 1827 (Lot 90) 'A View of Windsor from the Lime-Kiln in the Great Park at Bishop's Gate' suggests a possible source of the smoke seen in this drawing.

II. WINDSOR GREAT PARK AND VICINITY

87. 'View near Cranbourne Lodge'. An old beech tree in the left foreground; a girl with a child, cattle and sheep to left, and to right a woodland glade with women gathering sticks and a man with two horses cantering.

Pencil and watercolour, 37.5 × 54.3 cm. (14¾ × 21⅜ in.)
PLATE 50   *No. 14612.*

Inscribed on mount in block letters in pencil, 'View near Cranburn Lodg [sic] in Windsor Park'. The auction mark of the 1811 sale cut into and illegible, but this can scarcely be identified with Lot 71 on the third day, 'a portrait of an Old Beech tree in Cranburn Park' (bt. Colnaghi, for the Prince of Wales, £7 17s. 6d.), for that is described as in body-colour on canvas. (Cf. on No. 149.)

Perhaps dated after 1778 by the Windsor uniform worn by the rider in the foreground and probably to be placed early in the '80s, because of the careful drawing in the trees, the cool colouring and the effect of precise detail joined with a massiveness in the foliage which is far from the tinted outline popularly associated with Sandby's style. At the same time there is a spottiness of lighting and a diffusion of effect which mark a transitional period and a mixture of methods.

88. Woodland Scene. A group of large trees with a pool behind them, a man with a pack donkey in the left foreground.

Watercolour, with some touches in body-colour, 29.3 × 40.2 cm. (11½ × 15⅞ in.) *No. 14613.*

Apparently acquired locally in 1910 under the title 'In Windsor Park near the Wheelwright's shop, drawn by Paul Sandby', which is inscribed in pencil in a modern hand at the back. The view of high hills at foot, left, conflicts with this title.

A late drawing, about 1790.

89. 'In Old Windsor Wood', a cottage behind two large trees.

Pen and watercolour; the upper portion, more than a third of the whole, continued, without pen, on the washed mount, 27.7 × 29 cm. (10⅞ × 11⅜ in.) *No. 14614.*
PLATE 49

Signed in pen with initials P.S. on the base of the tree, to left, and inscribed by him, lower centre, with the title as given. In pencil on the back of the mount, 'Back of Bishops-gate, Windsor Gt. Park', perhaps taken from the front, now cut down.

Probably the 'Drawing, View of the Back of Bishopsgate Windsor Gt. Park' bought by the Prince of Wales from Colnaghi for 1 guinea on Feb. 6th, 1812 (Archives invoice No. 27673).

One of the brightest and daintiest drawings, retaining the sparkle of the Banks series without the precision of detail and with more effective lighting and atmosphere. The large tree to the left is especially well seen and rendered.

90. 'In front of the Honble. John [sic] Bateman's house at Old Windsor, 1750'.

FIG. 8. 'THE HONBLE. JOHN BATEMAN'S HOUSE AT OLD WINDSOR' (CAT. NO. 90)

An ornamental Chinese bridge with turnstiles over a stream. To the left, a road separating a substantial 17th century red brick house from a summer house behind some trees. Distance, to right, of meadow; a water-cart and other figures and animals on the road and river banks. Sunset sky.

Pen and watercolour over slight pencil indications, 24.7×36.5 cm. (9¾×14⅜ in.) *No. 14615.* *Fig. 8.*

The reflection of the bridge in the water in pencil only; an illegible word written in the sky. The title as given is inscribed in pencil along the bottom in the same hand as No. 1, etc. The date 1750 may be a later addition.

Reprod. Harwood, *op. cit.*, p. 306.

The minute brush-work and tentative washes recall the sketches of the Scottish period (compare especially the trees with those of No. 219) and suggest Paul Sandby as the artist rather than Thomas to whom it has been ascribed (W. Sandby, p. 214).

Accepted as a representation of Manor Cottage by Harwood, who also divined a portrait of the Hon. Richard Bateman in the common-form figure on horseback to the right, this drawing defies precise identification with the locality. The water cannot be either the Thames or the backwater at its confluence with the river.

91. The Old Oak in the Woodyard in Windsor Great Park, near the South End, 1792.

Pencil and watercolour, 29.7×47.7 cm. (11¾×18¾ in.)
PLATE 47　　　　　　　　　　*No. 14621.*

Signed on a log to the left 'Wood Yard W.P. 1792, P.S', and inscribed in (?) the artist's hand in pencil on the mount with the title as given.

The auctioneer's lot number 2—13/2 on both mounts identifies this drawing and No. 92 as Lot 13 on the second day of the 1811 sale, bt. 'Shepperd,' for the Prince of Wales, 2½ guineas. The two drawings are uniformly mounted.

The four drawings, 91-94, are in the loose, late sketching style, outline largely eliminated, softness replacing sharpness, and the scene studied and represented for light and atmosphere rather than for form. The large roller in No. 92 alone has the precision of the early drawings, but three drawings of wood carts at the British Museum (L.B.8 (*a*) and (*b*), and 9 (*a*) for which cf. No. 97) suggest that at the same time Paul Sandby continued to make accurate studies of objects for use in more elaborate drawings.

92. The Wheelwright's Shop in Windsor Great Park, 1792; the shop, a thatched shed, in centre.

Pencil and watercolour, 27.6×42.6 cm. (10⅞×16¾ in.)
PLATE 48　　　　　　　　　　*No. 14618.*

Signed and inscribed 'P.S. 1792' and 'Wood Yard W.P.' and inscribed in pencil on the mount, in the same hand as the preceding, q.v. 'The Weelwright's (*sic*) shop in Windsor G. Park 1792'.

The closed wagon and field roller on the ground to right recur in No. 94.

93. Worksheds and the Master Carpenter's shop etc. in the Woodyard in Windsor Great Park, 1792.

Pencil and watercolour, 18.1×29.7 cm. (7⅛×11¾ in.)
　　　　　　　　　　No. 14619.

Signed on a log to left: P.S. W.Y. W.P. (signifying Paul

Sandby, Woodyard, Windsor Park) and inscribed in pencil at back with title as given, and on the mount in pencil, 'Scene in the Woodyard Wr. Gt. Pk.'

Shown by the auctioneer's lot numbers on the mounts to have formed, with No. 94, Lot 12 in the 1811 sale, second day bt. 'Shepperd', for the Prince of Wales, £2. The pair uniformly mounted.

The shed in the centre appears on the right of No. 94, the tall outhouse on the right and neighbouring shed reappear in the large elaborated gouache No. 96.

94. Part of the Wood Yard in Windsor Great Park, looking to the East Entrance, 1792.

Pencil and watercolour, 18.5×29 cm. (7¼×11⅜ in.) *No. 14620.*

Signed: P.S./Wood Yard W.P./1792. Inscribed in the same hands as No. 93, q.v., at back, in pen, with title as given; on the mount, in pencil, 'Scene in the Woodyard in Windsor Great Park'.

The closed wagon and roller recur in No. 92 and the shed on the right in No. 93.

95. Entrance into the Wood Yard, 1792.

Pencil and watercolour, 27.3×44.5 cm. (10¾×17½ in.) *Fig. 9.*
　　　　　　　　　　No. 17308.

Signed with initials P.S. and inscribed by the artist with pen or brush, 'Enterance [*sic*] into the Wood Yard. W. Park 1792'. A pencil inscription on the old paper mount has been largely erased leaving only the words 'from the back of the Royal Cottage'. Acquired, 1944, from Walker's Galleries, No. 83.

A loose pencil sketch, lightly coloured in green, blue and ochre, of a landscape without incident. Similar lightly coloured sketches of the woodyard, dated 1792, are in the British Museum (L.B. 6 and 7), and compare No. 185A.

The statement in the half-erased pencil inscription regarding the locality of the Woodyard, hitherto unidentified, is confirmed by the description of Lot 80 in T. P. Sandby's Sale in 1827 (see on No. 86) 'Three Views (by Paul Sandby) of the Old Woodyard in Windsor Park, now the scite (*sic*) of His Majesty's Royal Cottage and Garden.'

96. The Woodyard in Windsor Great Park, 1792. Men loading a cart to left; sunset sky.

Gouache, 66×97.5 cm. (26×38⅜ in.) *No. 14622.*

Signed P. Sandby. 1792.

Probably Lot 72 in the third day's sale, 1811. 'A large highly finished view, Scene in the Woodyard of Windsor Park, painted in body colour, on canvas' bt. 'Shepperd', for the Prince of Wales, £12 12s.

The shed and tall out-house are those of No. 93.

Paul Sandby exhibited at the Royal Academy, 1793, two 'Views in the Woodyard, Windsor Great Park' (Nos. 541 and 603) with one of which this large dated drawing may plausibly be identified. Apparently careless, diffuse and gently picturesque, it is characteristic of Sandby's later work and of special interest in its freedom from artificiality on the one hand and from topographical purpose on the other. It is already a pure, unconventional pastoral, treated for its own sake.

FIG. 9. ENTRANCE INTO THE WOOD YARD, 1792 (CAT. NO. 95)

FIG. 10. VIEW IN THE FOREST, 1796 (CAT. NO. 97)

97. View in the Forest, 1796. A gigantic beech tree; brick-kiln and pond to left, timber carting in centre, peasants and lambs in foreground.

Watercolour, on card, with touches of gouache, gum and soot, with washed border in one piece, 40 × 57.2 cm. (15¾ × 22½ in.) *Fig. 10 No. 14616.*

Signed on the trunk of the tree: 'P.S. R.A. Winsor [*sic*] Forest', and in pencil, below, 'P. Sandby, 1796'. The mount inscribed in pencil (? by P. Sandby), 'A view in Windsor Forest', and again in a large 'Colnaghi' hand, 'Windsor Forest by P. Sandby'.

The group of the wood-cart, man, log and team in the foreground is a copy of a careful study from nature in the British Museum (L.B. 9 (a)).

A late, free and atmospheric drawing, intended to be seen at a distance with its loose and slimy brushwork and exaggerated lights and shades. The restless, sinuous lines of the branches and brushwood are emphasised with opaque soot or lamp-black and the shadows deepened with gum; detail is no longer precise, and there are gross disproportions in the figures, etc., of the foreground.

With its exaggeration of emphasis on natural forms, this composition is perfectly adapted to serve as the background for a goblin adventure in a pantomime; but, more seriously, it anticipates the emotional tree studies of Samuel Palmer and the deliberately 'expressionistic' distortions of the 20th century 'romantic' revival.

98. Thomas Sandby.

The Great [now Cumberland] Lodge; the old East front, stables to right, and trees to left, foreground of road and lawn.

Pencil, watercolour and Indian ink, unfinished, on three pieces of paper, joined vertically, 32.6 × 61.5 cm. (12⅞ × 24¼ in.) *No. 14625.*

Inscribed in pencil below, in T. or P. Sandby's hand, 'Old lodge in Windsor Great Park'. A price 10/6 in pencil on the back identifies it with the 'Drawing of the Old Lodge in Windsor Park by Sandby', bought by the Prince of Wales from Colnaghi, Jan. 20th, 1802, for that price (Archives invoice 27172). The title is not specified in the T. Sandby sale 1799.

A first sketch for the following. The pencil work is largely free, without ruler; the position of the trees to the left has been modified. The word 'stables' is written in pencil on the gable of the outbuildings to the right. The washes are loose and in the foreground crude; window panes are put in rather roughly but separately. There are no figures nor spaces left for them. The buildings, etc., are on a much larger scale than in the following.

The Great or Ranger's Lodge, built in the 17th century and enlarged for Charles II, was occupied by the Duke and Duchess of Marlborough and by William, Duke of Cumberland, as Rangers. (See also No. 190.)

99. Thomas Sandby. The same in greater detail with two coaches driving from the stables (one showing the Duke wearing the ribbon of the Garter), ostriches feeding among the trees in the right foreground, deer on the left.

Pencil, pen and grey wash, unfinished, squared, 31.2 × 56 cm. (12¼ × 22 in.) *No. 14626.*

The drawing has been laid down in a modern mount but is perhaps the 'Drawing by Sandby, the Lodge in Windsor Gt. Park' bought for 15s. by the Prince of Wales from Colnaghi on Feb. 13th, 1805 (Archives invoice No. 27293).

The near leader of the front coach is a repetition of the horse in an early etching by Paul Sandby 'after M. Lauron' (Laroon).

The squaring suggests that this version may have been prepared for the engraving by Mason after T. Sandby, 'The Lodge and Stables, etc.' in the Eight Views of Windsor Great Park, 1754, which, in general, follows it closely. Even the clouds which are outlined only in the drawing are exactly reproduced in the print, while shadows of foliage which are indicated in pencil to soften the crude washes of the drawing are carried out fully in the print. On the other hand, the print shows considerable changes in the figures; the second coach is replaced by three riders and two deer, the attitude of a coachman is changed and a hunt servant with hound is introduced in the foreground, left of centre. The buildings are drawn and washed with miniature delicacy; the trees and figures are outlined in pen over pencil, and they have not been superimposed on previous drawing; the trees on the right are mechanically hatched with the pen, those on the left and the leading coach partially washed. Much use is made of the ruler in the drawing of the buildings.

For the Duke of Cumberland's ostriches see Charteris, *William Augustus Duke of Cumberland and The Seven Years War* [1925], p. 23.

100. Thomas Sandby. The same.

Pencil and pen and watercolour, touches of gouache in the trees, 40 × 73.3 cm. (15¾ × 28⅞ in.) *No. 14627.*

PLATE 57

Collection, Paul Sandby, with his mark. Probably Lot 73 on the first day of the 1811 sale, 'T. Sandby, A long tinted drawing of the Great Lodge in Windsor Great Park, 1768, high finished'. Bt. 'Shepperd', for the Prince of Wales, £3 3s.

Exhibited Brussels 1929, No. 158.

An enlargement in colour from the preceding, coming nearer in some respects to the print. The foreground shadows are variegated and improved as indicated in pencil on No. 99 and as completed in the print; also, there are two trees on the right and the Duke has a companion in his coach as in the print, whereas No. 99 shows one tree only and the Duke seated alone. On the other hand, in all the main features of the figures, this drawing follows No. 99 where it differs from the print. A distant group beside a bench near the stables differs from both No. 99 and the print.

The drawing is exceptionally well preserved and the colour adds to the brilliance of the miniature, largely ruler-drawn, detail. A noticeable feature is the light blue colouring, as in an architectural plan, of cornices, piping, leading in the roof, some rails and the rims of wheels. The trees are highly stippled, and with their elaborate building up achieve an appearance of solidity in contrast with the detail of the architecture. The clouds are somewhat dull and heavy, and the underlying acrid green and violent yellow of Thomas Sandby's original characteristic colouring betray themselves in the foreground while the figures, as in the preceding, are inferior in execution to conception, again suggesting tracing or copying from his brother. The horses are especially clumsy. On the other hand, the tiny personages in the distance are well drawn; one of them is a reduction to microscopic size of the drawing of a Negro servant of the Duke, No. 348 in this collection.

The date 1768 affixed to the drawing in the catalogue of the 1811 sale is difficult to explain since the print with which it is intimately connected is dated 1754. By 1768 the Lodge had been remodelled and the Duke, who is represented in the scarlet uniform of Commander-in-Chief which he had relinquished in 1757, had been dead three years. Either the date is wrong or the drawing is a retrospective reconstruction, ignoring the print.

101. Thomas Sandby.
The new North face of the Great (now Cumberland) Lodge, with the stables to the right; in the foreground the stud-groom Barnard Smith lunging a colt; a string of horses being led by grooms from the left to the centre, trees behind.

Pencil, pen and watercolour, unfinished, on three sheets of paper joined vertically, 43.5 × 90 cm. (17⅛ × 35⅜ in.) *No. 14629.*

The drawing has been laid down, but a strong light reveals at the back under the mount an inscription 'By T. Sandby' and a price £1 11s. 6d., which identifies it with a 'Drawing of the Duke of Cumberland Studd' [*sic*] bought by the Prince of Wales from Colnaghi for that price on July 31st, 1799 (Archives invoice No. 27096). 'The Duke's Stud' figures twice in the Thomas Sandby sale, 1799, 2nd Day, Lot 76, and 3rd day, Lot 163.

Some of the drawing of the façade of the house is careful and helped by the ruler, but both there and elsewhere much is free and rough and the colour washes, where they occur, crude. There are many alterations especially in the figures. Large portions are left unfinished, but the trees on the left are worried with a niggling pencil and those above the house neatly hatched with small brush strokes. These details and a certain general freshness suggest that the drawing is an incomplete earlier draft of the following, without the Duke, rather than a repetition dating from a period when it was no longer desired to include him.

An anonymous writer of 1757 quoted by J. P. Hore (*History of the Royal Buckhounds*, 1893) states that the Lodge was then so out of repair that it had to be rebuilt, a plan being then in preparation. Meanwhile the Duke removed to Cranbourne Lodge (see No. 110).

102. Thomas Sandby.
The same, with the addition of a group in the centre foreground: the Duke of Cumberland, in blue with the Star of the Garter, and three attendant gentlemen.

Pencil, pen and watercolour, unfinished, on two sheets joined vertically, Villedary watermark, unmounted, 47.8 × 90 cm. (18⅞ × 35⅜ in.) *No. 14628.*
PLATE 144 (*detail*)

Inscribed in pencil in margin at foot 'Cumberland Lodge', and 'By T. Sandby 15/-' at back, in a 'Colnaghi' hand. Probably, therefore, this is the second drawing with the same title bought at the same time as No. 101 and for the price of 15s.

Studies of the centre group are Nos. 385 and 386 disposed precisely as in the drawing, that of the hussars on the right is No. 387.

The beginning of a more elaborate and generally tidier version with added figures of the Duke and three gentlemen, who are noted on the sketch as Sir Thomas Rich, Lord Albemarle and Thomas Sandby, and showing more care in the portrait of Barnard Smith and his colt. The action of the colt is different, that of the horses in a string and their grooms more varied and, to fit the presence of the Duke as onlooker, coaches and four are indicated as waiting at the door and the escort of hussars as standing at the stable entrance instead of driving and riding away, as they are in the preceding drawing. The architecture is also neater and more elaborate, pilasters flank the door, the cornice is represented more carefully in light and shade, and there are a dial and fence on the lawn to the left of the house. On the other hand, the trees and the other parts which are not completed, are barely indicated, and there is little colour.

103. Thomas Sandby.
Elevation of the new North front of Cumberland Lodge.
Pen and grey wash, the lines ruled throughout. 12.5 × 27.5 cm. (4⅞ × 10⅞ in.) *No. 14630.*
Inscribed in pencil, below, in the same hand as No. 1, etc., 'Elevation of the New front of the Great Lodge in the Gt. Park.'
Architect's elevation for the building shown in Nos. 101 and 102 showing a porch and centre windows of a less ornate character.

104. Thomas or Paul Sandby.
'Near the Great Lodge in the Park'. A sketch of woodland. Two boys, one carrying a kite.
Pencil, 8.3 × 18.4 cm. (3¼ × 7¼ in.) *No. 14631.*
Inscribed below in pencil: 'Near the Gt. Lodge Windsor Gt. Park', in the same handwriting as the preceding.
On the back is part of a receipt, in ink: 'Recd the 23d of June 1787 of Mr. Sandby the Sum of of [*sic*] Two Pounds Twelve Shilings and Six Pence for one Quarters Wadges Due 21th of June by me Francies Cart—[cut off here]—£2: 12: 6:'. Although it is natural to assume that a drawing of the forest on the back of a receipt is by Thomas Sandby who lived at Windsor and would have such scraps of paper in plenty around him, there is no reason why Paul when visiting his brother should not have made use of the local 'salvage' or even have happened to have one of his own receipts among his materials.

105. Gamekeeper's Lodge, Windsor Great Park. An elaborate stone-built Gothic house on the left, a distant view with water to right.
Pencil and watercolour, torn in the centre, 7.5 × 11.2 cm. (3 × 4⅜ in.) *No. 14632.*
Inscribed in pencil at top with the title, as given, in the same hand as the preceding.
The mansion shown on this very small sketch does not correspond to the inscription.

106. The Bishopsgate Entrance to Windsor Great Park, 1801. A red house in the background to right behind large trees which border the road to Englefield Green; the inn to left with a fence and poplars.
Gouache, 63.2 × 88.5 cm. (24⅞ × 34⅞ in.) *No. 14633.*
PLATE 45
Signed, P. Sandby 1801 on root of tree.
Probably No. 77 on the third day of the 1811 P. Sandby Sale 'View of the cottage of — Powney Esq and the entrance to Windsor Great Park at Bishopsgate, bodycolour on canvas'. Bt. 'Shepperd', for the Prince of Wales, £21 10s. 6d.
A full-dress exhibition drawing, remarkable for the effective note of light on the houses seen through trees.
Penyston Portlock Powney, Ranger of the Little Park and M.P. for Windsor, who sold the lease of the Rectorial Manor of Old Windsor in 1786 to Henry Isherwood (cf. No. 243), buying Ockwells, near Bray, with the proceeds (Harwood, *op. cit.*, p. 307), died in 1794 and is said to have been the last member of the family.

107. Attributed to Paul Sandby.
'A Fair at Bishopsgate'. An inn and outbuildings in the background; on the green in front, among trees, numerous figures dancing, drinking at a table, conversing, driving, etc.

Pencil and pen, folded and unmounted, Whatman paper, in border
41×55.7 cm. (16⅛×21⅞ in.) *No. 14623.*

Inscribed in ink on the reverse in an old hand 'Drawing of
a Fare [*sic*] at Bishops Gate Windsor Park £1' and in
another hand 'P. Sandby'. There are also ruled pencil
rectangles and pen scrawls.

Perhaps the 'drawing of a Fair at Bishopgate Windsor Park
by Paul Sandby', bought by the Prince of Wales from
Colnaghi for 15s. on Dec. 11th, 1809 (Archives invoice
No. 27485).

See on No. 108.

108. Attributed to Paul Sandby.

'Outside Bishopsgate'. The same buildings further in the
background; a youth and maiden in the foreground seated
with flocks; a coach and four driving across from the Right.

Pencil and pen, folded and unmounted, in border, 40.5×55 cm.
(16×21⅝ in.) *No. 14624.*

Inscribed in the border, top right, in a large (?) 'Colnaghi'
hand, 'Sandby f', and on the back, in the same hand as is
the preceding, 'Drawing of Winsor [*sic*] Park 2' and 'P.
Sandby' and in pencil at foot, 'a curious Drawing by
Sandby', perhaps in a 'Colnaghi' hand.

Reprod. Harwood, *op. cit.*, p. 254.

These two drawings are crude pastiches in which the figures
are copied or traced, probably from engravings of an earlier
date, but the buildings, being the same from different
aspects, may be genuine sketches of the locality stated.
Possibly the work of a very junior member of the Sandby
family, touched in places by his father or uncle, they yet
possess features which are disconcertingly similar to Thomas
Sandby's work at its worst.

109. Thomas Sandby.

The house occupied by Thomas Sandby in the Great Park,
now the Royal Lodge.

A drive crossed by railings leads straight from the left to the
Lodge in the mid-distance centre. A large tree and a group
of figures left; other trees, a coach, etc., indicated in pencil.

*Pencil, pen and watercolour, double sheet, Villedary watermark,
unmounted,* 50×74 cm. (19⅝×29⅛ in.) *No. 14634.*

Inscribed at the back in a large 'Colnaghi' hand 'Sandby's
House' and with the price 15s., which identifies it with
'A Drawing by Sandby, View of Sandby's House', bought
by the Prince of Wales at that price on Feb. 3rd, 1805, from
Colnaghi (Archives invoice No. 27293).

The house itself in the middle distance, the railings in front
of it and the near posts and rails carefully drawn with pen
and ruler; the railings with remarkable and excessive care.
The house and the trees near it daintily coloured, the
railings left white. All the rest is either left in tentative and
clumsy pencil or very crudely gone over with pen and
colour. The figures are exceedingly stiff and clumsy, some
of those in pen almost as puerile as those in the two preceding drawings.
The large tree with its smooth, bare trunk and heavily-
scrawled penwork in the foliage connects on one side with
No. 147 and on the other side with No. 85. The elaborately
worked and coloured sky recalls No. 90, which is poles apart
in other respects. The general combination of exquisite
detail in the minute architecture with clumsy incompetence
in figure, foreground and colouring may give the measure
of Thomas Sandby when unaided.

The house occupied by T. Sandby as Deputy Ranger
known as the Little or Lower Lodge or the Dairy and
described by Hakewill (*History of Windsor*, 1813, p. 294), as
the small lodge on the left of the road near Cumberland
Lodge, has been so completely remodelled as Royal Lodge
that it is impossible to identify with certainty the building
shown in this drawing. It possesses, however, features in
common with the house shown in later drawings by Paul
Sandby as his brother's residence, e.g., that reproduced
by W. Sandby, p. 20. Other views of that house at the
British Museum are L.B. 3 (*c*) and 4 (*a*).

110. Thomas Sandby.

Cranbourne Lodge—the back of a substantial red brick
house, with wings at right angles and a clock tower, on a
low grass terrace with a lawn below, to right.

Pencil, pen and watercolour, lines ruled, Villedary watermark,
30.5×38.3 cm. (12×15⅛ in.) *No. 14635.*

Inscribed at back 'Cranbourne Lodge' in pencil in the
handwriting of No. 1, etc. Figures 2-6 in the bottom corner,
left, may be either a lot number or the price.

With its crude greens and pinks and heavy washes, this
sketch is clearly only a beginning; the distance, to right,
beyond the lawn is left blank with rough pencil indications
for insertion of objects. The windows are coloured blue with
the details either roughly drawn over the wash in pencil or
pen, or omitted altogether. The sky bold and loose.
Cranbourne Lodge in Windsor Great Park was built by
Richard, Earl of Ranelagh, Paymaster of the Forces, in the
reign of Charles II. It belonged to William Duke of Cumberland who lived in it during the rebuilding of the Great
(Cumberland) Lodge circ. 1757-60. Subsequently occupied
by the Duke of Gloucester it was demolished, with the
exception of a tower which still stands, in 1830.

111. Thomas Sandby. 1752.

A Terrace and Bowling Green; a long straight gravel walk
between young trees to the right, a distant view to the
left, gardeners levelling worm-casts on the green and
gentlemen strolling and conversing on the lawn and walk.

*Pen, watercolour and gouache on two pieces of paper (watermark
Villeday) joined vertically, dulled and discoloured from exposure,*
42.5×111.5 cm. (16¾×43⅞ in.) *No. 14636.*

PLATE 51

Signed, lower right: T. Sandby delin. Septemr 19. 1752.

Exhib. *Country Life*, 1937, No. 479.

The small figure of the man reading as he walks, the man
looking through a telescope and the man walking along the
gravel path occur together in No. 231, also in green coats,
but in a different relation to each other. The gardener on
the extreme left is from a pen and grey wash study in the
British Museum (L.B.137, No. 12 (*a*)), where he is one of
three scythers.
The locality has hitherto been regarded as the old Bowling
Green at the eastern end of Windsor Castle which was laid
out by Charles II in 1663 as is shown by documents in the
Royal Library, and was displaced in or about 1786 for the
East Terrace under George III. As Sir Owen Morshead has
pointed out, there is no authority for this identification nor is
it borne out by the configuration of the ground. The drawing
most probably represents the Terrace and Bowling Green of
Cranbourne Lodge in the Great Park which are marked 'C'
on a manuscript 'Map of Cranbourne Chace' of about the
same date in the Royal Library (Fig. 11). Further, since one
of the four similarly shaped views of Windsor Great Park by
Thomas Sandby (No. 114) has also been hitherto wrongly

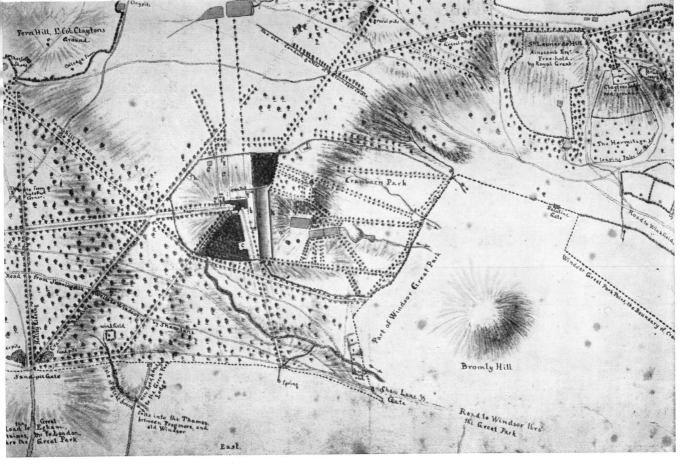

FIG. 11. CRANBOURNE CHACE. (FROM A MS. MAP OF C. 1750 IN THE ROYAL LIBRARY)

named and is shown by the same map to be a view in the neighbourhood of Cranbourne Lodge, it is more than merely tempting to find in this and the four following drawings the survivors of a set of 'Six Different views of Cranbourne Lodge and park' which are mentioned in the *Windsor Guide* of 1768, as decorating the Dressing Room in the Ranger's, i.e. Cumberland Lodge where, in the 'Bed Chamber', there were also 'four views of the Lodge and the Battle of Culloden'.

The figures were almost certainly furnished, and perhaps executed, by Paul Sandby; except some minute animals in No. 114, no others occur in this series of five landscapes. This, too, alone has been heavily worked with gouache which has become sadly discoloured.

The highly laboured foliage and bare tree trunks, the minute delineation of the fencing, the sharp rectangular spaces and perspectives and the crude colour washes, are distinctive of Thomas Sandby's manner at this date. The distance to the left, though much discoloured, shows the utmost minuteness of detail, and the darkening of the belt of trees which frames the middle distance displays picturesque feeling.

112. Thomas Sandby.

In Windsor Great Park. A rustic seat between trees on the extreme left; in the distance, beyond an open space with scattered clumps of trees, wooded hills on which are, left, a cottage among trees and, right, two houses or a house with large outbuildings, also among trees. Below, and somewhat to the left of, the latter, on another rise, a summer

house which may be that shown in the foreground of No. 113. Towards the extreme right a view over open country.

Pen and watercolour, much faded and damaged, on two sheets of paper, joined vertically, 42.5×110 cm. (16¾×43¼ in.)

No. *14637.*

The identification of the view, as stated on the frame, as 'from Sandpit Gate looking North', has no known authority and is probably as unfounded as those of No. 114 and the preceding drawing. The appearance of the park has been so much changed through the cutting down of all the woods which were full grown two hundred years ago and the planting of all those which exist now that, without more recognisable landmarks than the distant buildings in this drawing, any identification is most hazardous. Assuming, however, that these five uniform drawings were among the six hanging in the Dressing Room of Cumberland Lodge in the latter half of the 18th century, the distant house and its outbuildings may be supposed to be Cranbourne Lodge and the summer house in its neighbourhood would show the next drawing to be a view in the same vicinity, as is, without doubt, No. 114.

The drawing has been left unfinished in the foreground, where loose pencil outlines on rough washes of colour show that more foreground trees and vegetation were intended. Technically these indications, together with the unfinished fields of colour in Nos. 113 and 115, are of the utmost interest. The rough pencil work was not meant to be seen in the finished work, but the patches of loose colour, grey, green or blue, all now somewhat faded, were intended to be worked up into foliage in the same colour with the brush or with pen touches of black. This technique no more corresponds to the conventional description of the early watercolour method as limited to pen outline subsequently washed over with even tints than does the contemporary work of Alexander Cozens. It is nearer to that of miniature painting, the brushwork being truly painting, minute though it be, and the foliage distinctly articulated with the brush. So far from the pen being dominant in the drawing, it is merely used to help out the brush where a finer touch is needed.

113. Thomas Sandby.

Windsor Great Park. A rustic summer house under trees in the right foreground, a red brick house in a glade to right.

Pencil, pen and watercolour, on two sheets of paper (watermark Villedary) torn and discoloured, 43.5 × 110 cm. (17⅛ × 43¼ in.)
PLATE 53   *No. 14638.*

Some small trees and other details in the foreground are merely indicated in pencil and not coloured, and in the large trees to right some large patches of grey and blue-green wash have not been worked up as in the foliage generally. The pen is used for the timbers of the summer house and the fence around it. The clouds and shadows are lighter and more fluid than in the others of this series.

The minute house on the right, the only identifiable object in this panorama of woodland and open park, may be Cranbourne Lodge. The summer house may be the same as in No. 112.

114. Thomas Sandby 1752.

Windsor Great Park from near Cranbourne Lodge. The Castle, Eton College Chapel, etc., visible in the distance above a wooded hollow with two rectangular ponds.

Pen and watercolour on two sheets joined vertically (Villedary watermark) torn and discoloured, 42.2 × 109.5 cm. (16⅝ × 43⅛ in.) *No. 14639.*
PLATE 52

Signed T. Sandby delin Aug. 25 1752 (the date of the month torn).

Heavy shadows and a tendency to straight outlines and rectangular forms recall the drawing of the Bowling Green, No. 111, and, as in that drawing, a darker strip of forest separates and sets off the distance, which is of the utmost minuteness. The tiny cattle and horses are well drawn, the poultry dotted about the near field disproportionately large. The clouds are fluidly put in and the reflections in the pond elaborately worked up.

The two rectangular ponds in the hollow, which are prominent features in this view, still exist as marshy willow-beds below Cranbourne Lodge, and they are clearly marked on the contemporary plan of Windsor Park (Fig. 11). Even the dam across the lower pond, which is seen in the drawing, is marked on that plan. Trees crowning Bromly Hill now hide the Castle from the foot of Cranbourne Tower, but it is visible, as in the drawing, from the leads. The previous title 'From Bishopsgate, looking West', may therefore safely be discarded.

115. Thomas Sandby.

Windsor Great Park with Virginia Water; from near Fort Belvedere, looking North, the obelisk in the central middle distance, a house, a wooden bridge and the cascade at the end of the lake on the right, another house upon an island to the left.

Pencil and watercolour, a little pen, unfinished and faded, on two sheets of paper joined vertically, 43.7 × 111.3 cm. (17¼ × 43⅞ in.)
PLATES 54 and 55   *No. 14640.*

Boats, trees and reflections on the lake are indicated in pencil but left without colour and microscopic figures on a

FIG. 12. VIRGINIA WATER: THE CASCADE AND GROTTO. (UNPUBLISHED ENGRAVING, TOUCHED BY HAND)

road have been too much for the artist's brush. The foreground is bare and there are unfinished patches in the foliage where the ground colour of warm grey or blue green has not been worked up with the brush. The lines of the lake show the stiffness of the military draughtsman and map maker, but the disposition of the details is skilful and their colour in blue or green grey carefully graded under a pale blue sky with grey clouds.

This drawing is unique in showing the full extent of the lake before the destruction of the pond-head and the subsequent extension towards Egham (see on No. 120). The small bridge and the cascade are shown more fully in the engraving, 'The Cascade and Grotto', in the eight views of 1754 and in the unpublished plate of that series of which a touched proof is in the Royal Library (Fig. 12).

116. After Paul Sandby (by M. A. Rooker).

The New Lodge [the Belvedere] built by the late Duke of Cumberland on Shrubs Hill, Windsor Forest.

Pen and watercolour, 13.3 × 18.7 cm. (5¼ × 7⅜ in.) Album *Drawings of Windsor Castle*, p. 50.

Signed: M. A. Rooker 1776. (MAR in monogram).

Identical with the print by M. A. Rooker after Paul Sandby, of June 1st, 1777, with title as given above, No. 5 in Sandby's *150 Select Views*.

A companion view in the same album showing the Belvedere from another aspect, of the same size but without signature, may have the same origin. The signature (which may be accepted as genuine if only because a forger would have written 'Sandby') strengthens the suspicion, already aroused by the drawings themselves, that other versions of subjects by the Sandbys reduced to the size of the engravings, e.g. No. 196 and British Museum, L.B. P. Sandby, 31-33 and L.B. T. Sandby, 1, 2, 5, are copies or adaptations by the engravers of drawings by the brothers; see also on No. 8.

117. Removing a hulk (afterwards decorated as a Chinese junk) from the Thames near the 'Bells of Ouseley' to Virginia Water.

Pencil, 12.5 × 27.2 cm. (4⅞ × 10¾ in.) *No. 14641.*

Inscribed in pencil, at foot, in Paul Sandby's handwriting, 'Removing a vessel from the Thames at Old Windsor to the Great Park Lake' and in centre above the inscription, the pencil 'F' mark (see on No. 1).

On the reverse, rough pencil sketches of groups of spectators, some mounted and others on foot.

118. The same in greater detail. Old Windsor Church and houses in the distance.

Pen and watercolour, largely black, over pencil. Touches of gouache in the foliage, 22 × 63.5 cm. (8⅝ × 25 in.) *No. 14642.*
PLATE 56

From the Acland book of drawings.

Inscribed in ink at back in Paul Sandby's hand, the first eleven words over an older inscription in pencil: 'View on the Thames from the Bells of Ousley public House, taken during the removal of a Vessel from the Thames, to the Home Lake in Windsor Great Park, afterwards decorated as a Chinese Junck'. In the word 'Vessel' the short 's' precedes the long as in Nos. 78, 408 and 409.

Indications of colour, etc., pencilled in the sky above the distance.

The animation and variety of the figures, their studied complication of attitude, the free minute drawing of distant objects and the heavy blacks are all characteristic of Paul Sandby, if the bright raw colouring, blue green and amber, are more frequently associated with Thomas.

A completed drawing in gouache (until recently anonymous) is in the Victoria and Albert Museum, No. 113—1898 (reprod. Harwood, *op. cit.*, p. 256).

Since the junk appears complete in an engraving of 1753 and in the Sandbys' *Eight Views* of 1754, these two sketches can safely be dated a year or so earlier, whatever may be the date of the finished gouache.

119. Thomas Sandby.

'View from the North Side of the Virginia River near the Manour Lodge'.

In the centre under two large trees, the Duke of Cumberland wearing the ribbon of the Garter on his right shoulder addresses the (?) King who stands alone, and points with his outstretched left arm to the lake which occupies the right half of the drawing. Boats, including the Chinese junk, on the lake. Between the royal group and the lake a coach and six from which a lady descends. To the left, a crowd or spectators; hills and trees beyond.

Watercolour, 44 × 78 cm. (17⅜ × 30¾ in.) W. Sandby, p. 214.
No. 14646.

Perhaps the 'Drawing of a view of Virginia Water by Sandby' bought by the Prince of Wales from Colnaghi on Feb. 6th, 1802, for 12s. (Archives invoice 27174), but the low price would fit No. 138 better. The back and mount of this drawing cannot be examined.

The engraving, with the title as given, by P. Sandby after T. Sandby in the *Eight Views* of 1754, shows several variations of which the chief is that the enigmatic figure, without decorations, in the centre, who is taken to be George II, is replaced by an unmistakable youth bearing the Garter (also on the right shoulder), presumably the future King George III. The landscape, left, is also much altered, the boats somewhat differently disposed, and figures are altered and added.

Two pairs of figures among the spectators, the two young ladies facing right and the mother with a child in her arms and a girl leaning on her shoulder, are subjects of etchings by Paul Sandby, the latter dated 1756. Both pairs recur in drawings of the Piazza, Covent Garden, at the British Museum (L.B., Thomas Sandby, 17 and 18). With an alteration in one figure, which is also made in the print of this subject, the whole group of five persons containing these two ladies recurs in No. 163 in this collection, the young man on the left of the group being also No. 367 (in reverse). The principal lady between the Duke and the coach and the young lady beside a horseman in the background are respectively very close to No. 297 combined with 293, and Nos. 263 and 264. The study used for the young man standing beside a tree and raising his hat is in the British Museum (L.B. 136, No. 25 (*b*), red chalk and in reverse 137, No. 50, with grey and brown wash). Drawings or tracings of the junk are Nos. 407-409.

There is another version of this drawing, squared but not quite finished, at the British Museum (L.B. T. Sandby 7). It is in general more careful in execution, especially in the figures, and the distance beyond the lake is delicate. In this example, except for the junk, which is carefully if mechanically drawn, every feature is indifferent, the foliage perfunctory, the boats clumsy and the figures and horses especially coarse and ungainly. The Duke has ceased to possess any of his generally very recognisable features, and the figure supposed to be that of the King in the British Museum version and recognisably the Prince of Wales in the print, here wears a uniform plum-coloured dress without orders and has a white wig, while a different figure in a brown suit behind the Duke has the ribbon of the Garter, like the Duke himself, on the wrong shoulder. These details, together with the general clumsiness of the workmanship, may be held to absolve Thomas Sandby from the execution of this version, though it is not an exact copy either of the drawing at the British Museum or of the print.

Manor Lodge is stated by Lysons (*Magna Britannia*, 1806, Vol. 1, p. 415) to have stood at the entrance to the Park near Virginia Water, and is marked on the old maps as standing in the fork to the west of the arm leading north to Cumberland Lodge. It is perhaps shown on No. 115.

120. Paul and Thomas Sandby.

'The Great Bridge over the Virginia River'.

The old wooden bridge with, in the right foreground, the Duke of Cumberland in a green coat on horseback, directing a group of workmen. In the distance, above the Duke's head, Fort Belvedere.

Pencil, pen and watercolour with black border at foot, gouache in trees, rubbed and soiled, 31×57.4 cm. (12¼×22⅝ in.) *No. 14647.*
PLATE 58

W. Sandby, p. 215, who omits the part of the inscription which states that the drawing is the work of both brothers.

Inscribed in ink on the back of the mount (which is that of the drawings sold in 1811) in Paul Sandby's handwriting: 'View of the great Wooden Bridge over the Virginia River in Windsor Great Park built for His Royal Higness [*sic*] William Duke of Cumberland, by Mr. Fleetcroft [*sic*] in the year 1760, which went soon to decay, and an elegant Stone Bridge was afterwards Erected by T. Sandby Esqr— This drawing was made by the two Brothers T. and P. Sandby Esqrs' and again, to the right, 'Wrote by Paul Sandby 1807'. On the mount, at foot to right, 'The Late Duke of Cumberland', and, at top, traces of an attribution to Sandby, both in a large 'Colnaghi' hand. On the back of the drawing under the mount 'Windsor Great Park'.

Engraved with the title given above in the set of eight Windsor Views, 1754 (T. Sandby *delin*. P. Sandby *sculpsit*) with additional figures of workmen and elaboration of reflections, lighting and background.

The bridge, the construction of which is very carefully marked, has been left uncompleted, the further balustrade and figures being only indicated in pencil. Several pen lines are ruled.

Another version, also in watercolour, of the left half of this drawing, showing the bridge and figures under it, is at the British Museum (L.B. Thomas Sandby 27 (1)). The bridge and the figures upon it are completed and the distance more detailed, the water without boats but the reflections more elaborate, the figures and horses similar but somewhat slighter. Individual studies for the subject in the album (L.B. 138) of Paul Sandby's sketches at the British Museum are No. 58, the man digging in front of a horse and cart (the horse somewhat different and absent from the drawing just mentioned); No. 66, the man to the right dragging a wheelbarrow (with another digger absent from the finished drawing), and No. 21, a tamper similar to, but not included among, those in the finished drawing. Two of the workmen occur, in reverse, in one of Paul Sandby's early etched *culs-de-lampe*.

Thomas Sandby's 'elegant stone bridge', more fortunate than his other structures, still stands on the north arm of Virginia Water, below Johnson's Pond, then known as the Great Lake, and Cumberland Lodge. The previous bridge, built by Henry Flitcroft (1697-1769, Comptroller of the Works from 1758), figures largely in the old *Windsor Guides* as 'of most curious architecture, and on a bold and noble plan, being one single arch, one hundred and sixty-five feet wide in the clear, which is five feet wider than the boasted Rialto'. In the *Guide* for 1783 it is noted that 'a few years since, the pond head blowing up, the rapidity of the torrent did such material damage to the bridge that the whole was obliged to be taken down and is now rebuilding with five arches to it'. In 1791 and '92 a footnote was appended saying that the new bridge had 'lately been erected'. If, as is generally assumed, the damage to Flitcroft's bridge was due to the great storm of Sept. 1st, 1768, the effect of which on the pondhead and lake was mentioned by Mrs. Delany immediately afterwards (*Correspondence*, IV., 159), 'a few years since' is a strange way of describing 15 years. Moreover the *Guide* of 1774 says nothing about any damage but merely repeats the phrases of previous issues. It is conceivable but unlikely that there were two storms, the latter alone affecting the bridge.

It is characteristic of Paul Sandby's carelessness in these retrospective notes on his drawings that he should speak of Flitcroft's bridge as having been erected in 1760 when this very representation of it had been engraved by himself in 1754. The bridge also appears in his subscription plate for the 1754 series and in the print (by Canot after T. Sandby) of The New Building on Shrub's Hill in that series.

121. Thomas Sandby.

Design for an arch in Roman style embodying fragments of ruins.

Pencil, pen and watercolour, scaled. Compass and other pin holes, paper without watermark but apparently the same as that of No. 122 (q.v.), 40.5×57.8 cm. (16×22¾ in.) *No. 14648.*

122. Thomas Sandby.

Design for a Gothic arch among ruins.

Pencil, pen and watercolour, Villedary watermark, 37.5×61.2 cm. (14¾×24⅛ in.) *No. 14649.*

On the reverse the beginning in pencil of a large woodland landscape.

There were no ruins at Virginia Water in the time of the Sandbys; they were erected by Wyatville after 1826. The vista through the arch in this drawing which seems to show Virginia Water and, possibly, the tower projected in Nos. 145 and 146, suggest, however, that a ruined arch was already contemplated by Thomas Sandby as an appropriate embellishment of the ornamental water, and these two bold and pleasantly coloured drawings may be his projects for it. Alternative designs in Gothic and classical styles for the same bridge are shown on Nos. 123 and 124 (*verso*).

123—141. Thomas Sandby.

Sketches, elevations and plans for works in Windsor Great Park and at Virginia Water.

Of the two most considerable, No. 123 (14650) shows, in plan and elevation, an embattled Gothic bridge over a low cascade; No. 124 (14651) a plan for a drive at the edge of the Park crossing the water by a bridge which adjoins that for the main road from Egham to Bagshot. Pencil sketches on the back for a bridge of generally similar character but with classical features connect the two sheets. Both are on a coarse grey paper which is used for the bulk of the other sketches as well as for a smaller and more careful study of rocks among the Sandby studies at the Victoria and Albert Museum (D. 169-1901, with colour notes in pencil and therefore perhaps a study from nature) and for an elaborate sketch of some generally similar scheme bequeathed to that Museum by Mr. B. S. Long (P. 89-1937), which, however, though possibly connected with Windsor Park, cannot relate to Virginia Water.

Nos. 125 (14652), 126 (14653) and 127 (14654) are studies for the rock work of a low cascade, the latter pair when joined together showing on the reverse an uncoloured sketch for a similar detail, and Nos. 128-130 (14655 (on white paper)-14657), 131 and 132 (14663 and 4), sketches for a low rustic bridge or bridges, with rock work. Nos. 133 and 134 (14658 and 9) are elaborate sketches of a high cascade and Nos. 135-137 (14665-7), of a grotto which is perhaps combined with it in No. 136. These probably relate to the rebuilding of the dam and cascade at Virginia Water after the flood or floods (see on Nos. 115 and 120), but they show the grotto which, according to the *Windsor Guide* of 1783, p. 102, did not require rebuilding, in a different relation to the waterfall. Sketches for somewhat similar cascades in one of the volumes at the Soane Museum (wrongly described by W. Sandby, p. 223) are shown by a reference to the level of the Thames to be unrelated to Virginia Water.

Nos. 138-141 are on white paper of different manufactures. No. 138 (14660), which alone of these drawings is mounted (with a 'Colnaghi' inscription, see on No. 119) shows a portion of the lake with a bridge, a large brick house beyond and a public road with coaches and a rider. The same bridge, which is apparently quite unrelated to that of 124 and 125, is shown on the sketch plan No. 139 (14661). No. 140 (14662), a plan of roads round a portion of a lake, does not seem to be connected with either.

Several of these sheets have miscellaneous pencil sketches on the back and bear pencil inscriptions of various dates, 'Virginia Water', 'T. Sandby' and 'P. Sandby'. Eleven bear comparatively recent numbers up to 26, showing that they at one time formed part of some larger series. There is nothing to identify them with the anonymous '13 Plans of Bridges in Windsor Great Park', '3 Drawings of the Cascade and Grotto in Windsor Great Park' or 'Two Sections of the Head of Virginia River' mentioned on p. 169 (281) of the 'George III' Inventory as contained in a 'Portfolio of Drawings of the Royal Palaces'. Nor is it likely that any of them would have been attributed to Paul Sandby. Another provenance is suggested by a note on a very crude sketch of a single-span rustic bridge No. 141 (14668) in pen and sepia on white paper with Villedary watermark. 'Not T.S. From Palser's Collection of Plans of Virginia Water'. A sketch recognised as spurious would scarcely have been chosen by itself out of a dealer's stock. 'Various sketches for Virginia Water' were included in W. Sandby's list, p. 214, of T. Sandby's drawings at Windsor.

142. Attributed to T. Sandby.

Sketch-design for a summer-house with conical thatched roof, a Gothic window and an open front supported by rustic columns. Background of trees.

Pen and watercolour, unmounted, 22.2 × 23.7 cm. (8¾ × 9⅜ in.) No. 14715.

Signed or inscribed in ink, at foot, right, 'T. Sandby', and inscribed at the back in pencil by J. H. Glover, a former Royal Librarian, 'at Frogmore?'

A clumsy and insignificant sketch with just enough general resemblance to the summer-house in No. 113 to support the attribution to T. Sandby. Sketches by him for a somewhat similar but more restrained summer-house are at the Soane Museum (Nos. 227 and 8).

143. Attributed to T. Sandby.

Sketch elevation of a thatched cottage with a circular porch and wings.

On the reverse a slight but neat architectural sketch and an inscription 'at Frogmore?' identical with that on Nos. 142 and 144.

Pencil and watercolour, unmounted, 15.5 × 27.4 cm. (6⅛ × 10¾ in.) No. 14716.

Even more clumsy than the preceding.

144. Attributed to T. Sandby.

Sketch design for a rustic, two-storied hermitage or summer-house, formed of gnarled tree trunks with branches, thatched and preceded by a porch.

Pen and watercolour, 19.5 × 28.8 cm. (7⅝ × 11⅜ in.) No. 14669.

Inscribed T. Sandby in pencil at foot and on back 'at Frogmore?' in pencil, as on the two preceding drawings.

145. Thomas Sandby.

A Gothic Tower proposed to be erected at Virginia Water. Front elevation.

Pen, ink and watercolour, with scale in feet, on a double sheet, Pieter van der Ley watermark, unmounted, 99 × 66 cm. (39 × 26 in.) No. 14671.

Inscribed on the back in pencil in a modern hand, 'T. Sandby, Gothic Tower proposed to be erected at Virginia Water'.

See on No. 146.

146. Thomas Sandby.

The same, side or back elevation.

Pen and ink, some details in pencil, dimensions and paper as for the preceding.   No. 14670.

A very large number of studies and designs in Gothic architecture was contained in the Thomas Sandby sale of 1799. The colouring of these drawings, especially the meticulously executed brickwork of No. 145, is sufficiently characteristic to justify the attribution to him, although no tower of this description exists, or is known to have been intended, at Virginia Water.

147. Thomas and Paul Sandby.

Ascot Heath Races.

On the right, stands and marquees under a large tree and beyond it; in front, a crowd of race-goers, including some on horseback; the course with the winning-post and a finish from the centre to the left; beyond, further large crowds with coaches. In the distance wooded country.

Pencil, pen and watercolour on two pieces of paper joined vertically, Villedary watermark, water-stained and dulled through exposure, 49 × 90.6 cm. (19¼ × 35⅝ in.) No. 14675.

PLATES 59 and 60

Nos. 251 and 252 are studies used in this drawing; a very Seymour-like pencil drawing of a galloping racehorse and jockey at the British Museum (L.B. 137, No. 55a) may also have been used, much reduced. For the hussar in the foreground see on No. 387.

Reprod. Hughes, *History of Windsor Forest*, 1890, opp. p. 384. Cawthorne and Herod, *Royal Ascot*, 1900, facing p. 16.

'A drawing by Sandby, a View of Ascot Heath Races', was bought from Colnaghi by the Prince of Wales for 5 guineas on August 1st, 1799 (Archives invoice 27097), and was no doubt the 'fine View of a Horse Race' which formed, with three other drawings, Lot 11 on the first day of the Thomas Sandby Sale on July 18th preceding. The attribution to 'Sandby', unless it simply implies Paul, as is usually the case, may be due to the vendor's doubts whether the drawing could be by Thomas, among whose possessions it was sold. Certainly the large tree, the wooden booth under it, and the minute details of the distant landscape may be paralleled in his work; but the variety in the microscopic figures of riders, carriages, etc., which fill the space between the crowd and the distant trees, the invention and number of the principal figures and the facility in the grouping are far beyond anything that we know of his powers. There is no reason to doubt that the larger studies of figures used in this drawing are by Paul, and they are transferred to it with a greater sense of proportion than is common with him. In the nearest parallel, the drawing of 'The Bells of Ouseley' at the Victoria and Albert Museum for which the preliminary sketches are in the Royal Collection (Nos. 117 and 118), disproportion of figures and groups proclaims the piecing together in the studio of separately conceived details and goes far to counteract the freshness of the original sketches. That Paul was capable of contriving so homogeneous a crowd is shown by an elaborate drawing on a miniature scale of Edinburgh, dated 1751, which was in the market in London in 1939 or '40 but is now unfortunately untraceable In the 'Bells of Ouseley', too, the humour and action are more forced than in this drawing, but these characteristic qualities are observable even in the smallest details of the background where the drawing has the minute deftness of his etchings.

The drawing had probably suffered sadly while in Thomas Sandby's possession; otherwise it would scarcely have made so modest an appearance as one of a lot of four among architectural studies, plans and designs in the posthumous sale of his property. It does not appear to have been framed till recently in the Royal Library, and there is therefore no reason why it should have become still further discoloured. Had it retained its original brilliance of colour it would no doubt rank as Paul Sandby's masterpiece in this genre, and there is nothing but a certain stiffness and sense of effort in the individual figures to deny it a high position among such works or to explain why he abandoned figure subjects and reserved his talent of characterisation and humour for the incidents of his landscapes and occasional excursions into anonymous caricature.

The Races at Ascot were re-established by William Duke of Cumberland as Ranger in 1746. It is possible that he is represented in one of the carriages beyond the racecourse, but it is surprising that he is not placed in a more prominent position, even to the detriment of the composition, as he is in 'The Bells of Ouseley'.

148. Thomas Sandby.

A Design for the King's Booth at Ascot.

Pencil, pen and watercolour, 22.3 × 32 cm. (8¾ × 12⅝ in.)
                                                    No. *14676*.

Inscribed in pencil with the title as given above and 'by T. Sandby'. Probably the 'Design for the King's Booth at Ascot by Paul Sandby' bought by the Prince of Wales from Colnaghi on June 5th, 1811, for 1 guinea (Archives invoice 27637). The Lot number 3—5/5 which remains on the mount may, despite a difference in the number of drawings included, connect it with Lot No. 5 on the third day of the 1811 Sale, 'T. Sandby. 4 Architectural Sketches', bought by Colnaghi for £1 17s. This or the next lots may have contained Nos. 188 (which has the mark of Paul Sandby's collection) and 189, the mounts of which are identical with this and No. 66, the lettering and mount of which are very similar. Similar architectural drawings by Thomas Sandby at the British Museum (L.B. 27, Nos. 2 and 3) are mounted and inscribed in the same way.

The drawing is scarcely an architectural elevation but a completed sketch, at an angle from the left, of a two-storied pavilion in a railed enclosure, with a sentry on each side, trees and tents with persons regaling in the background left, and a horse race in progress on the right. It is comparatively freely drawn and washed with loose transparent colouring; the accessory figures and details recalling the Encampment scenes of 1780. This may represent Thomas Sandby's later manner, but it is equally likely that the drawing has been completed by Paul Sandby or 'dressed up' for the sale by his son.

The first permanent Royal Stand at Ascot was erected by Nash in 1822.

149. Landscape composition. An old beech tree, with faggot-gatherers at foot, on a river bank beyond which are cottages and hills.

Watercolour and gouache, watermark Whatman, removed from canvas, much dulled through exposure, 64.3 × 94.2 cm. (25⅜ × 37⅛ in.) *No. 14677*.
PLATE 72

Formerly No. 1342 in the Windsor Inventory of Pictures (Lord Chamberlain's Department). Conceivably the drawing referred to on No. 87 as bought at the 1811 sale.

W. Sandby noted on Feb. 8th, 1892, with reference to this drawing, 'The tree is said to be a stump beech in Sir R. Burdett's park in Staffordshire'. Four drawings of trees in that park formed Lots 92 and 93 in the Paul Sandby sale of 1817, first day. The subject might perhaps equally well be identified with the more famous beech tree near Sandpit Gate of which J. T. Smith tells in his *Book for a Rainy Day*, p. 113, that it served for years as the residence of a woodman, his wife, four children, a sow and a numerous breed of pigs, and when it was cut down its accumulated incrustations of peat-smoke furnished Paul Sandby with masses of the finest bistre.

III. THE DUKE OF CUMBERLAND'S CAMPAIGNS.

150. Thomas Sandby.

Plan of the Battle of Culloden, April 16th, 1746.
Pen and watercolour, with key and additional data below, folded and torn before mounting, 32 × 42.5 cm. (12⅝ × 16¾ in.) *No. 17177*.
                                                    Fig. 13.

Signed and dated: T. Sandby delint: April 23rd, 1746, at Inverness.

Transferred from the Cumberland Papers, Vol. x, No. 28.

A portion of a copy reprod. Evan Charteris. *William Duke of Cumberland, his early life*, 1913, facing p. 266.

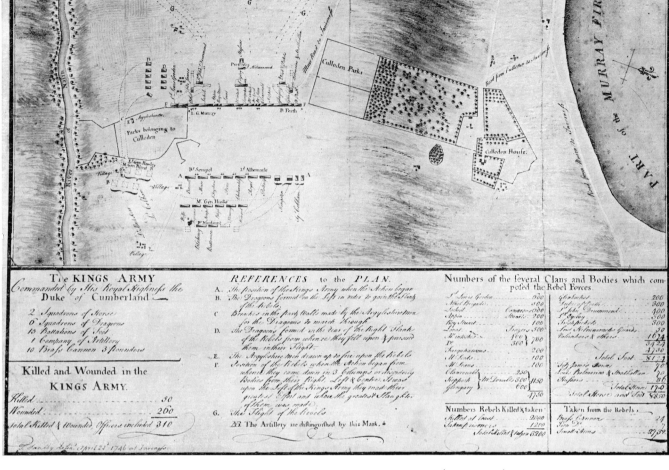

The KINGS ARMY

Commanded by His Royal Highness the Duke of Cumberland

2 Squadrons of Horse
6 Squadrons of Dragoons
15 Batalions of Foot
1 Company of Artillery
10 Brass Cannon 3 pounders

Killed and Wounded in the KINGS ARMY.

Killed........................50
Wounded.......................260
Total Killed & Wounded, Officers included 310

T. Sandby Delin. April 23. 1746 at Inverness.

REFERENCES to the PLAN.

A. The Position of the Kings Army when the Action began.
B. The Dragoons formed on the Left in order to gain the Rear of the Rebels.
C. Breaches in the Park Walls made by the Argyleshiremen for the Dragoons to march through.
D. The Dragoons formed in the rear of the Right Flank of the Rebels from whence they fell upon & pursued them in their Flight.
E. The Argyleshire men drawn up to fire upon the Rebels
F. Position of the Rebels when the Action began from whence they came down in 3 Columns or disorderly Bodies from their Right, Left & Centre. It was upon the Left of the Kings Army they made their greatest Effort and where the greatest Slaughter of them was made.
G. The Flight of the Rebels
N.B. The Artillery are distinguished by this Mark.

Numbers of the several Clans and Bodies which composed the Rebel Forces.

S.t Lewis Gordon	500	Glenbuket	200
Athol Brigade	500	Dukes of Perth	300
Lochel	Camerons 800	S.t John Drummond	400
Appin	Stuarts 200	L.d Ogilvy	300
Roy Stuart	100	Kilmarnock	300
Lovat	Frazers 500	Lord Kilmarnocks Guards	50
D.n	300 } 700	Volunteers & others	1674
Farquharsons	200		3424
M.c Leods	100		4750
M.c Intosh	100	Total Foot	8174
Clanronald	250	S.t James Horse	70
Keppoch	M.c Donalds 300 } 1150	Lord Balmerino's Battallion	70
Glengary	600	Huzzars	86
	4750	Total Horse	176
		Total Horse and Foot	8350

Numbers Rebels Killed & taken

Killed at least................2000
Taken & wounded................1200
Total Killed & taken 3200

Taken from the Rebels.

Brass Cannon.................24
Iron D.o
Small Arms....................2750

FIG. 13. THOMAS SANDBY. PLAN OF THE BATTLE OF CULLODEN (CAT. NO. 150)

A Sketch of the Field of Battle at CULLODEN by T Sandby 1746

FIG. 14. THOMAS SANDBY. THE BATTLE OF CULLODEN (CAT. NO. 151)

151. Thomas Sandby.

'A Sketch of the Field of Battle at Culloden 1746'; from a point looking down the lines; the Highlanders attacking; in the distance a view of Moray Firth.

Pencil and watercolour, a little pen, 29.2 × 53.1 cm. (11½ × 20⅞ in.) No. 14722. Fig. 14.

The title, as given, lettered in ink on the mount below the drawing, with 'by T. Sandby 1746'. Under the drawing at left, a pencilled inscription, explaining an indication 'A' on the drawing as 'Barrell's Regiment' and on the drawing itself, also in pencil, the 'Duke of Cumberland' (centre left), 'Kingston's Regiment' and 'Murray Firth'.

W. Sandby, p. 213. Exhibited Nottingham, 1884, No. 5.

A loose and rapid sketch, but if any part of it were made on the spot, the three Highlanders rushing forward and firing immediately in front of the artist's viewpoint are surely a subsequent addition.

152. Thomas Sandby.

Fort Augustus. The fort, partly ruined, in the centre middle distance with the camp to the left; in the foreground, a group of officers to the left playing 'nine-holes' and a team of four horses hauling a gun towards the centre; in the distance, mountains and a loch winding to the sea. An ornamental cartouche below with battle scenes on each side of the title-space.

Pen and grey wash lightly coloured, on a card with border and cartouche, 28.4 × 70 cm. (11⅛ × 27½ in.). No. 14724. Fig. 15.

Inscribed in pencil 'Fort Augustus' within the cartouche in a nineteenth century hand; and 'by Sandby', below, in a 'Colnaghi' hand (cf. on Nos. 154 and 157), a 'T' inserted later before 'Sandby'. At the back a price £3 3s. which identifies it with 'A Drawing of a Camp by Sandby' bought

by the Prince of Wales from Colnaghi for that price on June 20th, 1804 (Archives invoice No. 27266).

The two onlookers at the game in the left-hand corner are identical with two figures on the right of the etching 'South West View of Fort William', No. 5 in Paul Sandby's set of eight large Scottish views, 1751. (Cf. No. 154.)

For the game of nine-holes see Strutt. *Sports and Pastimes*, 1801, i.p. 204. The popularity of the game revived in the suburbs of London some twenty years before Strutt wrote, 'as a succedaneum for skittles' when that game was proscribed. In England it was played with a number of metal balls; in Scotland, as described by Dr. Johnson (in error under the name 'kayles'), with an iron bullet as in the drawing.

153. Thomas Sandby. The same.

Pen and watercolour, unmounted, 34.2 × 68.4 cm. (13½ × 26⅞ in.) No. 14723.

Inscribed in pencil on the back (a) in a Sandby-like hand 'Fort Augustus or Loch Ness' and (b) in a 'Colnaghi' hand, with the same words followed by 'by Sandby'. In the corner, in pencil, '£1.11.6', which identifies it as 'A Drawing of a View of Fort Augustus by Sandby' bought by the Prince of Wales from Colnaghi on January 1st, 1802, for that price (Archives invoice 27171).

A replica of the preceding with more colour but less precision in the buildings and less detail in the distant hills and woods. The only important differences are that the gun and gun carriage are heavier in this drawing and of a different type, the same drawing is no longer repeated for all four horses and the leading horse of the team turns, with the road, towards the spectator while the whole incident is brought somewhat to the right. There are no cattle, etc., on the low ground to the right nor boat on the loch.

FIG. 15. THOMAS SANDBY. FORT AUGUSTUS (CAT. NO. 152)

Expenditure of £2,000 *p.a.* on building Fort Augustus appears in the Military Ordnance accounts (in the Royal Archives) from 1734 to 1745, inclusive. The Duke of Cumberland, with eleven battalions of foot and Kingston's Horse, made it his headquarters, May 23rd, 1746, for that pacification of the Highlands to which he owed his posthumous evil notoriety (cf. Charteris, *op. cit.* (1913) p. 282).

154. Thomas Sandby.

The same; a more extensive view from a more distant point, of the fort, the camps and the surrounding country. In the foreground, left, four soldiers lead away a couple of Highland prisoners with a woman, baby and dog following.

Pen and watercolour, 31.7 × 70.1 cm. (12½ × 27⅝ in.)
No. 14725.

Inscribed on the mount in pencil 'by Sandby' in the same hand as on Nos. 152 and 157. The price £2.2.0 at the back in the bottom right hand corner identifies this with a second drawing bought for that price at the same time as No. 152 and under the same title.

The paper used as a mount has on the back a rough but powerful architectural sketch, partly in pen and grey wash, partly pencil with perspective lines, of a building with a curving colonnade.

The same sketch may have served for the chief buildings, etc., in this and the two preceding drawings; the penwork is still more microscopic both in architecture and figures.

The group of soldiers, etc., in the foreground is a repetition, apparently identical even to the spacing of the figures and the mound behind them, of a drawing which is among the sketches by Paul Sandby at the British Museum (L.B. 80(*a*)). The sketch is in fine black pen with grey and pink washes, the tartans pink and green. It is indeed conceivable that drawings by Thomas Sandby have become intermingled with Paul's in the various collections, but the double coincidence in this and in No. 152 and the etching-like minuteness of the cartouche below the latter suggest that even at this early date Paul furnished the figures for his brother, if sometimes only as models for him to copy.

155. Thomas Sandby.

A View of Diest from the Camp at Meldart, 1747. The allied camps on the right from the foreground into the distance, in the left and centre middle distance the town and church of Diest; hills beyond, and a large tree in the extreme left foreground.

Pen and watercolour, with border, 38.5 × 70.5 cm. (15⅛ × 27¾ in.) *No. 14726.*

The title, as given, lettered in the border below. Inscribed in pencil on the back in a large perhaps 'Colnaghi' hand, 'A view of Diest, with the camp of Meldart in 1747 by T. Sandby while with the Duke of Cumberland in Scotland'; and in a smaller, Sandby-like hand, 'Drawn by T. Sandby when with the Duke of Cumberland in Scottland [*sic*] against the Rebels'. Also 'very curious' in pencil at back, and, almost erased and torn, '£2.2', identifying it with 'A Drawing of a View of Diest by Sandby' bought by the Prince of Wales on January 1st, 1802, from Colnaghi for 2 guineas. (Archives invoice 27171.) For Diest see Charteris, *op. cit.* (1913), p. 307.

The reference to Scotland in the inscription is no doubt due to a confusion of Meldart with Moidart. A long drawing (7 ft. 6 in. × 1 ft. 9 in.) of the camp at Diest 1748, by

Thomas Sandby with small portraits by Gilpin was No. 124 in the T. P. Sandby sale, 1827.

156. Thomas Sandby.

A British camp in the Netherlands, 1748. The tents massed on the right towards a church in the middle distance, on the left a flat green with a village and scattered tents, others in the distant background.

Pen and watercolour on four sheets, Villedary watermark, joined vertically, unmounted, 24.5 × 132 cm. (9⅝ × 52 in.) *No. 14728.*

Signed below on the left, in ink: 'Drawn on the spot', by T. Sandby July 5th, 1748', and inscribed in pencil on the back, '2 (an illegible word) at Kenilworth in Warwicks'. A dealer's cypher at foot, right. W. Sandby, p. 212.

The Union Jacks are inscribed 'Cold Streams' on the horizontal red line and the tents 'I.B. No. 1; (No. 2 etc.) Colds. Regt.' A pen drawing for one of the tents, similarly inscribed, but with 'No. 11' and with a halberd set up beside it, is among the sketches by Paul Sandby in the Victoria and Albert Museum (No. 161-1901).

On July 5th, 1748, the British Army in the Netherlands was encamped at Eindhoven. 'Kenilworth', if that is the correct reading of a rubbed inscription, must be a dealer's mistake for some Flemish name.

157. Thomas Sandby.

The same from a greater distance and further to the left.

Pencil, pen and watercolour, unfinished and unmounted, on the same paper as the preceding, 25.3 × 72.1 cm. (10 × 28⅜ in.) *No. 14727.*

Inscribed 'Sandby' and '15/-' on the back in pencil in the same hand as on Nos. 152 and 154. The price probably identifies this with 'A Drawing by Sandby, The Encampment', bought by the Prince of Wales from Colnaghi for 15s. on Feb. 13th, 1805 (Archives invoice No. 27293).

158. Thomas Sandby.

'The Camp on Cox Heath, 1778'. In the left foreground a post-mill with round house; at its foot, further to the left, figures on a road beyond which are fields and woods and a large red mansion. To the right a panoramic view over fields and hedges to an extensive camp bounded on the extreme right by the houses of a large village.

Pen and watercolour on two sheets of Whatman paper, mounted on canvas with ties for rolling, 49.1 × 147.3 cm. (19⅜ × 58 in.)
No. 14729.

The drawing for the soldier conversing with a bystander at the foot of the mill is No. 378, q.v.

From the 'Cumberland' collection of military documents and papers, in the catalogue of which (after 1817) it is entered under the title given but without name of artist (Box XIV, No. 37). The collection contains several prints, drawings and plans of the encampment at Cox Heath in Kent under Lieut.-Gen. Keppel, May 28-November 11, 1778. These, however, give no indication of a windmill nor possess any recognisable common feature with this. It has been suggested that the camp at Blackheath in 1780 is intended, and certainly there is some resemblance between the drawing and the aquatint by Paul Sandby of that scene; but the mills are not the same and the general character of the drawing is so little removed from that of Thomas Sandby's scenes of the campaigns in the Low Countries and Scotland that an altogether earlier occasion seems to be represented. In fact, a camp of 10,000 Hanoverians at Cox Heath, reviewed by the Duke on Sept. 24th, 1754, is mentioned in the contemporary *Life of William Augustus Duke of Cumberland* by Andrew Henderson, 1766, p. 342. It is possible that the title of this drawing was intended to refer to this camp and not to that of 1778.

IV. RICHMOND, KEW AND LONDON

159. Ormonde or Richmond Lodge, Kew. The South Front; the Prince of Wales and Duke of York playing with a hobby horse in the foreground; a lady with them, a sentry with box to left.

Pen and watercolour over pencil, some body colour in the figures 38.7 × 61.9 cm. (15¼ × 24⅜ in.) *No. 14711.*
PLATE 65

'/38' on the back in pencil, perhaps the remains of a lot number.

The drawing in fine pen over pencil of the two princes and lady, identical in size, is at the Victoria and Albert Museum (D 154—1901); that for the grenadier on guard is No. 377, *q.v.*

Ormonde Lodge, which was at the Richmond end of Kew Gardens, was demolished by George III about 1770. This date would approximately fit the age of the two boys who would seem to be intended for the Prince of Wales and the Duke of York since they alone among the brothers received the Garter in infancy. On the other hand, the Windsor uniform which the two princes are precisely and deliberately represented as wearing was not introduced until 1778 (cf. O. F. Morshead, *Connoisseur*, May, 1935). The foundation may have been a drawing, or elevation, of the front of the house by Thomas Sandby. This is set square after his manner and has the meticulous minuteness of detail, left incomplete in places (e.g. the cornice of the pediment) which is characteristic of him. The foreground and figures have obviously been added at a later date, for while space has been left in the grass, etc., for the lower part both of the sentry and the group of the lady with the princes, her head and the upper part of the sentry are superimposed over the lines of the architecture. It is not impossible that the copying or tracing of these figures (including the Garter ribbon on the wrong shoulder) might be by Thomas, but the drawing at any rate of the chief group though somewhat wooden is easy and dainty, the washes throughout are more fluid and tender, the outbuildings on the left are more picturesquely handled, and even in the main building there is more free penwork and less of the ruler and compasses than is customary with him. The suggestion is therefore that the drawing is on the whole the work of Paul, retaining, because of its composite construction, the character of an earlier date.

160. The Prince's House at Kew. The Dutch House or Kew Palace, from the North-East; from the centre to the right a long avenue through which the river and Syon House are seen. In the left foreground five royal children, playing with a go-cart and accompanied by a lady; in centre, three horses.

Pen and watercolour with a little pencil, and body-colour and gum in the trees; some lines ruled. Much dulled and discoloured through exposure, 36.1 × 69 cm. (14¼ × 27⅛ in.) *No. 14712.*
PLATE 66

Transferred in Dec. 1940 from St. James's Palace (Cat. No. 126). Probably the 'Drawing by Sandby of Old Kew Palace

in a Burnished Gold Frame and Glass' bought by the Prince of Wales from Colnaghi on June 26th, 1804, for £7 7s. (Archives invoice 27267).

The mount, also much faded, is similar in colour and pattern to those of the Banks collection, and has a gilt band next to the drawing as have several from that collection. Its present inscriptions, with the title as given and the date 1776, are probably taken from the engraving by M. A. Rooker after Paul Sandby of June 1st, 1776, for the *Virtuosi's Museum.* Both that engraving and the drawing for it at the British Museum (L.B. No. 31 (*b*)), which is probably also by Rooker, show considerably less on the right-hand side.

In its original condition, this drawing must have exhibited the sparkling freshness and miniature delicacy of the drawings of Windsor from the Banks collection. The group of royal children cannot be identified with precision, and probably has a totally different origin, but the two princes in the go-cart must be intended for the Prince of Wales and the Duke of York, since the former wears the ribbon of the Garter (see No. 159) and the latter wears the ribbon of the Bath, which he was alone among the brothers to receive (Dec. 1767). In view of the strictness of court etiquette he could scarcely be represented as wearing it after 1771 when he was promoted, in his eighth year, to the Garter. Either, then, the drawing must date from between 1768 and 1771 or it must be deliberately retrospective.

160a. 'Sion House'. A stretch of river seen beyond a towpath with a gate, trees, and a ferry; in the distance, across the river, a mansion in a meadow bordered by trees. Indications of further buildings on the horizon.

Pencil and watercolour, 17.2 × 26.6 cm. (6¾ × 10½ in.) *No. 14717.* W. Sandby, p. 216.

This drawing is laid down in a modern mount and cannot be closely examined. 'Sion House' written in pencil on the back of the mount was perhaps copied from the back of the drawing which does not seem to have been previously mounted. It cannot well be the drawing bought by George IV from Colnaghi (Archives invoice No. 27637) on June 5th, 1811, as 'A Design for Sion House by Paul Sandby' for 1 guinea, the price paid for three other 'designs': Nos. 148, 188 and 189, which were bought with it or at about the same time. Nor does the pedimented building at all accurately resemble Syon House, but it is not a prominent feature in the drawing which is a loose sketch in Paul Sandby's later manner and somewhat similar to Nos. 95 and 185 (*a*) but more heavily coloured.

161. Paul and Thomas Sandby.

Old Somerset Gardens, looking West: part of Westminster Bridge, the Abbey, etc., in the distance, the Garden Front of Old Somerset House to the right.

Pencil and pen, watercolour and gouache, 29.5 × 36.5 cm. (11⅝ × 14¾ in.) *No. 14697.*

The mount lettered 'Westminster from Somerset Gardens. Drawn by T. Sandby 1752'.

Collection: Paul Sandby, with mark.

Reprod. *Connoisseur,* XCII (1933), p. 6.

See on No. 162. For the women with children in both drawings compare Nos. 3 and 5 in this collection. The upper part of the seated soldier appears to be from the same drawing as that in 'The North Terrace Windsor Castle' of 1800 at the Victoria and Albert Museum. (D.1832-1904.)

162. The same, without Somerset House but with the Surrey bank, the whole of Westminster Bridge with two centre arches under construction and the Abbey, Whitehall, etc., shown at a lesser distance.

Pencil, pen, watercolour and gouache, 31.3 × 44 cm. (12⅜ × 17⅜ in.) *No. 14696.*

The mount inscribed in pencil 'View from Old Somerset Gardens. 1752' and 'T. Sandby'. (The reconstruction of the defective pier had been completed by 1750.) Collection. Paul Sandby, with mark.

This drawing and No. 161, though similarly mounted, do not form a pair but, allowing for the auctioneer's licence of description, may have formed Lot 25 on the third day of the 1811 Sale 'Two extremely accurate Views of Westminster, and the Thames, from Old Somerset Gardens by Thomas Sandby', bought by 'Shepperd', for the Prince of Wales, £13 2s. 6d. That lot was returned but the drawings may have been bought back singly from Colnaghi shortly afterwards as 'A View from Old Somerset Gardens by Sandby' and 'View of Westminster from Somerset Gardens by Sandby' respectively invoiced to the Prince of Wales on Feb. 6th, 1812, at 6 guineas, and on Feb. 7th, 1812, at 7½ guineas (Archives invoices 27673 and 4). Lot 46 (framed and glazed), on the same day, bought by Colnaghi for £17 6s. 6d. for the Prince of Wales 'T. Sandby. A Pair, views of Westminster from Old Somerset Gardens, and view of London from ditto' was also returned.

The subject, obviously deriving from Canaletto, directly or through engravings, was constantly repeated by either or both of the brothers and, as is even more noticeable in Nos. 240 and 241, the various topographical details could be disposed with considerable fantasy. In these two drawings, apart from the remarkable difference in the scale of the view up the river bank, though it is seen at practically the same distance, the pillars and fountain which are generally found on the West side of the central avenue are brought to the East of it in No. 161 where there is a square lawn in No. 162. In both, the women and children are clearly later additions, the trees, foliage and flowers show differences of treatment, and it is evident that, whatever their origin, both drawings were heavily handled by Paul Sandby at a late period of his life. His collector's mark, which occurs on both drawings, is occasionally found on his own work.

163. Thomas Sandby.

Old Somerset House, the Garden or river front; the gardens to right with the central avenue, several scattered figures.

Pen and watercolour, 53 × 75 cm. (20⅞ × 29½ in.) *No. 14698.*
PLATE 63

Inscribed 'T. Sandby fect' in precisely the same hand as on No. 190 and 'Somerset House' in another hand, both in pencil on the back.

'A Drawing View from Somerset House by Sandby' was bought by the Prince of Wales from Colnaghi for £1 11s. 6d. on June 20th, 1804, with Nos. 152 and 154 (Archives invoice 27266), but the title does not fit this drawing which moreover appears to have been trimmed and framed as a companion to No. 190 (q.v.). W. Sandby, p. 213.

Exhib. B.F.A.C. 1919, No. 16; reprod. Pl. 10.

Thomas Sandby exhibited 'The Garden Front of the Royal Academy' at the Royal Academy 1772 (No. 230). A similar drawing from a slightly different angle and with earlier costumes is in the extra illustrated Pennant bequeathed by J. C. Crowle to the British Museum (L.B. 21) and compare that reproduced as by Paul Sandby in Whitley's *Artists and their Friends in England*, 1928, vol. 1, pl. 12.

The child in the group on the left is one of the girls in No. 296 (the 'Ladies Waldegrave'); the lady with her is very similar to the governess in the version of that drawing in the Victoria and Albert Museum, D.1835-1904, and, with her male companion, identical with a couple on 'North Terraces looking West', at Drumlanrig and in the collection of Mr. C. R. N. Routh; the man looking up from the arcade is No. 355, the lady and two children towards the end of the steps are No. 312 (q.v.), and the foreground group is repeated in entirety from No. 119 (q.v.) as altered in the engraving corresponding to it. Pencil indications show that the youth on the left, who now stands slightly apart from the rest of the group, was originally intended to be closer to them as in the prototypes. The man pointing in the foreground corresponds fairly closely with No. 253. Spaces have been left in the drawing for the figures which are stiffly copied and placed; the lines of the buildings are carefully ruled, the windows, cornices, etc., elaborately detailed, and the stonework and walks insensitively coloured.

164. Paul and Thomas Sandby.

The Piazza, Covent Garden; an angle of the arcade from within, a group of figures with dogs and a sedan chair to right, a window cleaner to left.

Pencil and watercolour, the figures in body colour, 27.6 × 30 cm. (10⅞ × 11¾ in.) *No. 14700.*

The mount (1811) lettered 'Piazza Covent Garden'. Collection Paul Sandby, with mark.

Exhib. and Reprod. Nottingham, 1884, No. 12; B.F.A.C. 1919, No. 14, Pl. 9. *Connoisseur*, XCII (1933), p. 7.

Lot 27 on the third day of the 1811 Sale, 'T. Sandby R.A. Two, the interior of Freemasons Hall, and Piazza, Covent Garden', bt. 'Shepperd', for the Prince of Wales, 10 guineas, was returned to Messrs. Colnaghi, but the latter title reappears in an invoice of Jan. 13th, 1812 (No. 27671) with the price £5 5s. and is no doubt this drawing.

One of the numerous Covent Garden subjects associated with T. Sandby. His exhibit at the Royal Academy of 1771 (No. 172), 'A view from the Arcade in Covent Garden', is noted by Horace Walpole (Whitley, *op. cit.*, ii, 395) as being a 'Perspective drawn for his lectures' and therefore must have been of a different character from both this drawing and the engraving by E. Rooker of the subject after Thomas Sandby in the six London views of 1766. In this drawing, the figures, etc., which are partly in gouache and very freely drawn, are late in date and all but certainly by Paul. The whole drawing shows a freedom of colouring and construction, without pen, or even pencil, outlines, which, though it occurs in other drawings attributed to Thomas, and the method, with erasure of carefully drawn pencil outline, is recommended by him to his pupils in his lectures, contrasts strongly with the treatment in the drawings of the same theme given to him in the extra-illustrated Pennant at the British Museum.

165. Thomas Sandby.

Whitehall, the Holbein Gate and the Banqueting House. Unfinished.

Pencil, pen and grey wash, the pencil work with ruler and compass. Villedary watermark, unmounted, 34 × 54.1 cm. (13⅜ × 21¼ in.) *No. 14702.*

Inscribed in pencil, at foot, in an old hand, '1743. White Hall, London', and, on the back, with the price, almost erased, 15s., identifying it with 'A Drawing by Sandby, Whitehall 1743' bought by the Prince of Wales from Colnaghi at that price on Feb. 13th, 1805 (Archives invoice No. 27293).

The buildings to left freely and competently completed in monochrome with soft pen; the gate itself and adjoining house carefully drawn with fine pen and wash; the Banqueting Hall and houses, etc., to right partly in pen, partly wash, and much in pencil only. The foreground and the spaces between the three groups of buildings entirely untouched except for one shadow. No figures. 'B' in pencil under the arch of the Gate.

In no sense a sketch but one of many replicas left incomplete.

166. Thomas Sandby.

The same, a completed version; warm, sunset light.

Pen and watercolour, compass and ruler used; Villedary watermark, rubbed, cleaned and retouched, 31.7 × 50.8 cm. (12½ × 20 in.)
No. 14703.

The signature 'Thos Sandby' in ink at foot perhaps genuine.

Acquired in 1934.

The subject occurs twice in the T. Sandby Sale, 1799, No. 33, on the first day, and No. 286 on the fourth.

Other versions of this subject are at the Guildhall (unfinished, reprod. *L.C.C. Survey* XIV, pl. 8), at the British Museum (presented by the N.A.C. Fund, 1941, No. 1238), a copy also at the British Museum (Crowle *Pennant*, VOL. IV, 21, not catalogued), and an engraving by R. Godfrey after T. Sandby, July 1st, 1777. They differ mainly in the extent of the view shown, much the widest being the Guildhall version, the least extensive being the two in the Royal Library.

The figures in this and the British Museum versions are identical, even to their partial superimposition on the architectural drawing. None of the examples deserves to be regarded as more than an indifferent replica, this one probably executed in Paul Sandby's workshop.

The Gate and the adjoining house (belonging to Mr. Van Huls) were demolished 1759. (Cf. *L.C.C., op. cit.,* VOL. XIV, pp. 10-22.)

167. Thomas Sandby.

The Old Gate, Whitehall, with the Additions intended for the Termination of the Avenue, Great Park, Windsor.
Elevation showing the gateway as in Vertue's print, etc., continued on either side by a lower arch with battlements ending in a short machicolated turret over a porch; the whole chequered and ornamented in keeping with the central gate. A lantern indicated in pencil above the right-hand turret.

Pen and brown and grey washes, compass and ruler, Villedary watermark, unmounted, 48.4 × 69.4 cm. (19 × 27⅜ in.)
No. 14701.

Inscribed in pencil with the title as given both on the back in T. Sandby's handwriting (reading 'Aditions' [*sic*] for 'the Additions') and above the drawing in the large 'Colnaghi' hand.

A drawing of the subject was in the T. Sandby Sale 1799, No. 196, on the third day. An aquatint of Jan. 1st, 1804, in J. T. Smith's *Antiquities of Westminster* (1807) 'from an original drawing by T. Sandby, R.A., in the possession of Mr. John Manson, bookseller', showing the proposed gateway *in situ*, would not appear to have been taken from this drawing. William Sandby who mentions (p. 70) the aquatint had evidently seen no drawing of the subject in the Royal Library.

According to Samuel Pegge, *Curialia*, Pt. 1, p. 69, the materials of the gateway were removed to Windsor by William Duke of Cumberland who intended to have it re-erected as a termination to the Long Walk. The death of the Duke prevented the execution of this plan. Some of the materials are said to have been used to ornament houses in Windsor Park.

168. Thomas Sandby.

The Interior of the Freemasons Hall.

Pen and watercolour, on two sheets of paper joined vertically, 43 × 56 cm. (16⅞ × 22 in.) *No. 14705.*

'A drawing by Sandby, A View of Freemason's Hall' was bought by the Prince of Wales from Colnaghi August, 1st, 1799, for £1 1s. (Archives invoice 27097), no doubt from the T. Sandby sale on July 18th, 1799, second day, Lot 108. Another by T. Sandby, 'The interior of Free Masons Hall', bought by 'Shepperd' for the Prince of Wales at the P. Sandby Sale, 1811 (Lot 27, third day, see on No. 164) was returned.

Pen drawings of details of the cornice, etc., are at the Victoria and Albert Museum (D. 226-1901, etc.). Another example, with figures, was bequeathed to the Tate Gallery by W. Sandby in 1901 (No. 1852). That bequeathed by him to the Royal Academy as the 'Freemasons Hall' has nothing in common with this subject.

An elaborate work with ruler and compass washed lightly with Indian ink and pale colour. The detail is not quite so precise as in some of T. Sandby's other designs and in places is characteristically left unfinished, the paper remaining white. There are no figures nor spaces left for them.

An engraving of the hall as in this drawing but containing allegorical figures of Truth, Faith, Hope, Charity and the Genius of Masonry was intended to accompany the 'Constitutions' of 1784, but was actually only published in 1786: the architecture by Fittler after Sandby, the figures by Bartolozzi after Cipriani (Cf. *Connoisseur*, Jan., 1903). For a description of the hall which was built in 1775-6 and damaged by fire in 1883, see Britten and Pugin *Public Buildings of London* (1825) and *L.C.C. Survey*, v., pt. 2 (1914), p. 62 and pl. 26. It was T. Sandby's only known building in London (W. Sandby, p. 65.)

Nos. 169-179. The Encampments in Hyde Park, etc., 1780.

A letter of June, 1780, from William Whitehead, the Poet Laureate, to Lord Harcourt (*Harcourt Papers*, VII, 343) describes the entertainment afforded by the troops who were brought to London on account of the Gordon Riots and remained encamped in various parks until August.

'The camp in St. James's Park is so extremely pretty that you would be charmed with the sight of it.

'Tents, ammunition, colours, carriages, cannons and kettle-drums.

'Only think of the lawn betwixt the Mall and the Canal thus spangled and ornamented in regular rows with the soldiery as spruce as the scene they are placed in. Hyde Park, I am told, is more warlike, but I have hitherto been contented with the milder appearance'.

Paul Sandby lived in St. George's Row opposite Hyde Park and was therefore well placed for the show. He exhibited at the Royal Academy of the following year three views of the camp in Hyde Park, two of St. James's Park and one each of the Museum Gardens and Blackheath. He also issued four large, and two sets of small, aquatints of these subjects. The latter bear titles such as 'Drumming a Prostitute out of Hyde Park', 'The Fair-stationer', 'the Jolly Landlady in Hyde Park', and are semi-comic rather than topographical in character. All occur also as outline etchings coloured by hand.

169. A Sutler's Tent near the Serpentine River, Hyde Park, during the Encampment. 1780.

Gouache, 31 × 46 cm. (12¼ × 18⅛ in.) *No. 14678*.

The title as given, the lot number and the price £3 5s., which are written on the back of the panel, are those of Lot 107 on the second day of the 1811 sale, 'painted in body colour on pannel', bought by 'Shepperd' for the Prince of Wales. Transferred from St. James's Palace in 1942 and shown by a label at the back to have come from Carlton House, where it formed part of No. 525 of the 'New Catalogue' of 1816.

Identical with the aquatint 'The Jolly Landlady in Hyde Park', No. VI in the small series of Encampments, except that in the print the woman at the door of the tent is brought forward, the tree on the right is omitted and more figures are introduced.

170. View in Hyde Park looking towards the Uxbridge Road during the Encampment in 1780.

In the centre middle distance, a large tree with a tent under it; to the right a larger tent and flag; a group of dancers, onlookers, etc., in front; a third tent among trees to the left. A group on horseback in the left corner of the foreground, and in the distance on the right, houses behind a long wall. Sunset effect.

Pencil, pen and watercolour, 26.5 × 44.5 cm. (10⅜ × 17½ in.) *No. 14679*.

The title as given inscribed on the mount in pencil in the same hand as Nos. 172-175 and 177-8.

Probably Lot 83 on the second day of the 1811 sale, 'high finished tinted drawing, many figures', title as given. Bt. 'Shepperd,' for the Prince of Wales, £6.

The figures are clearly superimposed, the trees roughly hatched with the pen, the drawing and colouring loose and perfunctory, suggesting a later repetition.

171. View near the Serpentine River during the Encampment. 1780.

Beyond an open space with a man wheeling a barrow drawn by a dog, left, and scattered figures, a wooden hut with tents, trees and the Serpentine receding towards the right.

Pencil, pen and watercolour, 25.5 × 48.5 cm. (10 × 19⅛ in.)
PLATE 67   *No. 14680*.

The title presumably from the back of the mount.

Probably Lot 80 on the second day of the 1811 sale, 'a high finished tinted drawing, many figures', title as given. Bt. by 'Shepperd,' for the Prince of Wales, £3 3s.

Exhib.: B.F.A. Club (1919), No. 23, reprod. Pl. 12.

A signboard outside the tent on the extreme right bears the name 'Pool's', which occurs twice in the large aquatint 'Encampment in Hyde Park', once in full as: 'Pooles Intire Butt Beer Fine Ale & Amber' and in the title-print (Blackheath) of the second small set. The hut on the left appears, seen from the other side, in the small aquatint 'The Camp Kitchen'.

The brushwork summary and somewhat perfunctory as in the coloured etchings and the figures superimposed, but the colouring cooler and more transparent, with greys and white, and of an earlier type than in the preceding drawing, No. 170.

172. View near the Serpentine River in Hyde Park during the Encampment, 1780.

Carts with beer barrels, a man kicking a horse, centre, and a party regaling, left. The Serpentine, with conduit head, behind trees in the mid-distance from centre to right. The hut shown in No. 171 and tents to the left; houses, a church and wooded hills in the distance.

Pencil, pen and watercolour, 27.5 × 44.7 cm. (10⅞ × 17⅝ in.)
PLATE 68   *No. 14681*

The title as given inscribed on the mount in pencil, in the same handwriting as on No. 170, etc., and the auctioneer's lot number 2-78/1 identify it as Lot 78 on the second day of the 1811 sale, 'high finished tinted drawing, many figures'. Bt. by 'Shepperd', for the Prince of Wales, £4 4s.

'Facing to Knightsbridge' added in the modern title is no doubt correct, for the situation is established by the wooden hut of No. 171 and the conduit-head of Nos. 173 and 4. The figures are superimposed and the colouring is of the same cool and clear character, with a delicate distance, as in No. 171. The incident of a man kicking a led horse occurs identically in No. 17 and (with somewhat less savagery) in a pencil and brown wash sketch in an album (L.B. 138, No. 72) at the British Museum.

173. The same, looking towards Knightsbridge, from nearer to the Serpentine with the conduit head at the extreme right, a large open mess-tent in front of a tree occupying most of the centre, scattered figures and, in the distance, left, a bridge and houses beyond the water.

Pencil, pen and watercolour, 26.8 × 48.5 cm. (10½ × 19⅛ in.)
No. 14683.

Inscribed in pencil on the mount in the same hand as No. 170, etc., and on the back 'View near the Serpentine River Hyde Park during the Encampment (Camp) 1780', and, on the face of the mount only and perhaps in another hand, 'looking to Knightsbridge'.

The auctioneer's lot No. 2-82/1 on the mount identifies the drawing with Lot 82 on the second day of the 1811 sale 'high finished drawing, view looking towards Knightsbridge, many figures'. Bt. by 'Shepperd', for the Prince of Wales, £4 14s. 6d.

The composition in a somewhat contracted and concentrated form appears in the aquatint No. VII of the Encampment series 'the Filbert Merchant in Hyde Park', the tent, the trees and the distance being the same, but the foreground figures altered or omitted and replaced by others. Of the figures there omitted, the man with the water buckets and the child with a hobby horse reappear in the 'Camp Kitchen' No. V of the same series.
The bridge in the distance, left, carried the road between the Serpentine and the small piece of water at its east end which extended to the place where Albert Gate now stands. (H. B. Wheatley, *Round about Piccadilly*, 1870, p. 236).

174. The same, from a different point, the conduit head on the extreme left, the mess-house at a different angle, more tents on the right and more figures in the foreground.

Pencil, pen and watercolour, touches of gouache, 26.5 × 48.5 cm. (10⅜ × 19⅛ in.) *No. 14682*.

Inscribed in pencil as on No. 170, etc., on a mount which is identical with that of No. 173, 'Hyde Park during the Encampment 1780 looking towards Kensington', the last three words perhaps in another hand; also with 'By Sandby' in the large 'Colnaghi' hand.

Exhibited International, 1862, No. 853.

Not identifiable with any drawing at the 1811 sale, it is nevertheless a clear companion to No. 173 with even looser and softer colouring and the same half-naked urchins outlined in pink playing in the foreground. Several figures are as usual superimposed. The initials T.S. barely discernible on the board at the entrance to the mess-tent may indicate the co-operation, probably in the colouring, of Paul Sandby's son, commonly known as 'young Tom Sandby'.

The footman and a boy galloping on a pony occur also in the large aquatint of the Encampment in Hyde Park and behind another similar couple in a pencil and watercolour study No. 41 in an album at the British Museum (L.B. 138). The repetition seems to show that in this case the gross disproportion is deliberate.

175. View near the Ring in Hyde Park during the Encampment, 1780. A marquee and shed with men at a table under the trees of an avenue in the middle distance; a group of men and women regaling in the left foreground, a horseman beside them and another galloping with a led horse in the foreground right.

Pencil, pen and watercolour, 29 × 47.5 cm. (11⅜ × 18¾ in.)
No. 14685.
Inscribed in pencil on the mount in the same hand as No. 170, etc., with the title as given and with the lot number 2-81/1 identifying it with Lot 81 on the second day of the 1811 sale. Bt. 'Shepperd' £5, for the Prince of Wales. Also, in pencil, on the back of the mount, 'View near the Ring'.

Apparently a late repetition, loosely coloured. The rider galloping with two horses, occurs also in No. 87, etc.

176. View in Hyde Park, looking towards Grosvenor Gate during the Encampment 1780. In a broken foreground a woman ironing linen on the grass with another woman, seated, and soldiers under trees; the tents of the camp beyond and, in the distance, more trees and the houses of Park Lane.

Pen and watercolour, 35.5 × 54.5 cm. (14 × 21½ in.) *No. 14684.*
Identified by the lot mark on the mount 2-84/1 as Lot 84 on the second day of the 1811 sale. Bt. 'Shepperd', for the Prince of Wales, £7 15s. Title as given. Inscribed in pencil on the back 'View near the Ring in Hyde Park, looking towards Park Lane during the Camp. 1780'.

The central portion is almost identical, but for some different figures, with No. VIII of the small aquatint Encampments, 'The Laundress, with a distant view of Lord Petre's House etc. from Hyde Park'.

The woman on the left who is ironing linen on the grass occurs in a pencil and light brown wash sketch at the British Museum (L.B. 137(18)) together with another engaged in the same task and a standing woman with a distaff, apparently two separate nature studies.

The drawing and colouring are more careful than in most of these drawings and suggest an earlier date. The size also is larger and the mount may be of an earlier type. As usual, the figures are superimposed.

177. Grosvenor Gate, Hyde Park, during the Encampment in 1780. A double avenue of trees seen from within, houses to the left, figures in the foreground and under the trees; the engine-house, tents and a fence in the distance and to the right.

Pencil, pen and watercolour, unfinished, 41 × 100.5 cm. (16⅛ × 39⅝ in.) *No. 14686.*

The lot number 1-118 1 on the mount identifies the drawing with Lot 118 on the first day of the 1811 sale, 'A long drawing, view of Grosvenor Gate in Hyde Park, during the Encampment 1780'. Bt. 'Shepperd', for the Prince of Wales, £5. Inscribed in pencil on the mount in the same hand as No. 170, etc., the title as given.

This drawing is entirely different, and differently mounted, from the generality of the Encampment series, all described in the sale catalogue as 'high finished' and 'with many figures'. Sandby exhibited at the Royal Academy, 1781, besides four encampments in the Anti-room (367, 371, 376 and 380) which were probably watercolours, and two in the Great Room (156 and 158) which may have been oils or large gouaches, a 'view of the Encampment in Hyde Park from St. George's Row', which was explicitly described as a sketch (213, also in the Great Room). It is conceivable that the last-named is this drawing, but more probably it was a companion drawing, carried further. Certainly this is a direct and spontaneous drawing with every appearance of being from nature. Much is left uncoloured, some lines are omitted where they could be supplied with the ruler. The trees are outlined, and the foliage articulated, with the pen and in places shaded with parallel hatching. The architecture is neat and there is much minute detail which together with the general build of the drawing would, were it not for the costume, have suggested an altogether earlier date. In particular, the minute tents, etc., of the camp on the right are very close to those of the views of Diest and 'Kenilworth', Nos. 155-7. The figures, carefully drawn with fine pen, are superimposed; a man marching with a boy in front of him in the mid-distance may perhaps have given a hint for the semi-caricature figures in the engraved 'Encampment in the Museum Gardens' (No. 179), etc.

The double avenue of walnut trees, planted in 1724, from Cumberland Gate nearly to Hyde Park Corner is recorded (H. B. Wheatley, *op. cit.*, p. 246). The engine house to the left of the avenue is also identifiable.

178. Encampment in St. James's Park, 1780.

Pen, watercolour and gouache, 27.5 × 48 cm. (10⅞ × 18⅞ in.)
No. 14687.

The title, as given, in pencil in the (?) artist's hand on the washed mount, 'Paul Sandby' in pencil in the large 'Colnaghi' hand at foot of mount. W. Sandby, p. 217.
Generally similar to the large aquatint of 1783, but with different figures, centre and right. The figures superimposed in gouache which peels off and discloses the underlying pen work. The colour rather stronger and the pen work more careful than in most of the 'Hyde Park Encampment' series; striking disproportions.

179. The Garden of the British Museum (Montague House) during the Encampment 1780.

Outline etching for the aquatint of c. 1783 hand-coloured.
No. 14688.

Exhibited (as a watercolour) Brussels, British Art, 1929, No. 157.

Inscribed below with the (supposed) names of the personages from left to right: 'Sir John Donelly [*sic*], Bart., Poor Knight of Windsor; Mr. Gandon, Architect of Dublin and his family; Sir Thomas Rich; Archbishop Moore; Mrs. Fitzpatrick, daughter of Mr. Vardy, Architect; a corporal in the York Regiment, remarkable for his great strength in the arms.' The name 'Donelly' presumably covers that of Sir John Dineley (– Goodere) who succeeded as 5th

Baronet in 1761 through the murder of his uncle, the execution of his father as instigator of that crime, and the death of his insane elder brother. He was a hunchback. Having wasted what little remained of his family estates, he made himself notorious by his ubiquitous appearance in an obsolete costume at public functions and by his persistent endeavours, through advertisement and otherwise, to find a wife sufficiently well endowed to finance litigation which would bring him a fortune. He was admitted as a Poor Knight of Windsor in 1798 and died, aged about 80, in 1809. (See also on No. 236.)

For Gandon and Sir T. Rich see Nos. 323 and 385. Dr. John Moore (1730–1805), Bishop of Bangor 1775, Archbishop of Canterbury from 1783. John Vardy, the architect, died 1765.

Nos. 180–183. Four small views in gouache of Hyde Park.

It has not been possible to examine these drawings closely. The titles on the modern mounts may have been taken from the old mounts, and the date 1797 from No. 185. In any case the titles are correct and the drawings can safely be identified with Lots 41 and 42 on the second day of the 1811 sale, 'A pair of small finished body coloured drawings. Views of the Magazine in Hyde Park', and 'Ditto, Keeper's House and Cheesecake House in Hyde Park', bought for the Prince of Wales for £1 11s. 6d. each by Colnaghi and 'Shepperd'.

180. The Powder Magazine in Hyde Park, with trees, sentry and box to the left; in front an open space with two cavalrymen fencing with sabres; in the distance, to the right, houses.

Gouache, 20.5 × 26.5 cm. (8⅛ × 10⅜ in.) *No. 14690.*

181. The same from the back, trees to the right, the road and sentry to the left; the Serpentine beyond.

Gouache in black border, 20.5 × 26.5 cm. (8⅛ × 10⅜ in.) *No. 14694.*

182. The Keeper's House in Hyde Park. The West view; showing the house in its garden with trees behind, a shed to the right beyond a track on a slope. In the left foreground a ditch with a high palisade, children playing.

Gouache, 20.3 × 26.5 cm. (8 × 10⅜ in.) *No. 14691.*

A watercolour version dated 1797, extended to left and shortened to right, and the figures differently disposed, is at the British Museum (L.B. 24).

183. The Cheesecake House in Hyde Park; the house, white with large gabled porch, in its garden beyond a green space. A large tree in the right foreground above a rider leading a horse. Water and trees in the distance left.

Gouache, apparently a join about 3 cm. from the foot, 20.5 × 26.5 cm. (8⅛ × 10⅜ in.) *No. 14692.*
PLATE 71

184. South East View of Cheesecake House in Hyde Park, 1797. The house on the left, approached by a wooden bridge over water, horses and trees in the meadow on the right.

Pencil and watercolour on two pieces of paper joined vertically. The top 5.4 cm. of the drawing are completed on the mount and the lines and washes of the mount are carried into the drawing in places. 30 × 54.1 cm. (11¾ × 21¼ in.) *No. 14693.*

Inscribed in ink below with the title as given and the date

1797. Remains of auctioneers' lot number 1–27 on edge of cut mount. Lot 27 on the first day of the 1811 sale, with another, probably No. 185: 'Two finished studies, tinted, views in Hyde Park'. Bt. Colnaghi, for the Prince of Wales, £1 8s.

Exhib. and Reprod. B.F.A.C., 1919, No. 47, Pl. 21. *Connoisseur*, VOL. XCII (1933), p. 10.

Without the penwork, but with the transparency and loose brushwork, of the Encampment drawings.

A note in the *Gentleman's Magazine*, May 1801, p. 401, with a print very similar to this but without the large tree, describes the building as 'a boat-house on the North side of the Serpentine River', and quotes Swift's reference to it as the Cake-house near the Ring in Hyde Park where the Duke of Hamilton was killed in a duel with Lord Mohun on November 15th, 1712. It was demolished in 1835.

185. 'The Serpentine River, Hyde Park'. Foreground of trees and broken ground with sandpits and a pond centre to right, a river to left; wooded lawns beyond. Two men at foot of near tree.

Pencil and watercolour, touched with gouache in the cows and high lights, and loaded with gum and soot or lamp-black. 34.4 × 54.4 cm. (13½ × 21⅜ in.) *No. 14695.*

Probably, with No. 184 (q.v.) Lot 27 on the first day of the 1811 sale. The mount cannot be examined.

A drawing of the '90's, effective when seen at a distance and of interest as showing the stage of development reached before Girtin or Constable (or the 'nature' poets) in the appreciation of a commonplace scene without conventional, topographic or sentimental appeal.

185a. In Hyde Park.

Pencil and watercolour, unfinished, 17.5 × 29.4 cm. (6⅞ × 11⅝ in.) *No. 17312.*

Inscribed and signed on the back of the mount 'In Hyde Park. P.S.', the title also below the drawing, without the initials.

Acquired Walker's Gallery, 1944.

A slight sketch from nature showing a single elm in the centre, an avenue leading to the right in the mid-distance and, beyond, the buildings of the N.E. corner of the Park and the hills of Hampstead. Similar in manner to No. 95.

186. Thomas Sandby.

A Bridge of Magnificence over the Thames at Somerset House. Vista to the East through the central portion showing St. Paul's and houses of the city.

Pen and watercolour over slight pencil, the top 2 cm. apparently an afterthought on the same sheet, 47.3 × 42.5 cm. (18⅝ × 16¾ in.) *No. 14699.*
PLATE 64

Exhibited: Nottingham, 1884, No. 13.

The architecture drawn with extreme precision of detail with the aid of ruler and compasses throughout. The washes effective but crude and mechanical. The blue and pink view of St. Paul's through the opening is delicate and the clouded sky in keeping, but the figures in the foreground, which are not superimposed on the pen drawing, are even more ungainly in drawing and, when they are not left white, in colouring than is usual with T. Sandby. The wheels of the two carriages, which are in full broadside, still show the pinholes of the compasses with which their circumferences have been drawn.

Designs for the completion of Somerset House and the erection of a Bridge of Magnificence joining it to the southern bank and having a vast hall at each end and another over the centre were, according to T. Sandby's obituary notice in the *Gentleman's Magazine* (1798, Part ii, p. 630), 'one of his latest plans'. Two drawings for this bridge were exhibited at the Royal Academy in 1780 (Nos. 450 and 462) where they were stated to be designed for his sixth (and final) lecture on architecture to the students. According to Sandby himself in that lecture the series was never completed. Such designs figure largely in the catalogue of his sale in 1799, and are to be found, in different degrees of elaboration, at the Soane, Victoria and Albert and British Museums, etc. An etching bearing his name (Soane Museum, cut) of something very similar was prepared as a receipt for a set of views before 1760 (reprod. W. Sandby, opp. p. 30) and a drawing showing a hall of the same type but closed in by an apse and called a Greek temple was given by the artist in 1777 to his colleague, Thomas Worsley, Surveyor General of the Board of Works, and is still in the possession of his descendant, Sir William Worsley, Bart.

187. Thomas Sandby.

'A Design for a triumphal arch intended to Commemorate the Victorys [*sic*] Gained by the British Arms in the late War'.

Elevation of a triple-arched gateway, with a dome above which George III in a quadriga is crowned by a Victory. The arch is further ornamented with statues, basreliefs and trophies; the main inscription, on the entablature beneath the dome, reads: 'George III of G B F and I King under whose auspicious reign the British arms by amazing and successful conquests triumphed over his enemies by which means he gave peace to most parts of the world and is crowned with Victory'. Four circular tablets over statues between pairs of Corinthian columns are inscribed: 'The French defeated at Minding [*sic*]' 'The French fleet distoyed [*sic*] by Admiral . . .' 'Admiral Boscowan beats the French' 'Canada reduced'.

Pen and watercolour with grey border, 41 × 58 cm. (16⅛ × 22⅞ in.) *No. 14706*.

The title, as given, cut from the old mount and pasted at the back of the present mount.

The references are to Minden (1759), Admiral E. Boscawen's victory at Lagos Bay (1759), and perhaps the conquest of Canada in 1763. W. Sandby's description of the arch (p. 213) as 'Triumphal Arch in St. James's Park to Commemorate the Victories, 1746', must be a confusion with the arch in the Green Park celebrating the Peace of Aix-la-Chapelle of which many prints were published in 1749 and a drawing, attributed to T. Sandby, exists in the Crowle *Pennant* at the British Museum (L.B.15). Neither that drawing nor this can be given to him without question.

188. Thomas Sandby.

Design for a Theatre in Leicester Square.

Elevation of a domed building with a long colonnade of ten Ionic columns between end blocks faced each with four Ionic pilasters; round grass plot in front with a horseman galloping, trees on each side.

Pencil, pen and watercolour with some bodycolour in the figures, 19.6 × 37.3 cm. (7¾ × 14⅝ in.) *No. 14707*.

The title presumably copied from the back of the mount, From the collection of Paul Sandby, with his mark (blind)

Bought by the Prince of Wales from Colnaghi on June 22nd, 1811, for 1 guinea (Archives invoice 27639). Cf. on Nos. 66, 148 and 189.

The architecture is drawn throughout with ruler and compasses, and with much careful detail, but the loose colouring, the lightly drawn and superimposed figure, the trees and sky suggest completion by another hand.

V. MISCELLANEOUS DESIGNS AND VIEWS

189. Thomas Sandby.

Design for Lord Portarlington's House in Ireland.

Front elevation of a domed building with an open colonnade on the first floor and a portico of round arches above, three niches with urns, statues and reliefs at the sides; landscape setting.

Pen and watercolour with some gouache in the figures, 20.4 × 31.7 cm. (8 × 12½ in.) *No. 14708*.

The title, presumably copied from the back of the mount, is that of a drawing by 'Sandby' bought by the Prince of Wales from Colnaghi for 1 guinea on July 3rd, 1811 (Archives invoice 27640). Cf. on Nos. 68, 148 and 188.

Similar in treatment to No. 188 (q.v.), details left unfinished and the washes still looser and cruder.

James Gandon, the architect, mentions the Earl of Portarlington (1744-1798: until 1785, Viscount Carlow) as one of the frequenters of Paul Sandby's Sunday afternoons at St. George's Row (Mulvaney, *Life of James Gandon*, 1843, p. 24). Sandby engraved at least one of his landscape drawings and in a letter to Gandon of February 3rd, 1783 (ibid. p. 63, Wm. Sandby, p. 165) spoke of him as 'full of building temples, but with insufficient income to meet his taste and love of the fine arts'. His successor, according to the *Complete Peerage*, died in great poverty; his younger son George Lionel Dawson Damer (1788-1856) married in 1825 Minney Seymour, the adopted daughter of Mrs. Fitzherbert and favourite of George IV.

190. Thomas Sandby.

A round brick tower in course of construction; in front of the tower, and apparently adjoining it on the left, a single-storied, irregular-fronted lodge; in the centre an arched gateway opening to a park, on the right a flat building, and the walls of a garden with closed door. Foreground of a yard with a large single tree, builders' materials, stonemasons to right and a lady with two children left.

Pen and watercolour, somewhat faded, 53 × 77 cm. (20⅞ × 30¾ in.) *No. 14704*.
PLATE 62

Inscribed on the back in pencil 'T. Sandby fecit' precisely as is No. 163. The two drawings are cut to the same size and bear marks of having been framed as companions. W. Sandby, p. 213.

The woman with two children is a stiff copy or tracing of part of No. 312 in this collection (replica without the man, in the Victoria and Albert Museum (D. 130-1901)). A reduced version appears in No. 163. The further of the two stonemasons is identical with a figure in the engraving 'St. James's Gate' by E. Rooker after Paul Sandby in the Six London Views of 1766.

It is difficult not to connect this puzzling drawing with 'A perspective view of the back-part of the Chapel of Windsor Great Lodge, as it appeared when building in the year 1765' which was exhibited by Thomas Sandby at the

Royal Academy, 1773 (No. 262), but as the old chapel has entirely disappeared any positive assertion would be unwarranted. The heavy and imposing, if mechanical nature of the drawing, the curiosities of perspective and sharp contrasts of light and shade, are all characteristic of T. Sandby and the group of a lady and child may well have been copied or traced by him. On the other hand, the stone-masons at work are so much more freely drawn and form so much more integral a part of their surroundings that they proclaim the collaboration of Paul Sandby, who may have had a part in the final colouring generally, since it is rather warmer, and the washes are more varied, than is usual with Thomas. The shadows of the bricks, etc., in front of the lodge door are in the opposite direction from the others, which also points to a difference of hands.

191. 'View from the back of Paul Sandby's lodging at Charlton, Kent'. The backs of houses in a town, taken from a window; a lady standing at another.

Pencil, pen and watercolour, unfinished, 48.1 × 36.8 cm. (18⅞ × 14½ in.) *No. 14720.*

PLATE 61

Probably with No. 39 (q.v.) Lot 26 on the first day of the 1811 sale.

Bold and highly competent fluid washes and free pen work, the roofs of the more distant houses left in pencil uncoloured. With its companion an example of Sandby's stronger manner and unconventional vision.

Two drawings of 'Charlton in Kent' were exhibited by Sandby at the Royal Academy in 1770 (Nos. 163 and 164) and others subsequently.

192. The Royal Military Academy at Woolwich; Prince Rupert's tower to left. Sunset clouds.

Pencil, pen and watercolour with gouache in the figures, 30.8 × 47.5 cm. (12⅛ × 18¾ in.) *No. 14721.*

PLATE 69

The mount lettered with the title as given above.

Lot 32 on the first day of the 1811 sale, 'A finished view of the Old Royal Military Academy, and Prince Rupert's Tower in the Warren at Woolwich', bt. Colnaghi, for the Prince of Wales, £1 18s. The lot number is still visible on the mount though almost erased.

Late repetition, slightly extended to right, of the drawing engraved by M. A. Rooker, Dec. 1st, 1775 (pl. 22, of the *150 Select Views*). Follows the print very closely with different figures which have been superimposed, partly in gouache. It is probably later than the demolition of Prince Rupert's Tower in 1786. The ruler used for railings, cornice, etc.

A 'View of Woolwich' was exhibited by P. Sandby at the Royal Academy 1786 (No. 510), and in 1808 'A View of Woolwich as it was in the year 1785' (No. 54).

Paul Sandby succeeded Gamaliel Massiot as Drawing Master at Woolwich in 1768; he resigned the appointment at the end of 1796.

193. A Park scene near Woolwich, 1796.

Pencil, black chalk and watercolour, 45.5 × 62 cm. (17⅞ × 24⅜ in.) *No. 17152.*

PLATE 70

Signed in ink 'P. Sandby, Woolwich Sept. 1796' and inscribed 'at Woolwich' in pencil, large, at back and 'Nov. 14, 1827, £1 4s.'

See on No. 194.

194. A similar view.

Pencil, black chalk and watercolour, 46 × 62.5 cm. (18⅛ × 24⅝ in.) *No. 17153.*

Signed in ink 'P. Sandby, Woolwich 1796' and inscribed 'at Woolwich' in pencil on back.

Purchased (with No. 193) 1942. Fine Art Society, Cat. Nos. 65 and 75.

Large companion studio drawings of a clump of trees on rising ground, sketched from much the same spot; the river with ships and hills in the distance, a large cottage in the middle distance on the right.

The figures of the Woolwich cadets in No. 193 retain the early neat technique and were doubtless inserted for the purpose of sale to his pupils. The use of lightly rubbed black chalk, almost as a powder, to give 'body' while retaining transparency is a new development of Sandby's processes.

195. The Great Gateway of St. Augustine's Monastery, Canterbury, from the West; St. Ethelbert's Tower in the distance towards the right; Lady Wotton's Green and the houses surrounding it in the foreground.

Pencil, pen and watercolour, with touches of gouache, 33.2 × 50.7 cm. (13⅛ × 20 in.) *No. 14719.*

Reprod. *Connoisseur,* XCII. (1933), p. 10.

Probably the 'high finished drawing' bought for the Prince of Wales by Colnaghi at the 1811 Sale (first day, Lot 36, £3 7s.) in which case it was misdescribed as 'A View of the Caemetery Gate and part of the Monastery of St. Augustine at Canterbury'. Sandby exhibited that subject at the Royal Academy, 1786 (No. 584) together with a 'St. George's Gate at Canterbury' (No. 576) and published aquatints of them with the date 1782. A drawing of the former is at the Tate Gallery (No. 1856, reprod. Hughes. *Early English Watercolours,* opp. p. 16). The date 1782 is affixed both to that drawing and this, probably from the aquatints, but costume and style indicate a somewhat later date for this.

196. Wynn Stay in Denbighshire, the Seat of Sir Watkin Williams Wynn, Bart.

Pen and watercolour, faded, 13 × 12.7 cm. (5⅛ × 5 in.) *No. 14689.*

Acquired at Sothebys, 1918, as 'Kensington Palace'.

Engraved Jan. 1st, 1775, by M. A. Rooker after P. Sandby for the *Copperplate Magazine* (No. 7, Wales, in the *150 Select Views*), with considerably more to the right. Possibly the drawing has been cut. (cf. on No. 116).

For Sir W. W. Wynn see No. 371.

197. Thomas Sandby.

Maidenhead Bridge, a three-arched bridge with balustrade; houses on both sides, those on the right merely indicated in pencil.

Pencil, pen and watercolour, on two sheets joined vertically, 34 × 71 cm. (13⅜ × 28 in.) *No. 14709.*

Inscribed below in ink 'Maidenhead Bridge' and on the back in pencil 'Maidenhead Bridge, Thos. Sandby', with the price 5s. in the bottom corner, right. This identifies the drawing with the 'Maidenhead Bridge by Sandby' bought by the Prince of Wales from Colnaghi, Jan. 9th, 1800, for 5s. (Archives invoice 27111).

Where the drawing has been completed and coloured as in the bridge itself and the houses to the left, the preparatory pencil work has been corrected with the ruler and compasses and then erased. The houses behind and on the right are only indicated in pencil and there are various squarings and diagonals for perspective. The combination of mechanical precision in some parts and all but total incompletion in others seems characteristic of Thomas Sandby, whether from diffidence, indolence or reliance on his brother or others to give his drawings a final form.

There is nothing to connect T. Sandby with Maidenhead Bridge begun in 1772 under the direction of Sir Robert Taylor, his fellow Surveyor to the Board of Works; but, apart from his constant preoccupation with the design of a 'Bridge of Magnificence' over the Thames at Somerset House (see No. 186) a large number of drawings for 'Buildings and Bridges' were included in his sale in 1799. This study of Maidenhead Bridge may have been connected with his commission, late in life, for the bridge at Staines, where according to Farington's unpublished Diary, May 17th, 1796 (reading Staines for Walton), the sinking of one of the piers during its construction caused him 'great tribulation', since 'by some it had been imputed to his neglect in not attending to the operations'. The old wooden bridge was not removed but continued in use when both Sandby's bridge and those constructed in 1803 and 1807 to replace it, had proved insecure (see W. Sandby, p. 69, and authorities quoted).

198. Perhaps by T. P. Sandby, junior.

Gresford Lodge near Wrexham; the house on the right, among trees, lawns on the left running down to a river with a stone bridge above a low waterfall. Three figures under a tree, left centre, an empty chair in the right foreground.

Pencil, pen and watercolour, unfinished, 35.4×68.5 cm. (13⅞× 27 in.) *No. 14713.*

Inscribed in ink on the back of the drawing under the mount and in pencil on the back of the mount 'from Wrexham to Chester'. The latter in the same hand as Nos. 62 and 80.

Engraved March 1st, 1793, by W. and J. Walker, Pl. 28, of the *New Copperplate Magazine* as from an original drawing by T. Sandby junior; with different figures. Those in the drawing are in Paul Sandby's daintiest manner. It is possible that the drawing used for the engraving was a finished copy by T. P. Sandby, from this or a similar sketch by his father. 'A Drawing of a view of Wrexham by Sandby' was bought by the Prince of Wales from Colnaghi on Jan. 20th, 1802, for 15s. (Archives invoice 27172), but the watermark of the mount, 1811, unless a mistake for 1801, forbids identification with this. The drawing is not listed by W. Sandby.

199. After Paul Sandby.

Bridgnorth, Shropshire.

Pen and watercolour, 32.7×51.5 cm. (12⅞×20¼ in.) W. Sandby, p. 216. *No. 14718.*

Copy from the aquatint by Paul Sandby of 1778.

200. Imitator of Paul Sandby, perhaps S. H. Grimm.

Riverside scene with Windsor Bridge in the distance, stocks surmounted by a pump in the centre; a tooth extraction outside a barber's shop on the right, a woman smacking a child on the left.

Pencil, pen, watercolour and gouache, much injured and discoloured, 34.8×52.8 cm. (13¾×20¾ in.) *No. 14673.*

Bought with the next drawing (q.v.), Sotheby's, May 28th, 1930, Lot 8 (Mrs. Hamilton Gell).

Sandby exhibited 'a Country Operation for the Teeth' at Spring Gardens in 1762 (No. 207).

201. Imitator of Paul Sandby, perhaps S. H. Grimm

A country footpath, with a distant view of Windsor Castle; on the left a gallant conversation over a fence along a footpath beside trees; to the right a group of a fallen milkmaid, her irate mother, and a pedlar taking snuff from a horn.

Pencil, watercolour and gouache, much injured and discoloured, 33.4×52.7 cm. (13⅛×20¾ in.) *No. 14674.*

These two drawings were clearly concocted with views by Sandby of Windsor Castle and Bridge in mind, but the architecture of the Castle is far too little understood to be credited to him. Further, the combination of stocks with a pump in such a way as to interfere with the function of either and the decoration of the pump with figured leaden plaques betray an unfamiliarity with the common objects of the countryside which is improbable in an English artist; and if two of the figures might be derived from Sandby, others are quite foreign. The clumsy humour and facile execution suggest Grimm.

Of other landscape drawings wrongly attributed to Paul Sandby, Nos. 14587 and 14611 (Windsor subjects) are by de Cort; 14714 (called Frogmore) by or after J. Malton; 14564 and 14710 by Dr. Fisher, Bishop of Salisbury; 14266 by John Harden; 14672 neither by Sandby nor of Windsor Forest as described. Nos. 14266, 14672 and 14714 have forged signatures.

VI. SUBJECT AND CARICATURE DRAWINGS

202. Tavern scene called 'Jonathan Wild', two men seated in an interior, one raising his glass, the other handing his to be filled by a maidservant standing on the left with a bottle.

Pencil, pen and watercolour in black border, 23.5×18 cm. (9¼× 7⅛ in.) *No. 14442.*

From the book of studies. W. Sandby, p. 218. The title 'Jonathan Wild', presumably transcribed, on the modern mount.

A full interior, mainly in grey with strong colour in the dresses. The lighting studied but without the crispness of the 'Sandpit Gate' interiors; the face of the girl and the heaped clothing on her squat and disproportionate figure recall some of the later drawings of children.

Jonathan Wild was executed in 1725.

203. Attributed to Paul Sandby.

A Prison Scene. Probably an illustration. Centre and right three men chained by the leg to the same ring on the floor, one of them lying down, his right hand holding a book, his left raised to take a cup offered by the gaoler; the second also lying on the floor, reading and apparently unconcerned, and the third standing and talking energetically to a visitor. In the foreground left, by the window wall, three further visitors.

Pen and brown wash, the paper patched and joined, 33.5×46 cm. (13¼×18⅛ in.) *No. 13765.*

A clumsy and enigmatic drawing now firmly embedded in a modern mount without any indication whence it came or why it should have been included, apparently without much confidence, in the collection as by Paul Sandby. It is, however, sufficiently like the large watercolour, 'the Magic Lantern' at the British Museum (L.B. 123) to forbid any immediate rejection of the attribution.

204. The Boot and the Block-head.

In the centre a dummy head in a Scotch cap on a pike which is fixed in a jack-boot; Scotsmen and divines kneeling in adoration before it and, on the left, William Augustus Duke of Cumberland, wearing the Garter and carrying a whip, descending a flight of steps with his nephew, Edward Augustus, Duke of York. Cartouches issuing from their mouths read: 'Come my dear Ned let us descend and correct their folly'. 'Ay my Dear Uncle we will down with their block head worship and make them remember 62 as well as 45'.

Pen and grey wash, 26 × 18.8 cm. (10¼ × 7⅜ in.) *No. 14730.*
Fig. 16

Inscribed in red ink below: 'An Original of Paul Sandby's Politicall (?) Satires. D', W. Sandby p. 217.

First sketch for a print of 1762 (*B. M. Sat.* IV, 3977) attributed by F. G. Stephens on somewhat slender grounds to Lord George Townshend. A further drawing for the print also at the British Museum (*ibid* 3976) is also inscribed in an old hand 'P. Sandby'. In it, as in the print, figures of Hogarth and Churchill replace the cleric in adoration on the left of the jack boot; there are a cockade on the Glengarry hat, a Garter and Star on the boot, and further personages on the right. The legends issuing from the mouths of the Duke and nephew are absent from the British Museum drawing which has, however, the remains of others from the personages below; the print has all with different wording. It is clear that the British Museum drawing represents a later stage in the composition than this; but the fact that the whip is already placed in the left hand of the Duke of Cumberland shows that engraving was intended from the first and indicates a professional hand. The elaboration of the pig tail into Hogarth's line of Beauty and the introduction of that artist as an afterthought also point to the authorship of Sandby. Later editions bear the name of 'M. Darly'.

The nature of this caricature and of some half-dozen of the same date issued anonymously but known to be by Paul Sandby, however appropriate to a henchman of the Duke of Cumberland, scarcely indicates any desire on the part of the artist to gain the favour of the young King, George III.

205. Lord Kirkcudbright and Miss Myddleton of Chirk Castle in Denbighshire.

Pen and watercolour, 25.2 × 36 cm. (9⅞ × 14⅛ in.) *No. 14731.*

Inscribed below in ink: 'A Sceine [*sic*] in Brook St. Grosvenor Square or the Little Lord's hopes Blasted,' and on the back in ink: 'Lord Kircubright and Miss Middleton of Churk Castle in Denbighshire—An occurrence that took place, lately, in upper Brook St P.S.' (the signature, if such it be, in monogram).

In a cartouche issuing from the mouth of the man: 'Madam, I understand you possess an estate in Denbighshire that brings you in an income of £4,000 pr. annum, upon my word, you will never have an opportunity again of such an offer, besides a Tittle [*sic*] attended with my elegant person'. The lady's reply reads: 'Sir I am surprized at your assurance I beg you will not mention the subject again it is true my Estates lye in Wales: but it was never ment [*sic*] to be thrown away upon such ugly deform'd Pigmées as you my Lord—I dare say I shall meet with an offer, in Shropshire with fortune equal to my own'.

Sholto Henry Maclennan, b. 1729, was recognised as 9th Lord Kirkcudbright from 1772 when his father's claim to the Barony was allowed. He became, about 1797-1800, a subject of caricature as the typical old and hunch-backed fop; but since he was already married (1768) and his wife survived him by 5 or 6 years, dying only in 1807, it must be supposed that it is merely for the sake of humorous juxtaposition that Sandby represents him as pressing his attentions on Miss Myddleton who had succeeded by her brother's death in 1796 to Chirk Castle and a very considerable property. She married in 1801 Robert Biddulph of Hereford and Worcester, thus fulfilling in part the aspiration credited to her in the drawing.

VII. EARLY FIGURE STUDIES AND GROUPS

Three on one mount (Nos. 206-208).

206. 'Nurse with William Adam (son of John Adam), a famous speaker in the House of Commons, and his Uncle John Clarke [*sic*], noted for many fine etchings of views in Scotland'. An old woman seated holding a baby who is toying with an open backgammon board. To right, a man, also seated.

Pencil, pen and watercolour, 11.8 × 17.8 cm. (4⅝ × 7 in.)
No. 14406.

'del 1752' in ink on the drawing is apparently in the same hand as the (copy) description on the recent mount and is

FIG. 16. THE BOOT AND THE BLOCK-HEAD (CAT. NO. 204)

probably an inference from the age of the infant said to be depicted. William Adam, son of John Adam, architect, of Kinross, brother of Robert and James Adam, was born on August 2nd, 1751. In 1774 he became M.P. for Gatton and obtained some celebrity in the House of Commons. The description obviously dates from long after the drawing, the rudimentary, not to say puerile, character of which would place it at the very beginning of the Edinburgh series instead of at the end.

John Clerk, of Eldin (1728-1812), noted as an amateur etcher from about 1770, continued to correspond with Sandby on artistic matters (see M. Hardie, *Print-Collector's Quarterly*, xx, 1933, 362). He did not become the uncle of William Adam until he married Susannah Adam in 1753.

207. 'At Edinburgh'. Two women in black dresses, panniers and caps facing each other, seated. A view of Edinburgh with St. Giles through the window, a mirror and a picture on the wall.

Watercolour over pencil, 11.8 × 18.6 cm. (4⅝ × 7⅜ in.) *No. 14407.*

One of the earliest and most rudimentary of the Edinburgh portrait studies; the interior view elaborated in detail but without perspective or interest in the lighting; the exterior, in the dainty blues and pinks of the London vistas, perhaps added later. The figures wooden, the arms and hands clumsy; the dress and perhaps one of the personages the same as in No. 209.

The same method of tying the corsage by a single ribbon, possibly a local fashion, occurs in Allan Ramsay's portrait of Lady Hall of Dunglass, 1752 (reprod. *Walpole Society Annual*, xxv, 1937, pl. 24).

208. 'R. Bell the engraver, Edinburgh', in lavender with yellow facings. 'Sir Samuel Chambers' and a Lady in red, seated, in conversation.

Pencil, pen and watercolour, unfinished, the centre figure in pencil only, 11.6 × 18.1 cm. (4⅝ × 7⅛ in.) *No. 14408.*

W. Sandby, p. 218, who also lists Gravelot.

The lady without panniers but otherwise in the same costume as in No. 209, etc., may be the same as on the left in the preceding drawing. The pencil work in the unfinished figure is tentative and shaky. No doubt the drawing was intended to be worked up as an interior scene.

According to the memoir of Paul Sandby by his son in the *Monthly Magazine* of June, 1811, Bell, an engraver of Edinburgh, first introduced him to etching. This was probably Alexander Bell, portrait engravings by whom are recorded 1750-1780.

Sir Samuel Chambers cannot be identified at this date; for 'Lady Chambers' see No. 275.

Four on one mount (Nos. 209-212).

209. 'The Wife of Dr. Franklin', half-length, seated, in blue and white cap, blue ribbons and blue striped sleeves with panniers and high waist, holding a cat in her left arm.

Pen, black wash and watercolour, unfinished, 11.9 × 10 cm. (4⅝ × 3⅞ in.) *No. 14334.*

Of the early wooden type of drawing, with fine pen line and deep black in the hair, etc. The right half of the background left blank, presumably for a view through a window as in No. 207, which is of precisely the same type and may show the same sitter in the same dress.

W. Sandby, p. 217, lists a drawing of 'Mrs. Franklin and her Mother', probably referring to No. 207. As these are Edinburgh drawings, the sitter cannot be identified with the Mrs. Francklin who was godmother to Thomas Sandby's second daughter (b. Sept. 13th, 1759, cf. W. Sandby p. 176) and beyond reasonable doubt the child's aunt. Dr Thomas Francklin, Greek Professor and, later, chaplain to the R.A., married on Jan. 20th, 1759, Mary Venables, who was, according to the *D.N.B.*, the daughter of a wine merchant. The second Mrs. T. Sandby, married April 26th, 1753, was Elizabeth Venables, and as Elizabeth Sandby was a witness at the Francklin marriage (details ascertained by the London Museum).

210. Mr. Bell, engraver of Edinburgh, half-length seated facing half left, wearing a blue-flowered dressing gown.

Pencil, pen and watercolour, 12.9 × 8.4 cm. (5⅛ × 3¼ in.) *No. 14335*

It has been suggested that the title of this drawing has been transferred to the mount of the next since the sitter is more like the man described as R. Bell the engraver on the left of No. 208; the blue dressing gown is that of No. 214.

Brushwork largely in black over fine pen outline; strong pen work with black over the brush. With its exaggerated contrasts of light and shade, this wooden figure recalls the efforts after Rembrandtesque effects in the early Edinburgh etchings, but also possesses some of the salience of the later 'Sandpit Gate' drawings Nos. 245 *et seq.*

211. A violin-player, half length profile facing left, wearing a green coat.

Pen and watercolour, 11.7 × 9.2 cm. (4⅝ × 3⅝ in.) *No. 14336.*

PLATE 74

'del 1758' on the drawing in pencil appears to be recent and imperfectly repented. It has been suggested that the description 'Mr. Bell engraver of Edinburgh' on the modern mount below this drawing has been transposed from the preceding Facile and lively but possibly still of the Edinburgh period

212. 'The wife of Bob Munn, Keeper at Sandpit Gate' seated, suckling a baby; another woman standing in the background.

Pencil, pen and watercolour, 16 × 11.4 cm. (6¼ × 4½ in.) *No. 14337*

Looser and softer than the Edinburgh drawings but still opaque through the heavy underlying monochrome and aiming at a strong effect of light and shade. The baby well observed if badly placed, its blue striped dress and the touches of brick-red in its socks bringing it well into the palette of the Sand-Pit Gate interiors. Nos. 245 *et seq.*

For Bob Munn, Nunn or Dun see on No. 254.

Three on one mount (Nos. 213-215).

213. 'Mr. Ford, Deputy Ranger, Windsor Gt. Park, succeeded by T. Sandby'. Full length, hand on chair in an interior; two ladies, in panniers, and a man seated at a table in the background.

Pencil, pen and black wash, some watercolour in the face, unfinished 12.8 × 9.2 cm. (5 × 3⅝ in.) *No. 14402.*

PLATE 73

A full interior in miniature, fine penwork, especially in the elaborate chair. Generally similar in character to the coloured miniatures Nos. 222, etc.

Thomas Sandby succeeded 'Mr. Ford' at his death in 1764 as Steward at Windsor to William Duke of Cumberland (*Gentleman's Magazine*, 1764, p. 603). Ford had previously been the Duke's Clerk of the Stables (until about 1753), and Sandby from 1750 the Duke's Draughtsman (*Court and City Register*). The Deputy Rangership being an unofficial post, it is not possible to say whether Ford ever held it or when Sandby obtained it; but if, as this (copy) inscription suggests, it was held by the Steward, the constant statement (W. Sandby, p. 20, *D.N.B.*, etc.) that the Duke appointed Sandby to the post immediately upon his becoming Ranger in 1746 is nearly twenty years out. On the other hand, the words 'Deputy Ranger' may have been supplied by the mounter (cf. No. 389).

214. 'Allan Ramsay', seated, in hat and blue dressing gown, at a table, and smoking a Turkish pipe which is elongated in caricature to reach diagonally across the drawing. A lady, in panniers, seated in the background, right. Candlelight effect.

On the reverse a pencil study of a woman standing.

Pencil, pen, black wash and a little colour, a second woman in pencil only to right outside the wash, 11.7 × 15.8 cm. (4⅝ × 6¼ in.)
PLATE 75   *No. 14403.*

An exercise in chiaroscuro intermediate between Nos. 207 and 210. The dress of the lady practically the same as in Nos. 207–9; the dressing gown of No. 210.

The title is more likely to be intended for the painter (1713–1784) than for the poet (1686–1758) as W. Sandby, p. 218 supposes.

215. 'Brig.-Gen. B. Deley, Engineer, 1750', full length, standing to left in a window embrasure, reading a book. Slight indications of a church and buildings through the window.

Pen, grey wash and watercolour over pencil indications, 10.2 × 10.3 cm. (4 × 4 in.) *No 14404.*

A miniature, largely in monochrome, of the same character as No. 213. The window washed with blue, the breeches and shoes heavily worked up with black; hatching with soft pen as in No. 214.

No Brigadier-General Deley is identifiable in the Army Lists of the period.

Three on one mount (Nos. 216–218).

216. A lady, playing cards, seated at a table, in profile to right.

Pencil and pen, grey wash, pink in the face; hands, arms and chair in pencil only, 11.5 × 14.3 cm. (4½ × 5⅝ in.) *No. 14430.*

A rough drawing in pencil, to the right, of a woman's head and shoulders, apparently unconnected.

Of the same type as No. 208, the lady not wearing panniers, and her scarf falling down her back. The penwork neat.

217. A similar figure, the attitude and occupation the same, but the features different and the dress crimson with blue ribbons and with a black cape.

Pen and watercolour, corners cut off and made up, 15 × 10.4 cm. (5⅞ × 4⅛ in.) *No. 14431.*

Of the same type as the preceding, with fine penwork and parallel shading, but highly coloured with a full brush over the grey foundation.

218. An old lady playing cards, seated, profile to left, in a crimson upholstered chair and wearing a fur-bordered dress and large cap.

Pen and watercolour, 15.2 × 11.2 cm. (6 × 4⅜ in.) *No. 14432.*
PLATE 76

No doubt of the same series as the preceding; but with greater ease in drawing and pose, and the character and humour more fully developed.

Three on one mount (Nos. 219 to 221).

219. 'A humble imitation of Vauxhall in the Grounds of Heriot's Hospital, Edinburgh'; a rude, covered bandstand in a park with promenaders in fashionable dress, the ladies in hoops. Heriot's Hospital in the background left.

Pencil, pen and watercolour, unfinished; a lady in the foreground, right, indicated in pencil only, 11.7 × 16.2 cm. (4⅝ × 6⅜ in.)
PLATE 80   *No. 14452.*

Microscopic miniature, highly coloured; the feathery trees are similar to those in No. 90. The date 1756 at the end of the (copy) inscription on the present mount is unintelligible.

For Heriot's Hospital at this date see Maitland's *History of Edinburgh*, 1753, plate facing p. 430 perhaps after Paul Sandby as are other plates also engraved by P. Fourdrinier in this work.

220. Figure studies, unconnected. On the right two men seated at a table spread for a meal, one reading, the other writing by the light of a single candle. On the left a man in outdoor dress and a violin player, both standing.

Pencil, partly gone over with pen, 11.2 × 17.5 cm. (4⅜ × 6⅞ in.)
No. 14453.

The F mark (nearly E) in pencil at foot.

Easier than most of the Edinburgh studies, but from the neatness of the pen-work possibly of, or about, that date.

221. 'On Windsor Terrace', three ladies and two men in groups promenading and conversing. In the background two men on a low parapet, one looking through a telescope.

Pen and grey wash over slight pencil indications, 9 × 13.6 cm. (3½ × 5⅜ in.) *No. 14451.*

The foremost pair of figures recurs with No. 301 in the 'North Terrace looking West' at Harewood (see on No. 4) where the lady has her hat on her head and holds a child by the hand; her companion appears in the aquatint of that subject.

Closely akin to Nos. 242 and 243, but the penwork is neater and the drawing tighter with a touch of caricature as in the aquatint. The costume of the two women in the background is earlier, and the waistcoat of the principal man is longer, than in the print.

Nine on one mount (Nos. 222–230).

222. A miniature, a lady in light brown and white, seated beneath a tree, holding a fan in one hand and with the other apparently raising the pannier of her dress. A man in a blue coat, and red waistcoat, and breeches approaching shyly from behind.

Pen, watercolour and gouache in black border, bottom corner cut off and repaired, 10 × 7.7 cm. (3⅞ × 3 in.) *No. 14469.*
PLATE 79

The figure of the man is also used in the View from the Gardens of Somerset House, looking East, attributed to Thomas Sandby at the British Museum (Crowle, *Pennant*), L.B.9.

The stiff miniature manner used for a completed composition, somewhat recalling Carmontel.

223. The same personages, the lady in brown with a blue and white striped apron and black gloves, the man in blue and red and furred hat, both standing in a landscape.

Pen and watercolour in black border, 8 × 5.8 cm. (3⅛ × 2¼ in.) *No. 14470.*

The figures, reduced and reversed, used by the artist in the etching of 1751, No. 4 in the series of Castles, etc., 1750-1753 (Nagler, No. 16). The man recurs in the same direction, but with a woman in another position, in the Bothwell Castle, No. 7, in his large Scottish series of 1751.

Stiffer and still more miniature in handling than the preceding.

224. A lady in a black dress and red skirt with hoops seated in a chair in a Park.

Pen, watercolour and gouache in black border, 10 × 7.5 cm. (3⅞ × 3 in.) *No. 14471.*

In the same technique as the preceding and with similar stiffness of attitude.

225. Two men standing, one in grey with green waistcoat, the other in crimson and orange.

Pencil, pen and watercolour, 8 × 6.5 cm. (3⅛ × 2½ in.) *No. 14472.*

The left-hand figure is a freer version of the man on the right in No. 235. Both the men recur in the same relation in the large drawing of Somerset House and Gardens, looking East attributed to Thomas Sandby from the Crowle *Pennant* at the British Museum (L.B.9).

In fine pen; the figures, though stilted, easier than in the preceding both in pose and drawing. The hands, always a difficulty with Paul Sandby, clearly evaded.

226. Two ladies, wearing panniers, standing with a child and a dog, a footman behind to left.

Pen and watercolour, 8.3 × 9.1 cm. (3¼ × 3⅝ in.) *No. 14473.*

Reprod. *Windsor Castle, Series C* (in colour) as 'North Terrace'.

Fine penwork in the stiff, early manner of the Edinburgh period.

227. 'At Ascot'. Two men, one in a blue coat, the other in reds with white waistcoat, leaning against a rail and conversing.

Pen and watercolour, some gouache, 7.7 × 6.5 cm. (3 × 2½ in.) PLATE 103   *No. 14474.*

The group is repeated in an outline drawing of the Piazza, Covent Garden, attributed to Thomas Sandby, in the Crowle *Pennant* at the British Museum (L.B.17).

Neat miniature penwork with strong colour.

228. An Illustration. A girl seated, bareheaded, in a blue and white dress, in an artificial landscape with waterfall, a bust and vases.

Pen and watercolour with black border, 9.5 × 8 cm. (3¾ × 3⅛ in.) *No. 14475.*

Minute penwork and transparent colour washes, but in general in the miniature French manner.

229. 'Mr. Powell, a celebrated pedestrian'. Full length, standing to left in black with grey coat, blue and white striped stockings; his hands in the pockets of his waistcoat.

Pen and watercolour, 9 × 4.6 cm. (3½ × 1¾ in.) *No. 14476.*

Early miniature manner.

230. 'A Scene from "Reality"', an illustration. An altercation between an artist and his wife before a picture on an easel which is surmounted by emblems and the legend 'I wont Alter'. A chair tumbling, a hat flying, a palette falling, a frightened cat and a screaming child on the floor.

Pencil, pen and watercolour in black border, 8.6 × 9.4 cm. (3⅜ × 3¾ in.) *No. 14477. Fig. 17*

A scene from "Reality"

FIG. 17. 'A SCENE FROM "REALITY"' (CAT. NO. 230)

The subject is not explained by the title, presumably copied, on the modern mount. The date would appear to be in the early '50s. The glorified 'Chippendale' chair is much that of No. 274.

Nine on one mount (Nos. 231-239).

231. Studies of three men, called 'Col. Deacon, Equerry to Henry Fdk. Duke of Cumberland'.

An elderly stalwart man in green coat and top boots, advancing with bent head reading a book; a younger man, also in green coat but wearing shoes, standing facing left, looking through a telescope; back view of a third, his head repeated in the corner above.

Pencil, pen and watercolour, the third man in pencil and grey wash only, 8.6 × 10.2 cm. (3⅜ × 4 in.) *No. 14502.* PLATE 99

All three figures occur separately in No. 111, the Terrace and Bowling Green at (?) Cranbourne Lodge, signed and lated by Thomas Sandby, 1752. They cannot, therefore, represent Major (subsequently Lt.-Col.) John Deaken who is noted in the *Court and City Register* from 1767 to 1790 as Groom of the Bed Chamber to Henry Frederick Duke of Cumberland, but are, as he was not, personages of his predecessor's household. Capt. John Deacon of the 1st Regt. of Foot is stated by J. Hakewell (*History of Windsor and its Neighbourhood*, i. 280) to have been the purchaser of Holly Grove House in Windsor Park (now known as Forest Lodge). A 'design for Colonel Deacon's House in Windsor Forest' by T. Sandby uniform with Nos. 148, etc., in this collection is at the British Museum (L.B. 27 (2)).

232. 'A Street Coffee-house, Edinburgh'. On the left, a man dressed in pink with blue waistcoat, advancing with head bent; beyond, in the centre, a small square erection like a watchman's booth with five men seated in discussion on low benches around it. Other personages lightly indicated in the distance.

Pen and watercolour, 6.1 × 7.9 cm. (2⅜ × 3⅛ in.) *No. 14503.*

The seated figures are drawn with great freedom. The somewhat inappropriate use of Sandby's favourite pink and blue colouring is noticeable.

233. A group or two separate studies; on the left a man seated in a short-backed, round chair, looking away; on the right a man standing, his hand held behind his back, talking to a woman in hoops and laced corsage, also standing.

Pen and grey wash, 8.1 × 9.6 cm. (3¼ × 3¾ in.) *No. 14504.*

Presumably at the end of the Edinburgh period; the penwork though fine is fluent and the faces carefully drawn.

234. In Somerset House Gardens.

Two women (or the same woman), the nearer leaning over the parapet of Somerset House Gardens, the other seated on it at a lower level beyond. They wear the same heavy dress, apron and black hood but have different hats.

Pen and watercolour, the prolongation of the parapet to left indicated in pencil only, 11 × 14.8 cm. (4⅜ × 5⅞ in.) *No. 14505.*
PLATE 81

Reprod. as 'North Terrace' in *Windsor Castle Series C* (in colour). 'At Edinburgh' written on the modern mount.

The seated woman occurs again, less happily, in No. 241, the other as the more distant of two figures in the large 'View from the Gardens of Somerset House, looking East', attributed to T. Sandby, in the Crowle *Pennant* at the British Museum (L.B.9). The step and the fall in the parapet have nothing in common with Windsor, nor presumably Edinburgh, but are clearly marked in the views of Somerset House Gardens.
The penwork is neat and especially careful in the face of the nearer woman; heavy grey underpainting.

235. Street Characters. Three women of the lower orders, two accompanied, each, by a little girl; on the right a young man fashionably dressed in pink and crimson with a blue coat.

Pen and watercolour, 7.5 × 11.2 cm. (3 × 4⅜ in.) *No. 14506.*

Presumably separate studies brought together; the youth, a typical, neatly-drawn mincing young buck, reappears in No. 225 and in the drawing quoted thereon; an almost identical

figure of the woman in the centre and the squat child at her skirt occur by themselves, the child holding a paper windmill, in a pen and grey wash drawing at the British Museum (L.B.88(*d*)).

236. Two studies of men (wrongly called 'Windsor Poor Knights'). On the left, a miller standing with folded arms; on the right, three old men, dressed in black, red and lavender, standing in conversation.

Watercolour, the miller over pencil; the others over pen, 8.1 × 10.2 cm. (3¼ × 4 in.) *No. 14507.*

A number (1) under the centre figure, and the modern mount inscribed 'Windsor Poor Knights. 1. Sir John Dineley?'

The three coarsely drawn and coloured figures of old men are not dressed in the purple cloaks with the St. George's Cross worn by the Poor Knights of Windsor. The group of old men as it stands recurs in the engraving by E. Rooker after Paul Sandby, 'The West Front of St. Paul's, Covent Garden' of 1766, in company with a group taken from a pencil drawing in the Victoria and Albert Museum (D.192-1901). As, further, Sir John Dineley (see No. 179) was only admitted as a Poor Knight in 1798 (Fellowes *Military Knights of Windsor*, 1945, p. 51) the title on the modern mount with its identification of one of the three old men as Sir John is at least thirty years out.

237. 'A Hanoverian who brought over despatches from Wm. Duke of Cumberland'. Full length facing half-left, in furred overcoat and hat, wearing top-boots and holding a heavy whip in his left hand.

Pen, watercolour and gouache; a landscape background indicated in pencil, 9.2 × 6.1 cm. (3⅝ × 2⅜ in.) *No. 14508.*

The opaque red over yellow is that of the Sandpit Gate interiors, Nos. 245 *et seq.*

238. Two studies of men. A countryman, left; on right, two elderly men, one with a patch over his right eye; all standing.

Pen, with traces of pencil (? offset), 8.8 × 7.8 cm. (3½ × 3⅛ in.) *No. 14509.*

The two old men recur, exactly, in the 'North Terrace Looking East', at Drumlanrig, referred to on No. 8.

With the perfunctory, mechanical evenness of a repetition or a tracing.

239. A ratcatcher, walking to left holding a (?) jar in his left hand and under the same arm a trap with a tail protruding from a hole in its end.

Pen and watercolour wash, 8.7 × 5.7 cm. (3⅜ × 2¼ in.) *No. 14510.*

Rapid work with a soft pen and light wash. The figure appears with increasing movement in No. 36 and in the aquatint of 1776 based upon it.

Two on one mount (Nos. 240 and 241).

240. Somerset House Gardens, looking East; a lady in yellow gown, blue petticoat and white apron, flat hat and hoops, conversing with a man in red with blue coat, both standing in centre; on the left a lady similarly dressed but in red, seated. Background of Somerset House, the river and St. Paul's.

Pen and watercolour, 10.6 × 16.1 cm. (4⅛ × 6⅜ in.) *No. 14446*.
PLATE 77

Exhib. Royal Academy (British Art) 1934, No. 598 (1291) with No. 241.

Reprod. *Windsor Castle Series C.*

The foremost group in the large drawing, 'View from the Gardens of Somerset House, looking East', attributed to Thomas Sandby from the Crowle *Pennant* at the British Museum (L.B.9) is composed of the man in this drawing and two women who share between them features reproduced from his companion here.

Early miniature work, delicately coloured in pinks and blues with fine pen in the buildings and minute brush strokes in foliage. The distance without outline. The figures careful but stiff and flat.

The topography is largely fanciful, most of the features of the garden being transposed, statues surmounting the pedestals and, above all, the back of old Somerset House closing the gardens to the East and at right angles to the River instead of lying to the North parallel with it. A similar fantastic treatment of London topography is to be found in the drawing of the Horse Guards with St. Paul's rising above it attributed to Paul Sandby in the Crace Collection at the British Museum (L.B. 134).

241. The same, but without Somerset House; the river walk much abbreviated and St. Paul's brought nearer. Two ladies, one in a red gown, white petticoat and black cape and hat, standing; the other, seated on the parapet, similarly dressed but with yellow gown.

Pen and watercolour, 10.9 × 16 cm. (4¼ × 6¼ in.) *No. 14447*.
PLATE 78

Reprod. *Windsor Castle Series C.*

The seated woman is nearly a repetition from No. 234, even the fringe of the cape being retained. The other bears a strong resemblance to a figure in the etching of Bothwell Castle referred to on No. 223. The topography, less fanciful than in No. 240, is also inaccurate; and the figures, though more careful, especially in the faces. are as wooden and without animation or relation to each other as in that drawing.

242-244. *Three on one mount lettered 'On Windsor Terrace'.* The drawings appear to have been remounted, in a different order, since they were exhibited at the Royal Academy (British Art), 1934, No. 594 (1287); and not only do the inscriptions on the present mount differ very considerably from those stated then to be 'under the mount', but there is also now no trace of the 'signature' *P. Sandby del* which each of the three drawings was stated in the catalogue to bear.

242. 'On Windsor Terrace'. Five figures promenading; on the left an officer in red with white facings and yellow waistcoat addresses a lady while his friend, in Windsor uniform, touches him on the shoulder; she indicates with one hand an old man hobbling away, his back turned. A third young man stands apart on the right. Slight indications of landscape.

Pen and watercolour over very slight pencil indications, perhaps offset, 8.1 × 13.4 cm. (3¼ × 5¼ in.) *No. 14448*.
PLATE 106

Exhib. as stated above. Reprod. *Windsor Castle Series C.*

According to the inscription on the present mount four of the personages are identified by pencil numbers at the foot of the drawing as (from left to right) (3) Mr. Howse, (2) Col. Watson, (1) Miss Clark and (4) Mr. Yeoman. The catalogue of the Royal Academy (British Art) Exhibition, 1934, has "(3) Mr. Hervey on the survey, Scotland. (2) Colonel D. Watson, on the survey, Scotland. (1) Miss Clark, Edinr. Mr. Yeoman, Edinb.' For Howse and Watson see Nos. 329, 366 and 273.

The group of three men and one woman on the left occurs in the version in gouache of the 'North Terrace looking West' from the Banks collection reproduced in fig. 6 and referred to on No. 1. The action is the same and the figures are of the same size and generally identical save that there is a wider gap, partly occupied by a dog, in the centre, and the men are less cramped and more elegant in form and movement. The woman wears grey, but otherwise the colours are the same. The indications of a landscape background here, while suggesting the North Terrace, are certainly not of the view looking West. This, together with the greater fluency of the drawing and general coarsening of the figures, suggests that this is not a preparatory study for the gouache but a later repetition from the same sketch intended, with its pendant No. 243, for still other views of the North Terrace. The figure of the old man hobbling away also recurs in the version of No. 31 at Harewood and elsewhere.

If any weight is to be attached to the Scottish names given to three of the figures, they are more likely to indicate a revision of some older sketch dating from the Edinburgh period than an excursion of North Britons to Windsor Castle. The blue coat with red collar (not cuffs) worn by 'House' both in the gouache and the sketch may be taken as an accidental anticipation of the 'Windsor uniform' instituted in 1778. (See on No. 2.)

243. A similar group of four young men, standing in conversation; indications of a landscape setting (? the North Terrace, looking East) and of further figures in the distance.

Pen and watercolour over very slight pencil indications, perhaps offset, 9.2 × 13.5 cm. (3⅝ × 5⅜ in.) *No. 14449*.
PLATE 105

Exhib. and reprod. as for No. 242.

In the same manner as, and apparently a companion to, the preceding, with similar pencil numbers under the figures identifying them, according to the inscriptions on the modern mount, as (3) J. Isherwood the brewer (in blue), (2) Davis the smith, (1) Cap. Archibald Campbell, in red coat, white facings and waistcoat. The Royal Academy (British Art) Exhibition catalogue has '(1) Capn afterwards Sir Archbd Comber, (2) Davis the Smith of Windsor Castle, (3) Isherwood, the Brewer of D.'

Henry Isherwood (1743-1797), M.P. for Windsor 1796, was the son of the founder of the brewery in Datchet Lane who died in 1772 (see Nos. 71 and 300). The Davis family were general furnishers of ironwork to Windsor Castle from the preceding century. 'Comber' cannot be identified, and the name is probably due to a phonetic confusion. 'Sir A. Campbell' may be intended to refer to the distinguished officer of that name (1739-1791) who entered the Fraser Highlanders in 1757 as captain, went almost immediately to N. America, and served there, with an interval in 1773-5, until 1779, when he returned on leave and married the daughter of Allan Ramsay. By that date both he and Isherwood would be too old for the representations in this drawing, though both were most probably known to Sandby.

244. Two young men (or rather the same young man in two different attitudes) seen from behind leaning on the parapet of Somerset House Gardens (*not* Windsor Terrace).

Pen and watercolour over pencil, the left-hand figure incised with stylus, 12 × 15.2 cm. (4¾ × 6 in.) *No. 14450.*
PLATE 82

Exhib. and reprod. as for No. 242.

Thos. Sandby' is inscribed on the modern mount under the figure on the right. The 1934 exhibition catalogue reads, 'Signed: *P. Sandby del,* and inscribed: *T. Sandby, R.A.* and on the mount *T.S.R.A.*'

With fine but free penwork and rich but harmonious colouring, this is one of the best and most mature watercolours among these drawings. The varied colouring, light blue coat with red waistcoat and crimson breeches for one figure, grey coat and blue breeches for the other, proves that whatever difficulty the 18th century artists experienced in obtaining properly prepared colours, lack of pigments was not the cause. The fluid treatment in the stonework of the parapet is also noticeable.

In spite of the incision of the outlines for repetition, this figure does not occur precisely in either attitude among the various instances of similar postures in the many views of Somerset House Gardens, etc., so far seen. The parapet clearly belongs to that locality and not to the Terrace at Windsor.

VIII. INTERIORS AT SANDPIT GATE AND WINDSOR CHARACTERS

245. The Kitchen at Sandpit Gate, Windsor Park, 1754; interior view along the window wall on the right; a man in the livery of the Duke of Cumberland, green coat and crimson waistcoat, pumping in the foreground; further within, two women washing kitchen utensils at a window and an old man seated with a dog by an open door.

Pencil, pen, watercolour and some gouache, lightly scratched out in the water from the pump, 25 × 32.5 cm. (9⅞ × 12¾ in.)
No. 14331.

Inscribed and signed in ink at the foot 'The kitchen at Sandpit Gate Wr. Park 1754. P.S.' probably a retrospective addition.

A development of the figure studies with strong, interior lighting effects already practised in the Edinburgh period; the heavy underpainting in grey black still causing some clumsiness, but the drawing much more fluent, the attitudes easier, the colouring more fluid and the general effect of the light flooding from the windows most successful. The glistening lights on metal, produced by a transparent wash over grey and black, are noticeable and characteristic. An opaque red used for the brickwork of the sink in shadow in the foreground, also characteristic of Sandby's early work, looks as though it were made from the material itself.

Sandpit Gate, if it was, as now, a house or lodge and not a locality, has been altered beyond all recognition. W. Sandby (p. 218) seems to have supposed it to be the house of the keeper whose wife is portrayed on No. 212. It would seem large for such a purpose. There is no record of Paul Sandby having occupied it; he may have lodged there, but it is clear from a letter of his to Gandon (W. Sandby, p. 173) that he never had a house in the country but stayed with his brother Thomas when at Windsor. Much later he visited

his son at Englefield Green. If Thomas Sandby only became Deputy Ranger in 1764 when he succeeded Ford as Steward (see on No. 213) he may have received the 'Deputy Ranger's Lodge' as his residence then, or shortly afterwards when he quitted London in 1766. Until then he may have lived at Sandpit Gate when at Windsor, and Paul Sandby would have stayed with him there. In that case the lady shown in these drawings may be the first Mrs. T. Sandby, or after 1753 the second. Paul Sandby was not married till 1757.

Two on one mount (Nos. 246 and 247).

246. The same, seen from the other side of the pump; a maid standing and making pies at a table beside the heavily barred window, left.

Pen and watercolour over slight pencil, 15.1 × 12.7 (6 × 5 in.)
PLATE 84 *No. 14333.*

The pump and bricked sink, now brought to the right of the drawing, are the same and similarly treated as in the preceding drawing; the interest being now in the chequered light falling through the criss-cross of the window on the woman, the wall and the objects on the table in front of it. With still heavier black underpainting because of the more concentrated contrast of light and shade, and more pronounced pen outlines for the woman's features something of the woodenness of the Edinburgh experiments recurs. The skill in the colouring of the utensils is still more pronounced than in No. 245 and the indication of foliage in the sunlight through the window is noticeable.

247. A kitchen-scene (?) in London.

A maid standing, full face, her left arm on her hip, her right resting on a table in front of a window through which are seen a yard with an archway under a street and passers-by, one of whom peers through the railings. Full sunlight, entering obliquely from above.

Pencil, pen and watercolour, 16 × 11.3 cm. (6¼ × 4½ in.)
No. 14332.

A microscopic inscription as though diamond-cut on one of the panes of the window may read: 'Assist me evry Sund. . . ./Oh send me all . . .'

A pencil drawing for the figure only is on the back of No. 279; a repetition (including the background) in pen and grey wash, in reverse and apparently over an offset, is in an album (L.B. 138) at the British Museum, No. 64.

Although generally of the same type as the preceding two drawings, this is shown by the view through the window to belong to, or to be intended to represent, some other locality, and with less grey underpaint and penwork and more modelling of the face in colour it may exhibit a slightly more advanced development in the use of watercolour. There is also more expression in the fully rounded face. The interest is still very largely in the lighting, which here floods the window embrasure and the figure from above as though the scene were in a basement. The dress is complicated; the maid wears a white petticoat with stripes of red bordered blue, another over it of thick red material, lined white, with a blue border, a blue and white check apron, a grey bodice with short white sleeves and a red and green check scarf above, and a white cap on her head. Her round apple-cheeked face, not unlike that of Bob Munn's wife (No. 212) but less clumsy, is very different from the clean-cut types of the Edinburgh period.

If the pencil study on the back of No. 279 is of the same date as the drawing on the face, a later date is indicated for this drawing than 1754, the date inscribed on the Sandpit Gate drawing No. 245.

248. 'At Sandpit Gate'. Two women laundering at a table by a window, right, seen through an open door, by which stands a Queen Anne chair.

Watercolour and slight pen over pencil, 23.6 × 17 cm. (9¼ × 6¾ in.) *No. 14330.*
PLATE 83

A print or drawing pinned to the partition wall, right, inscribed in minute pen 'P. Sandby Fecit Old Win[dsor] July 1751'.

Presumably also at Sandpit Gate, but not the same room as in Nos. 245 and 246; the same colouring, but the metals less bright and the underpainting lighter. The faces are strongly outlined in pen, the lady standing in a blue apron is probably the same as in No. 249, the round-faced maid not unlike No. 247. The shadow of a face just within the window must be intended to fall from a woman standing outside.

Two on one mount (Nos. 249 and 250).

249. 'At Sandpit Gate'. A seated woman sewing, right, her foot resting on the stretcher of an empty chair, at an open door, through which a fence and fields are seen. Behind her another open door, showing a living room flooded with sunlight.

Pen and watercolour, the paper joined near the middle, 19.3 × 22.2 cm. (7⅝ × 8¾ in.) *No. 14328.*

The outlines have been carefully gone over with a stylus, some apparently with the ruler.

Presumably also Sandpit Gate, since it is of the same type as the preceding, the woman probably the same as in No. 248, the ladder back chair recurring in No. 250. The double lighting is very effective, the underpainting somewhat heavy, the brushwork of the added portion with the view through the open door and a small portion of the empty chair lightly handled.

250. 'At Sandpit Gate'. A woman laundering, her tubs standing on chairs, left, another crouching and tending the fire at an open hearth. Bright sunlight.

Pen and watercolour, traces of pencil, 22.9 × 23.4 cm. (9 × 9¼ in.)
PLATE 85
No. 14329.

Of the same series as the preceding drawings, but with fine pen outline and more fluid and transparent colour, as suits the more generally diffused light. The utensils on the ledge above the hearth are lightly drawn and effectively coloured; the foreground chair is the same as in No. 249, the position of the others and the tubs and basins upon them is not easy to interpret.

The whole series, but especially this drawing, with its sensitive and sympathetic representation of a simple figure, recalls Chardin. Sandby must have been familiar with prints after him. The series is probably earlier than Henry Morland's and Walton's household scenes.

251. 'A Windsor Character'. A short stout man in blue-coat with red collar, standing facing half-right, waving his hat in his right hand.

Watercolour over black chalk, 28.7 × 19 cm. (11¼ × 7½ in.)
PLATE 86
No. 13552.

The figure recurs, much reduced, in No. 147, the large 'Ascot Race Meeting', where the man stands on a railing, with another, some 4½ inches from the right edge.

Freely drawn and coloured, the chalk indications light and presumably removed except for hatching in the shadows under the colour and for the hat, where they have not been followed. The hands unfinished and clumsy.

252. A Servant of the Duke of Cumberland, full length, facing left, wearing the Duke's livery, crimson coat with green facings, green waistcoat and crimson breeches.

Pencil and watercolour, 22 × 13 cm. (8⅝ × 5⅛ in.) *No. 13551.*
PLATE 90

The letter C in pencil in the lower left hand corner. The figure recurs in the centre foreground of No. 147, the 'Ascot Race Meeting'.

Freely drawn in pencil, the tentative lines not removed and the contours not finally strengthened, except in the face, which is strongly characterised.

253. A Young Man. (Supposed portrait of, or by, Thomas Sandby.) Full length, facing half right, his left hand holding his glove and his stick, the right extended sideways and pointing to left.

Black chalk over offset, 26.2 × 16.6 cm. (10⅜ × 6½ in.) *No. 13549.*

Inscribed in pencil at foot, left, 'T. Sandby R.A.' and in another, later hand, right, 'Sir Joshua Reynolds'. The 'F' mark (see on No. 1) in pencil at foot, centre.

Listed by W. Sandby, p. 218, as a portrait of T. Sandby, 1760, by Paul, and reproduced as Sir Joshua Reynolds in the *'Annals of the Club, 1764-1914'* n.d. (1914) frontispiece.

Sir John Fortescue's 'discovery' of this drawing as a portrait of Reynolds to celebrate the third jubilee of Sir Joshua's own club had already been rejected by the far from hypercritical William Sandby. His name was probably placed upon it—in a weak, somewhat illiterate hand which does not occur elsewhere among these drawings—through a notion that the object, probably a glove, held in the left hand is an ear-trumpet. W. Sandby's own suggestion that this is a portrait of Thomas Sandby is negatived by the character of the drawing itself. If an offset were not already proclaimed by the lack of 'bite' in the main underlying lines it is proved beyond doubt by the buttonholes which are visible on the right-hand side of the coat beneath the slickly drawn buttons and by the buttons which are still discernible on the other side under the buttonholes. Clearly the coat has been turned. The features are barely indicated and are purely conventional, and the whole pose is that of the stock figures with which both brothers enlivened, and sometimes actually point to the beauties of, their architecture or landscapes. It is, in fact, followed in Thomas Sandby's 'Old Somerset House', No. 163, and in the 'North Terrace' quoted thereon. In the former it demonstrates something outside the picture to a very inattentive little 'Lady Waldegrave' and her more appreciative 'governess'.

The inscription 'T. Sandby R.A.' is in the same handwriting as the (ink) 'Paul Sandby by Parry' on the drawing reproduced after Plate 156. The writing is not Paul Sandby's. It might conceivably be Thomas Sandby's; but, though he may have been capable of the superficially competent touching-up of an offset, from a drawing probably by his brother, there seems little reason why he should single it out, after 1769, for his signature. It is more probable that the person who inscribed the portrait by Parry provided it with a pendant in this easy way.

254. 'Bob Dun, one of the Duke's gardeners at the Great Lodge'. Full length standing, his right hand under his waistcoat at the collar; landscape background with two women, seen from behind, standing on the right.

Pencil and watercolour, 23.6 × 15.2 cm. (9¼ × 6 in.) *No. 14318.*
PLATE 87

"'A most facetious fellow" written on the back of the modern mount, presumably copied from the back of the drawing.

Exhib. *Country Life*, 1937, No. 482 (reprod. *Souvenir*).

A first pencil sketch is just discernible on the right of the figure. A somewhat similar figure, but with a spade, similarly tinted, is at the British Museum (L.B. 92 (d)). The figure, reduced and in reverse, is introduced into the gouache drawing of the 'Bells of Ouseley' at the Victoria and Albert Museum (113-1898), cf. on No. 118.

The drawing is looser and the washes more transparent than in Nos. 251, 252, 255 and 256, grey being used as a colour with a yellowish green, especially in the sketchy background. The sky, too, is floated in with a wet brush. A patch of blue, no doubt accidental, has been partly removed.

Sandby's freaks of memory and the vagaries of the transcribers being known, it seems legitimate to identify this gardener, Bob Dun, with the keeper Bob Munn of No. 212 and a Robert Nunn whose account for killing vermin is preserved in the Royal Library.

255. 'Voules, Wm. D. of Cumberland's bailiff'. Full length standing, wearing grey overcoat, deep crimson coat, red waistcoat and black breeches, his right arm extended and pointing obliquely downward, his left hand on his hip; a man moving to left indicated in a landscape background.

Pencil and watercolour, 19 × 10.8 cm. (7½ × 4¼ in.) *No. 14319.*
PLATE 89

Exhib. R.A. (British Art), 1934, No. 599 (743).

A somewhat similar figure occurs with that of the preceding in the gouache drawing at the Victoria and Albert Museum quoted thereon.

More elaborate than the others of this series, the strongly modelled head with emphasised features recalls Nos. 246 and 247 of the 'Sandpit Gate' interiors; the velvety black of the breeches approximates to that of No. 344. The background and figure of a man retreating are in grey wash only. It is noticeable that the supposed bailiff is not in the Duke's livery.

256. 'A running footman to Wm. Duke of Cumberland'. Full length, standing, with his right leg advanced and right hand on his hip, dressed in crimson coat and green waistcoat. Woodland background.

Pen and watercolour over slight pencil or chalk, 32 × 23 cm. (12⅝ × 9 in.) *No. 14320.*

The figure is of the same general character as the others. but the contours, the face and the hands have been worked over in pen, and while the colour is less strong than in 255, the tree and the landscape background have been carried further than in any of the others and the sky completed, entirely with the brush. The accessories all suggest a later date than the main figure.

The penwork in the hands and face, the awkwardly drawn hands and the green and crimson of the livery are all identical with those of the man in the foreground of No. 245.

IX. WOMEN: FULL WATERCOLOUR

257. 'Mrs. Mercier and her Son'. Full length, seated on a 'Chippendale' chair, dressed in a black gown over white, white cap with a black ribbon under the chin. She holds a baby in her lap with her left hand.

Watercolour with traces of pencil, in black border, 24.8 × 18.2 cm. (9¾ × 7⅛ in.) *No. 14385.*

W. Sandby, p. 217.

The most elaborate drawing of a woman in the collection, comparable to the portraits of men in interiors and in some respects to the Sandpit Gate watercolours. The lighting is equally effective, but the modelling, mainly in grey, is fuller than in the latter, and there is a continuance of the effort after solidity which was shown in the early Scottish drawings, and still something of their wooden appearance. The underpainting and blacks are heavy; the shadows on white noticeably blue. The floor and panelling are detailed, and the pictures on the walls have gold frames and almost recognisable reproductions of their subjects.

The sitter appears to have no connection with the 'Mrs. Mercier and her youngest son Henry' of No. 266, q.v., where the names are inscribed on the drawing by the artist, not, as here, merely written on the modern mount.

258. 'The celebrated Kitty Fisher' as a milkmaid, full length, standing at a gate, and lifting her skirt with her left hand, the dress left white with red in the ribbons and pink in the flat 'milk-maid' hat; a yoke on her shoulders and a bucket at her feet. In the background a man in red and trees, vaguely drawn in shadow.

Watercolour over slight indications in pencil, gouache in the background, the bucket lightly outlined with brush and brown, 16.4 × 13.5 cm. (6½ × 5⅜ in.) *No. 14376.*
PLATE 95

Exhib. Royal Academy (British Art), 1934, No. 590 (1149), reprod. pl. CL. Paris, 1938, No. 230.

Lit. and reprod. W. Sandby, p. 217. Binyon, *English Watercolour* (1933), p. 26, pl. facing p. 21, and as above.

Kitty Fisher was at the height of her fame in 1758-60 when a song, 'Kitty Fisher's Merry-thought', provided the subject for one of Paul Sandby's etched 'London Cries' (1760), and was also mentioned in the title-piece. If this charming and deservedly celebrated sketch has anything to do with the lady, it must date from about these two years, and it would give a *terminus ad quem* for the Sandpit Gate interiors which are recalled by the effective lighting and the heavy blacks and brick red jacket in the background (clearly an afterthought), but are surpassed by the daintiness of pose and handling and the delicacy of the lightly touched head and features.

259. A lady, full length, in profile to right, in a green dress with ribbons at the back, white apron, black ribbon at neck and pink-ribboned 'Dolly Varden' hat, seated painting at an artist's table with colours in oystershells. View through a large open window over a river to houses. A blue striped curtain to right.

Pencil and watercolour, 19.5 × 15.2 cm. (7⅝ × 6 in.) *No. 14377.*
PLATE 94

Exhib. Royal Academy (British Art), 1934, No. 601 (1142).
Lightly coloured over the usual grey foundation, the hatching in shadow with the brush, the head and shoulders delicately modelled, and the face and right hand carefully drawn, almost entirely with brush. The distant view pink and blue without outline.

The exquisite drawing and delicate modelling of the features are those of the well-known watercolour, the 'Waldegrave Children', in the Victoria and Albert Museum. (D. 1835-1904) for which see on No. 296.

X. WOMEN: RED CHALK

Two on one mount (Nos. 260 and 261).

260. A lady, full length, standing, head turned to left, in short skirt, hoops, narrow waisted embroidered corsage with scarf on shoulders, flounced sleeves and beehive-shaped straw hat, her right arm bent and holding a fan across her at shoulder level. Background of trees.
Red chalk, 16 × 9.5 cm. ($6\frac{1}{4} \times 3\frac{3}{4}$ in.) *No. 14321.*
PLATE 97
The short dress is unique in this series and altogether unusual. Were it not for the hat (which reappears in No. 267) a dancer would be suggested.

261. A man and a woman sauntering in a Park, full length; the woman, with full skirt and panniers, holding her flat hat with her right hand.
Red chalk, 16.5 × 13.6 cm. ($6\frac{1}{2} \times 5\frac{3}{8}$ in.) *No. 14322.*
Numbered 62 in red in top right corner. The modern inscription on the mount, 'Paul Sandby and Lady' may or may not be copied from an older.
The numbers on this drawing and on 263, 266, 267, suggest that they come from the same sketch book from which some or all of the others in the same material may derive. The dresses of the women are also similar, panniers, narrow waists and flat hats predominating. The French influence deriving from Watteau, perhaps through Mercier, is manifest. In this drawing the subject is akin to the miniature conversations Nos. 222-4, the attitude of the man even more mincing, while the billowing skirt over high panniers connects it with No. 262. The minute hands and stick-like arms of the woman are noticeable, and belong to the artificial, miniature-like manner.

Two on one mount (Nos. 262 and 263).

262. Two ladies walking in a high wind, back view, their skirts over panniers; ribbons, scarf and flat hats blown to the right. One woman wears a 'Watteau' sacque gown.
Red chalk, 19 × 13.7 cm. ($7\frac{1}{2} \times 5\frac{3}{8}$ in.) *No. 14323.*
PLATE 98
The two figures occur, less agitated by the weather, in a 'Somerset House Gardens' belonging to Captain Brinsley Ford (reprod. Royal Academy (British Art), 1934, plate CXLIX).
The undulating line connects this drawing with Nos. 269-271, the parallel hatching of the shadows and background with 273 and 267, the 'Watteau' gown, small scarf and upturned flat hats with the next drawing.

263. Two ladies in sacque (Watteau) gowns, small pointed scarves or capes and flat, ribboned hats, walking to right; seen half from behind. The foremost woman points with a fan to the right, where a boy stands.
Black and red chalk, 19.7 × 17.6 cm. ($7\frac{3}{4} \times 6\frac{7}{8}$ in.) *No. 14324.*
PLATE 92
Numbered 15 in red in top right-hand corner.
The group, identical but much reduced, is used in the background of the engraving 'The Cascade and Grotto' in the 'Eight Views' of 1754. The left-hand figure, which is connected with the fine pencil drawing No. 264, also occurs in the 'View from the North Side of Virginia River' in the same series and the drawings related to it: No. 119, and L.B. Thomas Sandby, 7, at the British Museum, where the omission of the right hand, although there is no figure in front, proves a not too intelligent copyist.
The workmanship in this drawing is neater than in the others; the shading and ground in parallel hatching. The drawing of the left hand figure is entirely in black except for the face, and all the black appears to be posterior to the sanguine.

Two on one mount (Nos. 264 and 265).

264. A similar figure but with a 'Dolly Varden' hat, no ribbon at neck, no cape, and with her left hand holding her gown at her side.
Pencil, 18.6 × 11 cm. ($7\frac{3}{8} \times 4\frac{3}{8}$ in.) *No. 14386.*
PLATE 101
A study in very fine pencil, clearly connected with the figure on the left in the preceding, and either an elaboration from it or from a common original. Even in the points of difference there is similarity; the bow of the ribbon at the back of the neck has become a curl, an unexplained piece of drapery at the back is the remaining fragment of the cape. With the same hat and curl, but with the more voluminous coat and cape of No. 263, this figure occurs in the engraving and drawings there quoted. It was also used in the engraving 'The Moat Island' in the same series.

265. 'Lady L. Clayton', full length, standing to left in a very full red striped black gown and cape and high round hat with streamers, landscape background.
Watercolour over slight pencil, 14.3 × 11.5 cm. ($5\frac{5}{8} \times 4\frac{1}{2}$ in.) *No. 14387.*
W. Sandby, p. 217, as 'Lady Clayton'.
Somewhat heavily coloured but the face of the same neat type as the preceding; the hands evaded.

266. 'Mrs. Mercier and her youngest boy Henry'. Full length, seated, in flounced and embroidered gown and petticoat over hoops; a boy in the background, left, pointing. An indication of landscape.
Pencil and black chalk, with red in the faces and hand, 22.3 × 17.2 cm. ($8\frac{3}{4} \times 6\frac{3}{4}$ in.) *No. 14384.*
Numbered 11 in black in top right corner. Inscribed in ink, in the same hand as on the following drawing, with the title as given.
W. Sandby, p. 217.
Neat work with parallel hatching, notably in the sky.
The sitter seems to have no connection with No. 257; if it represents the same persons, this drawing would be some six or eight years later.
Neither portrait fits with the little that is known about the family of Philip Mercier the portrait painter (1689-1760). His widow was granted ten guineas by the Society of Artists the year after his death and afterwards given small employment by the Society. (Whitley, *op. cit.* i, 232.) His son Philip, according to the *D.N.B.*, was a captain in the Welsh Fusiliers and died in 1793 aged 54; he, or another of the same name, received assistance from the Royal Academy 'in its early years' (Whitley i. 318). The wife of the painter would appear too old for these portraits of the '50s, the wife of the son too young. An H. Mercier appears in the lists of the Drawing Office of the Tower given in the *Court and City Register.*

267. Mrs. Lane. Full length, seated, wearing a 'beehive' hat and apron, spinning, facing left; a maid threading a needle in the background, left.

Red and black chalk, 22.5 × 17.5 cm. (8⅞ × 6⅞ in.). *No. 14383.*
PLATE 96

Numbered 14 in black, in top right corner. Inscribed on the drawing at foot in ink in the artist's hand, 'Wife of Mr. Lane who purchased first the (pictures) by Hogarth of Marriage Alamode', 'pictures' written over a tear in the paper.

W. Sandby, p. 217.

The hat of No. 260, the chair (Queen Anne) of No. 287. Complete interior background with pictures indicated on the walls and a pattern in the carpet. The faces, hands and arms and the chair-back in red. Much hatching.

Mr. Lane's own story of his purchase from Hogarth in 1750 for 120 guineas of the six pictures after the failure of the artist's attempt to auction them is told in Nichols' *Biograph. Anecd. of William Hogarth*, 1781, p. 107, etc.

268. A lady sewing. Full length, seated, in profile to left; her gown, collar and sleeves laced, small cap; the chair, plain stuffed 'Queen Anne'.

Pencil, 21.5 × 18.2 cm. (8½ × 7⅛ in.) *No. 14382.*

Dated 1760 in pencil, at foot.

Without a number and with red chalk only where it has been rubbed against a sanguine drawing on an opposite page; but it is of the same character as the portraits in that medium, especially Nos. 266 and 267. The chair is identical with that of No. 315. The parallel hatching similar to, but less precise than in that drawing.

Three on one mount (Nos. 269 to 271).

269. 'A Girl from Norwich'. Full length, standing, profile to right, in negligé skirt and jacket, cap and ribbon.

Red chalk, 19 × 11 cm. (7½ × 4⅜ in.) *No. 14325.*

Inscribed at foot in pencil 'A Girl from Norwich (kept) *erased* by Wm. (here cut off and completed in another hand) Duke of Cumberland 1760'. The pencil mark F (see on No. 1) in lower corner, left.

The flowing lines of the drapery are similar to No. 261; the feet show several alterations. Parallel hatching in background.
A red chalk drawing at the Victoria and Albert Museum, D.96-1901, may represent the same girl in more elegant costume, head and shoulders only as in the next two drawings.

270. The same, half-length, facing half-left, holding cards.
Red chalk, 15 × 12.2 cm. (5⅞ × 4¾ in.) *No. 14327.*

Drawn in the same strong manner and showing the same dress as No. 269.

271. The same, the upper half only, repeated more carefully.
Red chalk, the eyes and brows in black, 16.9 × 10.3 cm. (6⅝ × 4 in.) *No. 14326.*

The F mark (see on No. 1) in pencil in lower corner, right. The fluent strong line is still more marked than in the previous sketch which has been closely followed.

272. 'Miss Marsden'. Full length, standing, head turned half right, in fur-bordered cape, flat hat with ribbons, hooped skirt and apron. Landscape setting.

Black and red chalk heightened with white, some pencil, on brownish or stained paper, 25.3 × 16.3 cm. (10 × 6⅜ in.) *No. 14436.*

Inscribed in pencil on the drawing at foot, 'Miss Marsden'. W. Sandby, p. 217.

The red and black chalk are used for local colour rather than decorative effect; the black is heavily worked and overpowering; softened with stump in the clouds and trees, it has a Gainsborough-like effect. The face and one hand are well touched in; the arm, as usual at this date, poor, the feet very prominent.

A companion drawing of the same size and with an identical inscription, also on brownish paper and in the same materials but without black, showing the same girl from behind with the same hat and ribbon hanging to the side but without the cape is in the collection of Sir Robert Witt. It has the initials (modern) 'F.H.' and was reproduced as by Hayman in the *Connoisseur*, Jan. 1926, p. 7, and Royal Academy (British Art), 1934, No. 571 (1308), plate CXLIV. It bears the F mark. Other drawings of the same type in the same and other collections, with or without the false initials or the name Hayman, in full, upon them (see on No. 274) are also presumably by Sandby, while one of them, in the writer's collection, without the false initials but bearing the 'F' mark and hitherto attributed to Hayman, is proved to be Sandby's by an offset from it among his drawings at the British Museum (L.B. 137, (27)).

XI. MAN: RED CHALK

273. 'Col. David Watson'. Full length, in uniform, seated cross-legged to left on a 'Queen Anne' chair.

Black and red chalk, 19.8 × 14.8 cm. (7¾ × 5⅞ in.) *No. 14405.*
W. Sandby, p. 218.
PLATE 93

Inscribed on the modern mount 'Col. David Watson on the Survey of Scotland, 1748'.

The date 1748, if not merely an inference of the transcriber, is probably a general reference to the period during which Sandby served on the Survey of the Highlands under the supervision of Col., later Major-General, Watson (c. 1713-1761). Though the drawing in red and black chalk (numbered 75) of a Scottish incident at the British Museum (L.B. 96) is not inscribed as stated by W. Sandby (p. 17) 'sketched on the spot, 1745'—nor, indeed, if it had been, could the statement receive credit—it is not impossible that at any rate by the end of his period in Scotland Sandby could practise in the 'Mercier' manner (see No. 261), as well as produce dainty miniatures. The charm and elaboration as well as the inherent weakness of this drawing are, however, precisely those of the rest of the series, which certainly belongs to the next decade. The studied elegance of the twisted attitude is noticeable and characteristic of the moment in English portraiture; the position of the sword and the cross-hatched background are also points of interest. (See also No. 242.)

XII. WOMEN AND CHILDREN: PEN, PENCIL AND WASH

274. A Lady writing a letter. Full length, in white flowered dress and lace cap tightly tied under the chin, seated in profile to left at a side table.

Watercolour over slight pencil, 24 × 20.7 cm. (9½ × 8⅛ in.) *No. 14381.*

The letter on the table reads, in microscopic characters, 'I should have honour . . .'

A version in pencil, probably earlier, of approximately the same size is in the collection of Sir Robert Witt. Like the 'Miss Marsden' referred to on No. 272, it bears the initials F.H. (twice) and has been reproduced (*Connoisseur*, Jan., 1926, p. 8) as by F. Hayman. In most respects the two drawings are identical down to the position of the flowers on the dress; in certain minor points, e.g. the position of the right hand and the pen, the ink bottle and the shadow on the panelling, the watercolour may have gained. Even in the chief difference, which is in the chair, the replacement of squared legs by the more unorthodox spirals and club feet of the watercolour version probably appeared an improvement, as are, certainly, the perspective and the reduction in the rake of its 'Chippendale' back. In both versions the relation of the body to the seat of the chair is no happier than in No. 268. The pencil drawing appears to have a partly erased pencil F at the foot and on the reverse an outline drawing, with several unequal figures, of a drunken carousal after the manner of Hogarth's 'Midnight Modern Conversation', probably a tracing.

The orange scarf and the mahogany chair have the sheen of Sandby's metal utensils and horses' coats.

Paul Sandby was married in 1757. A similarity in the features of this and other drawings with the painting by Cotes of his wife (exhibited 1761, engraving by E. Fisher reprod. W. Sandby opposite p. 186) would be more convincing if the chief points of resemblance, the high forehead and straight nose with little bridge, had not already been prominent in the heads of the Edinburgh period.

Two on one mount (Nos. 275 and 276).

275. ' Lady Chambers' and child. Full length, facing half right, in flounced dress, small cap, plain high-waisted corsage, apron and scarf with frills, seated on a sofa and holding a child on her lap.

Pencil and black chalk, brown wash, touches of colour, 20.5 × 12.5 cm. (8⅛ × 4⅞ in.) *No. 14409.*

W. Sandby, p.217.

This drawing and Nos. 277 and 278 are uniform in size and manner; they show the same features and, with some care, the same details of dress. The awkward treatment of the hands in this and 277 is identical. All might have been drawn on the same day from the same sitter. The character of the heads connects them with the red chalk 'Mercier-like' studies as does, perhaps, the use of the same material in 278, but they are later both in costume and in the more assured handling which leads to a new carelessness, most observable in the child in this drawing. It contrasts unfavourably with the perhaps wooden but conscientious study of No. 212 and even of the quite primitive No. 206.

See on No. 278. Lady Chambers cannot be identified—perhaps the wife of the non-existent Sir Samuel Chambers of No. 208. The *D.N.B.* credited both Sir William Chambers the architect and Sir Robert Chambers the Indian judge with marrying, simultaneously, the only daughter of Joseph Wilton, the sculptor, a noted beauty. This has been corrected, but no information is given about the wife of the former, who was married by 1752 and knighted by the King of Sweden in 1771.

276. Perhaps the same sitter, with a visitor, both full length seated, and both wearing capes or scarves; the visitor wearing a coalscuttle hat.

Pencil, touched with pen, and yellow-brown wash, 17.3 × 14.3 cm. (6¾ × 5⅝ in.) *No. 14410.*

The pencil work is slight and rapid, but the faces are rounded, neat and carefully outlined with the pen. Similarity in the features has caused this drawing to be grouped with the preceding on one mount and the rough pencil work, especially in the hands, is similar. But the dresses are not quite the same and the wash is of a different (generally later) colour. The figures are awkwardly placed in relation to each other and slightly different in scale, suggesting that, as in No. 280, two single studies have been pieced together.

Three on one mount (Nos. 277-279).

277. The same sitter as in No. 275, full length seated, facing to right and (?) knitting.

Pencil and grey wash with touches of white and faint indications of red chalk, 18.7 × 12.3 cm. (7⅜ × 4⅞ in.) *No. 14433.*

More rapidly sketched and less finished, but without doubt the same woman and in the same costume as in Nos. 275 and 278. The hands and their action are more studied than in those drawings, the face intermediate between them.

278. The same, full length, seated on a chair, facing right and holding a letter, the dress identical with Nos. 275 and 277 save for one added frill at the neck.

Black chalk and pencil over slight red chalk, grey wash and touches of white, 19.3 × 12.5 cm. (7⅝ × 4⅞ in.) *No. 14434.*
PLATE 112

Reprod. Evan Charteris, *William Augustus Duke of Cumberland and the Seven Years' War*, n.d. (1925), opposite p. 210, as 'Miss Elliot who lived under the protection of the Duke of Cumberland'; a note (p. 211) adding that nothing is known of this lady except this sketch, 'which appears in a volume containing portraits of the Duke's household'. W. Sandby, p. 217, lists 'Mrs. Elliott' among the sketches at Windsor, but the name is not on any of the present drawings or mounts. Possibly there has been a confusion with the actress Anne Elliot to whom Prince Henry Frederick, later Duke of Cumberland, 'was for two years devoted' (*B.M. Satires*, IV, p. 592), or perhaps by supplying the name of the 'Dam of Gimcrack' (No. 388), the whole story may be dismissed as a mare's nest. It is worth remarking that the sitter for this drawing is almost alone in the collection to display a wedding ring (the other instance being No. 276).

279. A lady, full length, profile to right, seated by a window, her left hand on the sill, her right holding a letter which she is reading.

Pencil and watercolour, a little pen, 20.2 × 13.3 cm. (8 × 5¼ in.) *No. 14435.*

On the reverse, a pencil sketch for No. 247 (14.5 × 9.5 cm.) without background and the head at a different angle.

Loosely washed mainly in grey, the scarf in green, much in the manner of the preceding, but the profile of the 'Greek' type associated in No. 274 with Mrs. Paul Sandby. The hand redrawn.

280. Two ladies, seated full length under a tree; one (? Mrs. Eyre) playing the guitar, wearing red with black apron and scarf, a cap on her head; the other, loosely holding a music book, in blue, with blue hat much turned up behind.

Pen and watercolour, 22.7 × 16 cm. (8⅞ × 6¼ in.) *No. 14378.*
FRONTISPIECE

The likeness between the lady on the left in this drawing and 'Mrs. Eyre' in No. 283 appears more than merely generic, while her companion is clearly derived from the next drawing, No. 281. The dress is, on the whole, similar to that of the preceding group, but the colouring is carried much further, with transparent washes, and the drawing in pen is consciously calligraphic, showing, with the use of the following sketch, that the juxtaposition is artificial, a piece-work of separate studies. The elegance is that of a painting or drawing by Sandby's friend Cotes.

Two on one mount (Nos. 281 and 282).

281. A lady, full length seated. Study used for the right hand figure in the preceding drawing, the hat and the upper part of the dress in black, sleeves and petticoat yellow.
Pencil and watercolour with traces of red chalk, 17.2 × 11.7 cm. (6¾ × 4⅝ in.) *No. 14379.*
The title 'Idleness' on the modern mount is a recent invention.
Exhib. Country Life, 1937, No. 481, with No. 282. Reprod. *Windsor Castle Series C.*
A change in the expression of the face, an added ribbon or two and a complete difference in colouring, have done much to disguise the fact that this is the drawing, probably from nature, from which the preceding has been worked up. The apparent differences are as significant as the resem-blances. Where the left hand differs, it and the book held by it in No. 280 are completely confused, while the recog-nisable ruffles in this drawing have become part of the background foliage in the other. The hat is the same in outline but has a semi-circle added in No. 280. The colour-ing was no doubt added to this drawing, at least in part, after it had been used in the composition of the other.

282. A lady, in flowered dress, full length seated, sewing by a kitchen table in front of a diamond-paned window.
Pencil, red and black chalk, grey wash and touches of colour, 18 × 12.7 cm. (7⅛ × 5 in.) *No. 14380.*
PLATE 110
Exhib. and Reprod. as on No. 281, under the title 'Indus-try', which has no authority. The two drawings are entirely unrelated.
A rapid drawing of the figure, with delicate profile. The careful hatching in pencil and chalks and the chair back of 'Queen Anne' type, which is entirely out of relation to the body, were no doubt subsequent additions. The blue of a ribbon is precisely that of Nos. 281, 289, etc.

Four on one mount (Nos. 283-286).

283. 'Mrs. Eyre'. Full length, seated, profile to right, at a spinet, wearing a blue flounced and frilled dress, a cap with crimson ribbon and a rolled scarf of the same colour round her neck.
Pencil and watercolour, 16 × 12 cm. (6¼ × 4¾ in.) *No. 14424.*
W. Sandby, p. 217.
PLATE 121
Apparently the same sitter as the guitar player in No. 280, and with a similar dress. The watercolour transparent, the drawing neater and more precise than in 280. The diffused light well suggested and the action of the hands well caught; but the spinet an afterthought.

284. A lady, in undress. Full length, seated, facing to left, one hand on her lap, the other hanging loosely.
Pencil and grey wash, 16 × 11 cm. (6¼ × 4⅜ in.) *No. 14425.*
Of the same type as No. 275, the hands and arms a difficulty as there. One of the very few among these drawings in which the sleeves are without ruffles.

285. A young girl, full length, seated to right, her head facing front over her right shoulder.
Pencil and watercolour, 17.5 × 10.8 cm. (6⅞ × 4¼ in.) *No. 14426.*
The colour, yellow for the dress and blue for the ribbon of the cap, lightly and loosely thrown over the monochrome; the momentary attitude of a young body in a somewhat stiff costume caught with spirit.

286. A girl, full length, seated, in profile to left, beside a window, reading.
Pen and watercolour, 17 × 12 cm. (6¾ × 4¾ in.) *No. 14427.*
PLATE 111
The fine but rapid penwork and the loose and transparent wash of colour (as in the preceding), show a completely assured and developed art. The conscious, complicated postures of Sandby's earlier work are no longer needed to give life to the figure. Direct and unpretentious, it has the grace and simplicity of the best English painting.

Two on one mount (Nos. 287 and 288).

287. 'Mrs. Gandon, Wife of the Architect'. Full length, seated on a 'Queen Anne' chair, facing half-right, her right arm resting on a table. She is dressed in black gown and dress, flounced and frilled, black hat and black scarf crossed in front.
Watercolour over pencil, 17.5 × 11.8 cm. (6⅞ × 4⅝ in.)
No. 14396.
W. Sandby, p. 218.
Though in every way heavier and more wooden in effect, the drawing and pose of the hands are similar to those of No. 258, the delicate workmanship in the face to that of 259, though the contours are largely left in pencil.
For Gandon the architect see on No. 323; unfortunately, his biographers do not give the date of his marriage, but it can scarcely have been before 1769.

288. Two girls, called 'The Misses Berry', in large straw hats with black ribbons, standing full length to right. They have long ringlets hanging over their shoulders; one, a white dress with capacious black shawl, fastened in front; the other, a spotted single-piece dress with tight sleeves and the black collar and facings of a man's coat. Landscape background with two ladies walking.
Watercolour over pencil, 15.5 × 11.7 cm. (6⅛ × 4⅝ in.)
No. 14395.
Reprod. W. S. Lewis. *Horace Walpole's Correspondence*, VOL. XI (1944), opposite p. 12.
This drawing was not known to W. Sandby, at any rate under the title at present on the mount. Had he known it, he could not have failed to include the sisters among the notabilities mentioned in his list. It might possibly come from the Acland book; but as it is entirely different in style and date from all other studies in this collection, it is more probably an interloper, separately acquired. The face of the nearer girl alone retains the character of Paul Sandby's figure studies; the coarse outline and clumsy colouring, if they are not the work of another hand, must have been deliberately employed by him to emphasize the caricature of the hideous costume.
In any case, the identification of the two girls as the Misses Berry must be abandoned. They are represented as between 15 and 20 years of age. The Berry sisters were born in 1763

FIG. 18. 'MISS SANDBY'S OF NORWICH' (CAPT. BRUCE INGRAM)

and 1764, and until 1783 they lived at Chiswick where even if they had by some accident attracted Sandby's notice they would not have been wearing this costume. In 1783 they went abroad, returning only in 1788, and then for the first time they met Horace Walpole and might therefore have become subjects for Sandby's pencil. But by then they were respectively 25 and 24 years of age, too old to be the models for this drawing.

Moreover, Sandby himself gave other names to the two girls. A drawing (Fig. 18) in Capt. Bruce Ingram's collection, lightly washed over slight, perhaps off-set, pencil indications, presents the same two figures, somewhat smaller, in reverse and in different costume, but in precisely the same attitudes and relation to each other. They wear bonnets in place of extravagantly large hats and the open sunshade held by the foremost girl in her left hand explains the action of her arms which in the present drawing are purposelessly, if not painfully, crossed in front of her as she walks. Underneath these figures Sandby has written in pencil 'The Miss Sandby's [sic] of Norwich', meaning no doubt the daughters of Dr. Sandby, Chancellor of Norwich, drawings of whose seat, Denton Lodge, Sandby exhibited at the Royal Academy in 1798 and 1799. The costume shows that the figure sketch dates from about that time. The correctness of this description is to some extent confirmed by a companion drawing in the album from the Burney family in which Capt. Ingram acquired it, a sketch in the same manner and of the same date showing three figures which are inscribed below with the names of Mrs. T. P. Sandby, her sister Augusta (characteristically written 'Agusta') and a Sandby boy.

Two on one mount (Nos. 289 and 290).

289. A lady, full length, standing, profile to left, carrying a kettle in her left hand, the right extended from the shoulder. 'Peg Woffington' hat, narrow-waisted corsage laced with two ribbons, hoops.

Pencil, red and black chalks and watercolour, 18.7 × 12 cm. (7$\frac{3}{8}$ × 4$\frac{3}{4}$ in.) *No 14389.*
PLATE 120

The red chalk is used as a colour in the petticoat, hands and kettle, but it seems also to have been used very lightly for a first rough drawing and heavily for the feet, where it has not been followed. The face is very delicate as in No. 259, etc., the outline with the brush. The watercolour strong only in the blue lining and ribbon of the flat 'Peg Woffington' hat and the pink ribbons; elsewhere, a mere light wash of grey on the dress, yellow green for the ground and trees indicated in the background and blue in the sky, as in No. 290. Much parallel hatching in pencil.

290. 'Lady Mary Churchill, Aunt to the Duchess of Gloucester'. Full length, standing to right, full face, the right arm extended from the elbow, wearing a heavy gown, black bowl-shaped hat and black scarf. A castle vaguely indicated in the right background, a hill on the left.

Watercolour with slight indications of pencil, 18.3 × 12.4 cm. (7$\frac{1}{4}$ × 4$\frac{7}{8}$ in.) *No. 14388.*

W. Sandby, p. 217.

Almost monochrome except for the background and the face. There is more brushwork in the gown than in the preceding (No. 289), but the same grey wash; and the delicate work in the face is similar to that drawing. The foot as first drawn in pencil was in a very incorrect position.

Lady Mary Churchill was the daughter of Sir Robert Walpole and Maria Skerrett, whom he subsequently married as his second wife. She was therefore, as stated, the aunt of the Duchess of Gloucester (previously Lady Waldegrave), who was the natural daughter of Sir Edward Walpole, Sir Robert's second son, and Dorothy Clements. Lady Mary was granted the rank of an Earl's daughter by George II, and married Colonel Charles Churchill, the illegitimate son of General Sir Charles Churchill and Anne Oldfield the actress. In 1764 she succeeded Mrs. Handysyde as housekeeper at Windsor Gate (see on No. 13), and held that appointment until 1800. If, therefore, the castle in the background can be accepted as Windsor, it tends to confirm the description of the lady represented and would date the drawing after 1764.

Five on one mount (Nos. 291-295).

291. A girl, full length, standing, in white dress, looking at a book which is placed on the seat of a chair.

Pencil and watercolour, mainly grey, 12.5 × 8.7 cm. (4$\frac{7}{8}$ × 3$\frac{3}{8}$ in.)
PLATE 107   *No. 14411.*

The head of the girl, who is in full adult dress, scarcely reaches to the top of the large very rustic 'Chippendale' chair which, no doubt, and the rather unusually strongly marked floor, panelling, etc., have been thrown around her originally independent figure. They form a good design; the arm, with pretty hand, is noticeably bad in drawing.

292. 'Mother of the Dss. of Gordon: dau. of Sir William Maxwell'. Full length, standing to left, in flowered dress with panniers, blue tippet and flat 'Peg Woffington' hat.

Pen and watercolour, 13.7×8.8 cm. (5⅜×3½ in.) *No. 14412.*
PLATE 102

W. Sandby, p. 217.

Of the Edinburgh period or soon after (cf. Nos. 219 and 240 and 295). The grey blue of the tippet as in Nos. 210 and 214.

Jane, the second daughter (b. 1748) of Sir William Maxwell, was married on 23rd October, 1767, to the 4th Duke of Gordon. The inscription with its roundabout description of Lady Maxwell by reference to her celebrated daughter is therefore considerably later than the drawing.

293. A lady. Full length, standing half left, in embroidered narrow waisted dress and full gown and round hat; her left arm hanging down, the right not finished.

Pencil, 12.3×7.4 cm. (4⅞×2⅞ in.) *No. 14413.*

A highly finished pencil drawing similar to, but smaller than, No. 264 and, like it, connected with the 'Virginia Water' prints of 1754. With the head in profile it occurs much reduced in 'Moat Island' of that series, and it seems to have been used for the principal lady in the 'View from the North Side of the Virginia River', where, as here, the right arm appears unfinished, though in the associated drawings in this collection (No. 119) and at the British Museum (L.B. T. Sandby, 7) the lady holds a fan as in the kindred drawing No. 297, and her other hand is different.

294. A girl. Full length, standing, facing half left, wearing a green, high-waisted, fringed dress and black scarf.

Red chalk, washed with watercolour, 18.3×8.3 cm. (7¼×3¼ in.) *No. 14414.*

A very rough version of this figure is used, with a repetition of an Edinburgh sketch at the British Museum (L.B. 83 (c)), in a pencil composition (also at the British Museum (L.B. 97), possibly a tracing) for the frontispiece of the etched series 'London Cries'. The etching itself is totally different.

Though the watercolour wash considerably alters the effect, this is completely in the later 'Mercier' manner of Nos. 260 *et seq.*) It must be before 1760, the date of the 'London Cries'.

295. A lady. Full length, standing in profile to left, hands in the pocket of her apron which is worn over her brown dress with panniers. Blue tippet and 'Peg Woffington' hat.

Pen and watercolour, 11×6.8 cm. (4⅜×2⅝ in.) *No. 14415.*

Of the Edinburgh period. It might be another study of No. 292 differently coloured save for the blue.

Five on one mount (Nos. 296–300).

296. 'The Ladies Waldegrave'. Three children, full length, standing; the two elder on the left with linked arms.

Pencil and pen with light grey wash on toned paper, 10.5×12.4 cm. (4⅛×4⅞ in.) *No. 14390.*
PLATE 119

Inscribed in pencil on the drawing (gone over) 'Lady Waldegraves', and with two indications of colour written in pencil against the ribbons.

The three girls are repeated in a finished watercolour bequeathed by W. Sandby to the Victoria and Albert Museum (D.1835-1904). In that drawing, which is said to have a date, 1760, at the back, the gap between the girls is filled by a governess and another child. There is a slight alteration in the pose and the clasped hands of the second girl; and the figure of the third girl of this drawing is slimmer and placed lower. The two elder girls recur in a group in the aquatint, 'The North Terrace looking Westward' of 1776; while the third appears, together with a lady resembling the governess of the watercolour at the Victoria and Albert Museum, in the 'Old Somerset House' by Thomas Sandby, No. 163, and the drawings referred to thereon. The whole group, as in the drawing at the Victoria and Albert Museum, reappears in a 'North Terrace looking East', one of a series of five large gouaches lately in the possession of Mrs. Angerstein.

The three daughters of Lady Waldegrave were born in 1760, 1761 and 1762 (see Violet Biddulph, *The Three Ladies Waldegrave*, 1938, where the Victoria and Albert Museum drawing is reproduced). If, therefore, they are correctly named, and still more if the additional child is, as supposed, their cousin, Laura Keppel, who was born in March, 1765 (and her sisters would be even less possible), that drawing cannot date from 1760; nor is it easy to suggest a date which would fit the apparent ages of all four girls. The drawing in the Royal Library is not affected by this complication, but it is open to the suspicion that, as in other cases (see Nos. 300 and 244) the detached figure is an independent study in another position of the second of the two girls on the left. Presumably this is a sketch from nature; it combines the precise outline of the earlier period with the freedom and sensitiveness of Sandby's maturity. The repetition at the Victoria and Albert Museum with its delicate colouring loses nothing of the charm.

297. A lady. Full length, standing, nearly full face, wearing a cape and down-turned flat hat. The right arm extended from the elbow and holding a fan.

On the reverse, pencil, a horse with halter and pack-saddle.

Pencil, 10.7×7.5 cm. (4¼×3 in.), *with the F mark below*. (See on No. 1.) *No. 14391.*

Neat, but free pencil. Connected with No. 293, the engraving after Thomas Sandby, 'View from the North Side of the Virginia River near the Manour Lodge' of 1754, and the drawings associated with it, No. 119 of this collection and L.B. T. Sandby, 7, at the British Museum.

298. A group, two ladies wearing large straw hats, brims turned down, seated at the foot of a tree; a man behind, standing against it. A slight architectural note, a lantern, cut into, on the left edge.

Pencil, with the F mark (see on No. 1), 10.5×7.5 cm. (4⅛×3 in.) *No. 14392.*

A rapid note in fine, easy pencil; the faces delicately dotted in.

299. A young girl, half length, seated to right, wearing a large down-turned straw hat.

Black chalk, heightened with white on brown paper, much torn and repaired, 9×8 cm. (3½×3⅛ in.) *No. 14393.*
PLATE 118

On a larger scale, but similar in type and treatment to No. 296 and possibly showing one of the same children. The drawing of the sleeve and hand is especially careful. It thoroughly deserves the care taken by the artist to preserve it in its fragmentary condition.

300. 'Miss Isherwoods, the Brewer's daughters, Windsor'. In riding costume, one standing against a tree, the other seated, with whip. A third figure lightly indicated in the background.

Pencil, grey and violet wash, 11 × 14 cm. ($4\frac{3}{8} \times 5\frac{1}{2}$ in.)
PLATE 114 *No. 14394.*

Almost entirely drawn with a lightly-handled brush. As in other cases, this might well be a study of the same person in two positions.

The two sisters of Henry Isherwood (see on No. 243) were stated (*Gentleman's Magazine*, LXVIII, p. 536) to be living at Bushey at the time of his death, 1797. Their father died in 1772 (*Ibid*, XLIII, p. 201).

Four on one mount (Nos. 301-304).

301. 'Lady Ladd'. A girl, full length, nearly facing front, in blue dress, crimson lined, white apron, black scarf crossed; the head bound in a kerchief with feather or cockade; hand on hip.

Pencil and watercolour, 17.2 × 8.8 cm. ($6\frac{3}{4} \times 3\frac{1}{2}$ in.) *No. 14420.*
PLATE 108

The figure occurs with the mother and daughter of No. 312 in the version of No. 31 at Harewood (Borenius, No. 428, dated 1768); with No. 221 in a 'North Terrace looking West' in the same collection; and in the gouache of the same subject lately acquired by the Victoria and Albert Museum (P.7—1945). In all the drawings the girl appears as an attendant, as the dress suggests.

No Lady Ladd is recorded. The name may conceivably have been intended to refer to the notorious Lady Lade, the mistress—and from about 1789 the wife—of Sir John Lade, 2nd Baronet.

302. The same, full length, standing and holding her apron to her face.

Pencil and watercolour, 16.5 × 10 cm. ($6\frac{1}{2} \times 3\frac{7}{8}$ in.) *No. 14421.*

Companion to the preceding but still slighter.

303. A young girl, full length, standing, facing half right, in blue dress, pinafore, brown petticoat and large black sun hat with ribbons. She has her dress tucked under her bent right arm.

Pencil and watercolour, 17 × 10.5 cm. ($6\frac{3}{4} \times 4\frac{1}{8}$ in.) *No. 14422.*

The figure, in reverse and apparently an offset, occurs with three others in a sketch in pencil and light brown wash at the British Museum (L.B. 137.(44a)).

Somewhat of the same type as Nos. 296 and 299, and with the same easy but delicate treatment of the arms and hands but looser in handling.

304. A young girl, full length, standing, facing half left, holding the skirt of her heavy green dress under her joined hands, brown petticoat, red shoes, large cap. Landscape background.

Pencil and watercolour, 15 × 10.5 cm. ($5\frac{7}{8} \times 4\frac{1}{8}$ in.) *No. 14423.*

The hands and arms careful as in the following drawings, which are also fully coloured, but the outline rather lighter. The clumsy appearance is partly due to the too voluminous garments.

Three on one mount (Nos. 305-307).

305. A group of two women, a girl and a boy, beside a table, looking at a picture book.

Pen and grey wash, a little colour, 15 × 14.7 cm. ($5\frac{7}{8} \times 5\frac{3}{4}$ in.)
PLATE 113 *No. 14439.*

The large figure of the woman in a voluminous gown is perhaps an afterthought; it is more heavily drawn, going far to spoil the freely posed and easily drawn child in the centre whose hands and arms are close to those of the girl in the following drawing.

306. A girl, full length, facing front, in blue with white pinafore, a ribbon in the hair, her right arm on the shoulder of a boy who is looking back and pointing left.

Pen and watercolour, 19 × 10.8 cm. ($7\frac{1}{2} \times 4\frac{1}{4}$ in.) *No. 14440.*
PLATE 115

See on No. 307.

307. The same, full length, seated at a table, profile to right; the dress striped pink on white.

Pen and watercolour, 19.3 × 10.7 cm. ($7\frac{5}{8} \times 4\frac{1}{4}$ in.) *No. 14441.*
PLATE 116

The figure makes a remarkable reappearance, reversed, in the 'North Terrace looking East' at Drumlanrig (see on No. 8). There she is on her feet, bent forward, watching the Terrace raven attacking a dog.

Stronger in outline and with more feeling for volume than in most of these sketches. As in No. 305, great attention is given to the hands and arms, but in No. 306 the doubled hand on the waist has proved beyond the artist's powers. The variation in the colour of the dress in these two drawings, which seem certainly to belong together, proves how little weight can be attached to details of costume. The colour was no doubt added subsequently and arbitrarily.

Two on one mount (Nos. 308 and 309).

308. 'Lady Wallace'. A girl, full length, half-reclining on a sofa, in pink with blue-grey pinafore, a ribbon in the hair.

Pencil and watercolour, 14.5 × 16.8 cm. ($5\frac{3}{4} \times 6\frac{5}{8}$ in.) *No. 14428.*

See on No. 309.

309. The same, seated on a large log at the foot of a tree, the dress yellow.

Pencil and watercolour, 16.7 × 19 cm. ($6\frac{5}{8} \times 7\frac{1}{2}$ in.) *No. 14429.*

A pair with the preceding, both possibly from the same girl as in No. 307, the accessories and colouring also clearly added as afterthoughts. The treatment of the complicated attitude and casually disposed drapery in No. 309 is the most assured and successful in the whole series; the legs in No. 308, on the contrary, among the least happy.

Six on one mount (Nos. 310-315).

310. A lady, in narrow-waisted dress, with panniers and large cap, seated on a window-seat.

Pen and watercolour, 8.8 × 6.4 cm. ($3\frac{1}{2} \times 2\frac{1}{2}$ in.) *No. 14454.*

Thin and perfunctory penwork of the early miniature type but, though superficial and awkward, the drawing has life.

311. A girl, full length, standing, her right arm half-extended, seen from behind; large sun hat, gloves and cape.

Pencil and brown wash, with traces of white on buff paper, 12.2 × 7.2 cm. (4¾ × 2⅞ in.) *No. 14455.*
PLATE 117

Of the best period; fresh, fluent and broad in treatment, it goes with Nos. 296 and 299.

312. A Group. A lady in outdoor dress, full length, standing, a boy and girl on either side, accosted by an elderly man, right, hat in hand.

Pencil, pen and brown wash, 7.8 × 9.3 cm. (3⅛ × 3⅝ in.)
PLATE 104 *No. 14456.*

A replica with grey wash at the Victoria and Albert Museum (D.130-1901) without the man. These figures repeated in No. 190, precisely the same size, in No. 163 reduced and in the version of No. 31 at Harewood without the boy but with No. 301.

Rather formally but still prettily drawn with the pen over loose pencil.

313. A young girl, full length, facing half left, her left hand raised to her hat.

Pencil and grey wash, 8.8 × 5.5 cm. (3½ × 2⅛ in.) *No. 14457.*

See on No. 314.

314. The same (a tracing).

Pen and brown wash, with some hatching from left to right in pencil, 9 × 4.8 cm. (3½ × 1⅞ in.) *No. 14458.*

A third example in pencil, pen, grey and brown washes is at the British Museum (L.B. 137 40(a)), the dress rather less full but the pencil outlines apparently the same. The figure occurs in combination with No. 382 in a drawing, 'The Gate at Reading' in the collection of Mr. Leslie J. Wright, and was perhaps used in the drawing for the small print of the encampment at Montague House, No. xcix in the *150 Views.*

315. 'Lady Eliz. Harcourt'. Full length, seated, in riding costume, at a needlework frame. Seen from behind.

Pencil, 17.1 × 12.1 cm. (6¾ × 4¾ in.) *No. 14459.*

The name inscribed on the drawing, at foot, perhaps in the artist's handwriting. W. Sandby, p. 217.

The chair, which is identical, and the careful parallel pencil hatching connect this drawing with No. 268; though this is more solid and finished. The costume as in No. 300.

Perhaps Lady Elizabeth Harcourt, sister of George Simon, 2nd Earl, born 18th June, 1739, married in 1763 Sir William Lee. This would confirm the date, 1760, on No. 268.

Two on one mount (Nos. 316 and 317).

316. A country girl, full length, facing front, leaning against a fence and a tree.

Pencil, a little pen, and watercolour, 19.5 × 13.5 cm. (7⅝ × 5⅜ in.) *No. 14438.*
PLATE 122

In the fully developed, free manner, structurally uncertain but graceful and elastic, the face briskly touched in and adequately modelled. The grey shadows and fluid colour are those of No. 320 but on a much happier foundation.

317. 'Susan Carrol', a maid servant. Full length, seated on a table by a window, her left hand on the table, her left foot on the stretcher.

Pencil and watercolour, 16.5 × 11 cm. (6½ × 4⅜ in.) *No. 14437.*

Of a comparatively late type among these drawings (1770-1780), hasty and assured pencil work with brown monochrome foundation; the drawing not too correct, but the whole effect lively and graceful.

Two on one mount (Nos. 318 and 319).

318. A maid-servant or lady in undress. Full length, seated with arms crossed, face in profile to left.

Pencil and watercolour, 14 × 9.9 cm. (5½ × 3⅞ in.) *No. 14521.*

Freely drawn but careless, conspicuously in the arms and hands, and loosely washed with light brown and blue ; of a comparatively late type.

319. 'A Cottage Girl at Wynnstay'. Full length, seated to right, holding a flagon; cottage or kitchen interior.

Pencil and watercolour, mainly brown, 17.2 × 15.3 cm. (6¾ × 6 in.) *No. 14522.*

The interior is unusually fully indicated, but there is no care for detail nor effect of lighting. The drawing is rapid and loose, the washes perfunctory.

For Sandby's visit to Wynnstay see on No. 371.

Two on one mount (Nos. 320 and 321).

320. 'Martha Collins, Thomas Sandby's Cook'. Full length, seated, mending a garment, a child at her knee, right, holding up an apple.

Pencil and watercolour, 16.5 × 13 cm. (6½ × 5⅛ in.) *No. 14339.*

Late, hasty and clumsy work but with character. The drawing mainly with the brush, but there is hatching in pencil; the bright colouring over light grey is that of No. 316. Of the period of the Wynnstay drawings (Nos. 319, 371 and 374).

321. 'The wife of Mr. Whitbread's gardener at Woolmer, Herts, 1784'. Full length, seated, facing front, holding a saucer in each hand on her lap. A round summerhouse and trees in the background.

Pencil and watercolour, 14 × 9.8 cm. (5½ × 3⅞ in.) *No. 14338.*

A replica in pencil and grey wash at the British Museum, L.B. 98a, with the F mark and inscribed in Paul Sandby's hand (as on No. 1 in this collection), 'Servant of Mr. Whitbread at Woolmer's'. A basket at the foot of that drawing is not in this; otherwise, even the background of building and trees is the same.

As the replica may indicate, not a *plein-air* drawing, but its complete abandonment of the early precision and interest in form shows a landscape artist's study of a figure in sunlight. The background where it is in shadow is no doubt purposely confused and dirty in order to make contrast. The grey shadow in the figure has a violet tinge.

XIII. MEN

Three on one mount (Nos. 322-324).

322. 'Samuel Cotes, the Painter'. Full length, seated, full face, in crimson with red waistcoat, at a table with a book in his right hand; a blue and white-striped curtain in the background, right; lamplight.

Pen and watercolour, 20 × 13.2 cm. ($7\frac{7}{8} \times 5\frac{1}{4}$ in.) *No. 14399*.
PLATE 123
W. Sandby, p. 218.

A full interior with marked study of the light which falls from the lamp standing on the table; similar to, but rather more immature than, the 'Mrs. Mercier and her Son', No. 257—the seat uneasy, the hands clumsy and the perspective of the table insecure.

Samuel Cotes, 1734-1818, portrait and miniature painter, was the brother of Francis Cotes, who painted portraits of Paul Sandby, his wife and Mrs. Thomas Sandby. He would appear to be about 20 in this drawing.

323. 'Mr. Gandon, Architect'. Full length, seated cross-legged on a window seat reading a book; grey coat with yellow facings, pink waistcoat and red breeches.

Pen and watercolour over slight pencil, 133 × 9.7 cm. ($5\frac{1}{4} \times 3\frac{7}{8}$ in.) *No. 14397*.
PLATE 131
W. Sandby, p. 218.

Lightly coloured over fine pen with special delicacy in the architecture and details of furniture; the lighting through the window is carefully observed. Much use of the ruler.

James Gandon (1742-1823), the well-known architect in Dublin, was an intimate friend of Paul Sandby, according to his biography by Thomas Mulvaney, 1846, p. 17, from about 1765. Stylistically, this drawing would appear to date from much earlier, if not from a period when the supposed sitter was little more than a boy. For 'Mrs. Gandon', see No. 287.

324. 'J. W. Levison'. Full length, seated to right, the face turned to front, in grey with red waistcoat, holding a paper on the arm of his short-backed round chair.

Pencil and watercolour, 13.5 × 13 cm. ($5\frac{3}{8} \times 5\frac{1}{8}$ in.) *No. 14398*.

Awkwardly posed and drawn, the face flat and the hands entirely evaded, but delicately and loosely washed and with careful study of the light falling through the window to the left. Details of pictures, etc., on the walls.

Two on one mount (Nos. 325 and 326).

325. The same, a preliminary study, figure and chair only.

Pencil, pen, grey wash and body colour on grey paper, 19.8 × 13.3 cm. ($7\frac{3}{4} \times 5\frac{1}{4}$ in.) *No. 14401*.

Discoloration of heavily plastered body colour may account in part for the dissimilarity between the faces here and in the preceding drawing; but the pose and the chair are identical, only the right leg being altered and somewhat improved in the smaller study. The lighting is already strongly marked, mainly by means of heavy white body colour, and the shadow is stronger and falls on a lightly indicated striped curtain (as in No. 322), which is the only suggestion of the interior. The coat and hat are very much less smart. The red of the face recalls the Sandpit Gate interiors (Nos. 245 *et seq*), its general modelling is that of No. 326.

326. 'David Morier, the Artist'. Full length, seated to half left on a simple 'Chippendale' chair with striped covering to the seat; dressed in blue coat, yellow waistcoat and buff breeches, his right foot raised and resting on a piece of furniture; he is reading a book, which he holds on his knee.

Pencil, pen and watercolour, 18 × 12 cm. ($7\frac{1}{8} \times 4\frac{3}{4}$ in.) *No. 14400*.
PLATE 129

Altogether more happy in pose and draughtsmanship than the preceding but also marked by a preoccupation with lighting and an effort after solidity which here involves some heaviness in the face. The hat and hands are still clumsy.

David Morier (c. 1705-1770) was much employed by William Duke of Cumberland and was no doubt well known to the Sandbys, but it is impossible to accept this figure of a young man as his portrait. If the inscription on the modern mount is a correct copy of an older, this may be an unrecorded artist son.

Four on one mount (Nos. 327-330).

327. 'Sir Henry Elwes, Bart.' Full length, seated, face turned half left, his right hand resting on his cane, in grey coat, red waistcoat and black breeches; indications of a room.

Pencil and watercolour, 18.2 × 10.8 cm. ($7\frac{1}{8} \times 4\frac{1}{4}$ in.) *No. 14418*.
PLATE 124

Generally similar to the preceding (No. 326), the pose more conscious, the head, hat and hands more happily treated, the shadow equally strong.

Perhaps Sir Henry Elwes, 4th Baronet, of Stoke by Clare, who succeeded Sir William Elwes, his brother, in 1778 (*Complete Baronetage*, VOL. III, 51). Their dates of birth are not known and they seem to have lived in obscurity and reduced circumstances.

328. 'Mr. Ord of the Ordnance Office'. Full length, face in profile to left, in grey coat, long flowered waistcoat and crimson velvet breeches, seated on a low backed chair with box-seat and short cabriole legs.

Pencil, pen and watercolour, 18.2 × 11.3 cm. ($7\frac{1}{8} \times 4\frac{1}{2}$ in.) *No. 14419*.

Similar to the preceding, the light fuller and more diffused; consequently the features are less heavily marked. The interior is more complete, a framed seascape on the wall in monochrome.

Mr. Ord cannot be traced among the officers (military or civil) of the Board of Ordnance.

329. 'Mr. Howse, now the Rev. Mr. Howse, who was on the Survey of Scotland'. Full length, standing to right in uniform.

Pen and watercolour over slight pencil, 17.8 × 8 cm. ($7 \times 3\frac{1}{8}$ in.)
PLATE 135 *No. 14416*.
W. Sandby, p. 218.

Lightly coloured pen sketch of a complicated posture of ease, the hands careless in form, the legs far from convincing in spite of several alterations in the pencil outlines.

For another drawing called 'Mr. Howse', later in style, see No. 366; his name is also attached to a figure in a group, No. 242.

330. 'The Grave Digger of St. James's Parish 1758'. Full length, standing to left, in bright blue coat and blue and white striped waistcoat.

Watercolour and gouache, over slight pencil, 18 × 7.7 cm. ($7\frac{1}{8} \times 3$ in.) *No. 14417*.

Loose in drawing and colouring; discoloured and brick-red gouache in face and hands.

Nine on one mount (Nos. 331-339).

331. A man seated on an ornamental garden seat reading a book.

Pen and faint watercolour wash, mostly grey, the corners cut off and made up, 11.2 × 7.8 cm. (4⅜ × 3⅛ in.) *No. 14460.*

Early and careless; the seat preposterous in design and construction.

332. A young officer, full length, standing to left.

Pencil, 10.2 × 5.2 cm. (4 × 2 in.) *No. 14461.*

Pencil work of the prettiest careful type.

333. A man taking snuff, standing to left.

Pencil, pen and watercolour, 11.5 × 7.6 cm. (4½ × 3 in.)
PLATE 128 *No. 14462.*

A rapid note, somewhat ill-drawn and more elongated than customary. Lightly washed with green for the coat and pink for the waistcoat, but with heavy blacks in the trees indicated behind.

334. A man standing. Full length, facing front, arms folded, blue coat and waistcoat, red breeches.

Pencil and watercolour, 12 × 5.9 cm. (4¾ × 2⅜ in.) *No. 14463.*

Without background, but a completed watercolour with full, flat, heavily featured face as in No. 322 and the rich colouring of No. 244. The hands evaded.

335. 'An Undertaker'. Full length, standing to right, his left arm resting on a rail; dressed in black riding dress, lavender coat, top boots and spurs, garters above the knee, a riding whip in his hand and a rose between his teeth.

Pencil, pen and watercolour, the railings and steps indicated in pencil only, 15.1 × 9.5 cm. (6 × 3¾ in.) *No. 14464.*

A pencilled date 1744 at the foot of the drawing and the title, 'An Undertaker' on the modern mount are both difficult to understand. Unless the latter is merely the interpretation by the mounter of the black dress (which, incidentally, is much the same above the knee as is worn in No. 229 by a 'celebrated pedestrian'), the word may have had some such technical meaning in connection with a race meeting as the *O.E.D.* records for the theatre.

The penwork is fine and of the early type; the blacks deep, the colouring delicate.

336. A young officer, full length, standing to half left, in green uniform with crimson facings.

Pen and watercolour over slight pencil, 13 × 6.5 cm. (5⅛ × 2½ in.)
PLATE 126 *No. 14465.*

Repeated with slight variations in a later and freer manner in No. 367. The figure occurs in both views of Somerset House Gardens attributed to Thomas Sandby in the Crowle *Pennant* at the British Museum (L.B. 8 and 9), in the foreground of the former, well in the background of the latter; and, in reverse and in an attenuated and degenerate form, in the group common to Nos. 119 and 163.

Neatly drawn with fine pen and lightly coloured over grey in the early manner. Hands carefully evaded.

337. Two Coachmen.

Pencil, pen and grey wash, 9.4 × 6.7 cm. (3¾ × 2⅝ in.)
PLATE 139 *No. 14466.*

Perhaps a companion to No. 354 without colour and the penwork less expressive, as though traced. The hands noticeably evaded.

338. A boy, full length, seated, looking up.

Pencil and pen, 8 × 6.5 cm. (3⅛ × 2½ in.) *No. 14467.*

The markedly contorted attitude is prettily noted; the penwork apparently over a pencil offset.

339. A man leaning, full length, against a parapet and sketching, a perspective glass in his left hand; the Water-Gate and Somerset House Gardens are indicated in the background.

Pen and grey wash, 10.3 × 6.8 cm. (4 × 2⅝ in.) *No. 14468.*
PLATE 130

Fine early penwork, the washes loose, especially in the accessories.

Six on one mount (Nos. 340-345).

340. A young man, full length, advancing with head turned to right, in buff coat, crimson waistcoat and black breeches.

Pencil, pen and watercolour, landscape background indicated in pencil, 14.3 × 7.3 cm. (5⅝ × 2⅞ in.) *No. 14478.*
PLATE 127

Early, mainly in grey with delicate washes of colour; hand evaded.

341. 'A London Pieman'. Full length, standing in profile to left.

Pencil and watercolour, 17.3 × 6 cm. (6¾ × 2⅜ in.) *No. 14479.*
PLATE 88

Loosely drawn and coloured, almost a caricature (cf. No. 254). It has some relation to the figure of a pieman in the etched series of London Cries, 1760.

342. A young man, full length, standing to right looking down, in pink coat, buff waistcoat and crimson breeches.

Pen and watercolour, 14 × 6 cm. (5½ × 2⅜ in.) *No. 14480.*
PLATE 125

Free but fine penwork, not of the earliest type. Hands evaded.

343. A man, full length, standing to left, beckoning with his right hand.

Pencil and grey wash, the whole toned yellow, 14.2 × 6.6 cm. (5⅝ × 2⅝ in.) *No. 14481.*

Easier in pose and drawing and approximating to the later type of No. 345.

344. A man, standing looking down, the hands crossed inside the sleeves, wearing buff coat, crimson waistcoat and black velvet breeches.

Watercolour over slight pencil, 20 × 8.4 cm. (7⅞ × 3¼ in.)
PLATE 91 *No. 14482.*

Highly finished with colour over full modelling in grey; without the background, but with the strength of colour and the elaborate lighting, of Nos. 326-328.

345. A young man, full length, standing, holding a whip in his right hand and pointing to left with his bent left arm.

Pencil and pen with grey and buff washes, touches of colour, 15×8 cm. ($5\frac{7}{8} \times 3\frac{1}{8}$ in.) *No. 14483.*

Feeble in pose and indeterminate in drawing, of a later type. The deep lapels of the coat perhaps indicate a livery.

Nine on one mount (Nos. 346-354).

346. A coach-boy seated to left on the box, holding a whip and looking over his left shoulder.

Pencil, pen and grey wash, 6×3.2 cm. ($2\frac{3}{8} \times 1\frac{1}{4}$ in.) *No. 14484.*

A prettily noted thumb-nail sketch of a characteristically contorted attitude.

347. A young man, full length, standing against a parapet, facing front.

Pen, the whole washed brown, 9.1×4.7 cm. ($3\frac{5}{8} \times 1\frac{7}{8}$ in.) *No. 14485.*

Possibly a tracing.

348. 'Servant to the Duke of Cumberland'. A negro boy, full length, standing in profile to left, in the livery, crimson coat with green facings and green waistcoat, of William Duke of Cumberland.

Pen and watercolour, 12×6 cm. ($4\frac{3}{4} \times 2\frac{3}{8}$ in.) *No. 14486.*
PLATE 109

Highly finished with fine pen and rich colour, the pose easy.

The figure, reduced to microscopic size, occurs in the background of No. 100 (but not in the corresponding print); the boy also occurs in quite another position in the Ascot Race Meeting, No. 147.

349. A coachman, full length, standing, profile to right.

Pen, 9.5×4.8 cm. ($3\frac{3}{4} \times 1\frac{7}{8}$ in.) *No. 14487.*

A thumb-nail note.

350. A Servant of William Duke of Cumberland in two positions, both half-recumbent.

Pen and watercolour, 7×13.2 cm. ($2\frac{3}{4} \times 5\frac{1}{4}$ in.) *No. 14488.*

Mechanical line and perfunctory colouring, red for the coat, green for the waistcoat. A tracing.

351. The same, in another attitude seen from behind.

Pencil and watercolour, 7×9.8 cm. ($2\frac{3}{4} \times 3\frac{7}{8}$ in.) *No. 14489.*

The figure occurs in reverse and much reduced in the unpublished engraving of Virginia Water (Fig. 12).

A companion to the preceding but without the mechanical pen line; probably over an offset, the shading from left to right.

352. The Duke of Cumberland's Postilion, seated, flourishing a whip.

Pencil, 6.8×4.9 cm. ($2\frac{5}{8} \times 1\frac{7}{8}$ in.) *No. 14490.*
Inscribed in pencil on the drawing 'W.D.C.'

353. The same, from behind.

Pencil, 6.8×4.9 cm. ($2\frac{5}{8} \times 1\frac{7}{8}$ in.) *No. 14492.*

354. A coachman, full length, facing front, in plum-coloured livery with green facings.

Pencil, pen and watercolour, 9.7×6.5 cm. ($3\frac{7}{8} \times 2\frac{1}{2}$ in.)
PLATE 138   *No. 14491.*

The inscription on the modern mount 'Barnard Smith body coachman to Wm. D. of C.' is perhaps copied from an older, but this is not a portrait of Barnard or Barney Smith (see No. 386), nor was he the Duke's coachman. He is recorded as the Duke's stud groom from 1761 (*Court and City Register*).

The livery is approximately that of the Duke.
Strong and free pen, the features heavily shaded in grey as in the larger portraits.

Nine on one mount (Nos. 355-363).

Exhib. Royal Academy (British Art), 1934, No. 600 (803).

355. A man standing, full length, with legs crossed, one hand on hip, a stick in the other, head slightly upturned.

Pencil, pen and watercolour, 8.5×4.5 cm. ($3\frac{3}{8} \times 1\frac{3}{4}$ in.) *No. 14495.*

The figure occurs in the 'North Terrace looking West' at Harewood referred to on No. 4 and in at least three drawings by T. Sandby, No. 164 in this collection, the drawing of a 'Greek Temple' in the collection of Sir William Worsley (see on No. 186), and the architectural composition, called Freemasons' Hall, bequeathed by William Sandby to the Royal Academy. The pen line mechanical, no doubt over a tracing or offset.

356. A similar figure, in top-coat, standing and looking skyward.

Pen and watercolour, probably a tracing, 8.5×4.8 cm. ($3\frac{3}{8} \times 1\frac{7}{8}$ in.) *No. 14493.*

The figure is of precisely the same type as the preceding, and is no doubt to be found admiring the cornice or other feature in the exterior of a building designed or drawn by Thomas Sandby.

357. A man seated, full length, facing half left, legs crossed, reading a book.

Pencil, pen and grey wash, faintly coloured, 8.3×6.1 cm. ($3\frac{1}{4} \times 2\frac{3}{8}$ in.) *No. 14497.*

Nearly uniform with Nos. 355 and 356, and also apparently a tracing.

358. A man standing, full length, profile to right, in red coat against a pillar.

Pencil, pen and watercolour, 9.6×4.5 cm. ($3\frac{3}{4} \times 1\frac{3}{4}$ in.) *No. 14494.*

Early, neat pencil and penwork; tight and stiff.

359. A woman standing, full length, facing half right, hands meeting in front; green dress with panniers and large cap.

Pencil, pen and watercolour, 9.4×6.3 cm. ($3\frac{3}{4} \times 2\frac{1}{2}$ in.) *No. 14496.*

Early fine pen work, probably of the Edinburgh period, but has the appearance of a tracing.

360. A group. A woman full length, standing, profile to left, in pink gown and white petticoat over panniers and ribboned cap, and conversing with a man behind her.
Pencil, pen and watercolour, the man indicated in pencil only, 7.8×5.5 cm. (3⅛×2⅛ in.) *No. 14498.*
PLATE 100

The woman occurs, in combination with a man in a different position, in the view of 'Somerset House Gardens looking West', attributed to Thomas Sandby in the Crowle *Pennant* at the British Museum (L.B. 8).

Similar to the miniature couples Nos. 222-4, but much daintier in pose, and, if only because less coloured, more sensitive in handling.

361. A woman standing, full length, in profile to right, dress with panniers.
Pencil, pen and light wash, 9.7×5 cm. (3⅞×2 in.) *No. 14499.*
With some of the daintiness of the preceding but with mechanical pen work as though traced or over pencil offset.

362. A similar figure, full length standing, right hand on hip.
Pencil, pen and watercolour, 8.9×4 cm. (3½×1⅝ in.) *No. 14501.*
Clearly a tracing with fine pen.

363. A man in great coat lying asleep on the ground.
Pen, with faint watercolour wash, 4.3×8.8 cm. (1¾×3½ in.)
No. 14500.
An early but ambitious attempt at a difficult perspective. The line hard and suggestive of a tracing.

Four on one mount (Nos. 364-367).

364. A woman, seated to left on a kitchen chair, reading.
Pencil and warm brown wash, 14.1×9.6 cm. (5½×3¾ in.)
No. 14511.
With the ease and choiceness of attitude of the earlier portraits, and with their careful lighting and clumsy extremities, but with features such as the carelessness in detail, formality in the pencil hatching and uniformity in the wash which suggest the later monochrome drawings in this series (see Nos. 369 *et seq.*).

365. A man standing, full length, his right hand to his chin, his left under his right elbow.
Pen and pencil, 12.4×4.3 cm. (4⅞×1¾ in.) *No. 14512.*
Neat early manner.

366. 'H. Howse on the Survey of Scotland, later Rev. Mr. H. of Norfolk'. Full length standing, looking up to right, his right hand on his hip.
Pencil and light brown wash, 21.2×7.6 cm. (8⅜×3 in.)
W. Sandby P. 218. *No. 14513.*
An offset, gone over with pencil and washed with light brown is in the album L.B. 138 at the British Museum, No. 1.
Of the loose character, with uniform or nearly uniform brown wash, attributable to the later among the drawings of this series. For Howse see on No. 329.

367. A young man standing, full length, to left.
Pen over pencil indications, grey wash, 12.4×5.8 cm. (4⅞×2¼ in.) *No. 14514.*
A copy, possibly a tracing from No. 336 (*q.v.*) with less detail, altered costume and hand, and drawn in a more summary manner.

Six on one mount (Nos. 368-373).

368. A young man standing, full length, half to left, his head averted to right, hands on hips.
Pen and grey wash, 12.1×5.7 cm. (4¾×2¼ in.) *No. 14515.*
Soft broken line; mature easy manner.

369. A huntsman with raised arms, beckoning and pointing with his whip; a hound behind him.
Pencil and warm brown wash, 15.7×10.3 cm. (6⅛×4 in.).
PLATE 134 *No. 14516.*
The figure was used, in the same direction but with a slight change in dress, for a man flying a kite in the large aquatint 'Entrance of Warwick Castle from the Lower Court' of 1776, and for a man leading a horse with roller in the 'North Terrace looking East' referred to on No. 296 as once in the possession of Mrs. Angerstein. In the most mature and easy manner, the wash flat, hatching in pencil.

370. A man standing, full length, profile to left, his hands in his pockets; a collie fawning with its forepaws on his knee.
Pencil and brown wash, 12×6.9 cm. (4¾×2¾ in.) *No. 14517.*
Similar in technique to the preceding, but the wash somewhat darker, and the whole figure inferior, the dog especially clumsy.

371. Sir Watkin Williams Wynn, seated at the foot of a tree, sketching, his dog beside him; slight landscape background.
Pencil and brown wash, 13.9×11.6 cm. (5½×4⅝ in.).
PLATE 136 *No. 14518.*
Inscribed in ink on the drawing at foot 'Sir W. W. W.' in the artist's hand. W. Sandby, p. 217.
According to his son's memoir, Paul Sandby first visited Wynnstay when Sir W. W. Wynn went there to meet his tenants on coming of age. That would be about 1770. The second set of aquatints, the 'Twelve Views in North Wales being part of a tour . . . under the patronage of the Hon. Sir W. W. Wynn Bart. . .' was issued in 1776. This may give an approximate date for this drawing, Nos. 319, 374 and 404, and generally for the more rapid and careless figure studies lightly washed with brown.

372. 'Jefferies, Map and Printseller of St. Martin's Lane' asleep on two chairs; a bottle on the floor left.
Pencil and warm brown wash, 13.9×11.3 cm. (5½×4½ in.)
PLATE 132 *No. 14519.*
W. Sandby, p.218.
The attitude easy and well drawn, the accessories careless. Presumably Thomas Jefferies the younger, map engraver of St. Martin's Lane and Geographer to George III from 1761-1783. He sold Sandby's collected prints in 1765 (W. Sandby, p. 28).
The sketch in an album at the British Museum (L.B. 138, No. 29), inscribed, apparently by William Sandby, with the same name, has nothing in common with this drawing but the medium.

373. 'George Morland when a Boy', seated fast asleep in a large Windsor armchair.

Pencil, warm brown and grey washes, 10.1 × 8 cm. (4 × 3⅛ in.) W. Sandby, p. 218. *No. 14520.*

PLATE 133

Uniform with the preceding and of the same date, which would be appropriate to the age of the boy George Morland (1763-1804).

Three on one mount (Nos. 374-376).

374. 'Buckhurst or Buckhorse a Welsh poet of Wynnstay, inspired by ale and roast beef 1775'.

Pen and watercolour, 21.4 × 14.7 cm. (8⅜ × 5¾ in.) *No. 14444.*

The title inscribed on the modern mount and, on the back presumably copied from the back of the drawing or the old mount, 'Buckhurst or Buckhorse, a man noted in the time of Broughton the Bruiser, he used to permit any person to strike him in the face for a penny. Wynnstay 1775'. A deliberately rough caricature.

375. 'A Strolling Player at Luton as Hamlet', three-quarter length, his left arm raised.

Pencil, pen and watercolour, 23 × 17.3 cm. (9 × 6¾ in.)
PLATE 141
W. Sandby, p. 218. *No. 14445.*

The pen line harder and more careful than in the preceding or No. 376; the first pencil outline not followed.
For a caricature, careful and elaborated.

376. 'A strolling player at Luton as Macbeth', three-quarter length, profile to right, holding dagger.

Pencil, pen and watercolour, 20.7 × 11.7 cm. (8⅛ × 4⅝ in.)
PLATE 140
No. 14443.

The penwork soft as in No. 374, but otherwise closer to No. 375. The head is repeated in the background in pencil, probably a preliminary sketch.

Three on one mount (Nos. 377-379).

377. (? Thomas Sandby.)

'British Grenadiers in the Allied Army'. Private in uniform with bayonet, facing half right; another, without musket, seen from behind in the background, left.

Pen and watercolour over slight pencil, 21.2 × 12.1 cm. (8⅜ × 4¾ in.) *No. 14371.*

Inscribed with the title, as given, in pencil at the foot of the drawing.

The figure occurs in No. 159.

A stiff and wooden figure with the attention centred on the details of the uniform. The legs would appear to have been redrawn several times. The background figure is somewhat more successful. Clearly very early and akin to Thomas Sandby's elaborate drawings of camps, etc., in the Low Countries, whether the figures in those drawings are by himself or copied from his brother; the uniform of the Coldstream Guards of that date.

378. A foot soldier, full length, standing facing right, his musket carried over his left shoulder and held by the barrel.

Pen and watercolour over slight pencil, right-hand corners cut, 18.1 × 10.1 cm. (7⅛ × 4 in.) *No. 14369.*

The figure occurs with signal ineptitude, in No. 158 (Thomas Sandby); in No. 20 with the musket on the right shoulder and in a view of Shrewsbury at the British Museum. (L.B. 31 (a).)

Boldly outlined with the pen and coloured with flat washes of red and yellow for the uniform.

379. The same, facing front, the musket inverted under his left arm.

Pen and watercolour on slight pencil, 16.2 × 7.5 cm. (6⅜ × 3 in.) *No. 14370.*

Uniform with the preceding, the outline even stronger.

Four on one mount (Nos. 380-383).

380. The same, without musket.

Pencil and pen, black and brown wash, top corners cut, 13 × 4.7 cm. (5⅛ × 1⅞ in.) *No. 14372.*

Except for the replacement of red by brown and less strength in the black, uniform with the preceding. In the absence of accessories the attitude is difficult to interpret, but may be nearly that of the figure in the following drawing seen from in front.

381. The same, leaning against a wall, facing half left, hands crossed.

Pencil, pen and brown wash, the top corner cut, 13.5 × 4.2 cm. (5⅜ × 1⅝ in.) *No. 14373.*

Companion to preceding.

382. The same, seated on the ground, in two positions.

Pencil, pen and grey wash, top corners cut, 11.5 × 14.5 cm. (4½ × 5¾ in.) *No. 14374.*
PLATE 137

The left-hand figure used with No. 313 in a drawing 'The Gate at Reading' in the collection of Mr. L. J. Wright, also (without the child) in the engraving of that subject by M. A. Rooker, 1st May, 1775, and in the engraving of 1st October, 1776, by W. Watts, 'West View of Nottingham Castle'.

383. 'Duke of Cumberland's Hussars'. Full length, standing nearly full face, the right hand within his bandolier, the left on his curved sword.

Pencil, 18 × 7.9 cm. (7⅛ × 3⅛ in.) *No. 14375.*

A finished drawing in pencil, the counterpart of the detailed costume drawings of ladies in fine pencil, No. 264, etc.

XIV. THE GREAT LODGE, ITS OWNER AND OCCUPANTS

384. The Duke of Cumberland's old mare, standing at grass. A thistle, etc., in the background.

Black chalk and pencil on toned paper, 21.5 × 28.7 cm. (8½ × 11¼ in.) *No. 14354.*

On the reverse, another horse, also at grass.

Pencil, black chalk and light grey wash.

Inscribed at the foot of the drawing in pencil in the artist's hand, 'Portrait of a Mare ridden by Wm. Duke of Cumberland in his Campaigns in Flanders, afterwards turn'd out for life in Windsor Gt Park and paddocks'. The remains of an apparently similar inscription in the opposite corner (right) erased. The F mark (see on No. 1), at foot, centre.

The drawing, identical but reduced, is repeated in the bottom left-hand corner of No. 58, and in an 'Eton from the South West' at the British Museum (L.B.13). A closely similar drawing of the same size but washed with colour and with the accessories of a stall is in the collection of Sir Robert Witt.

The pencil work careful, with cross hatching. Probably contemporary with the larger drawings of women, Nos. 268, etc.

Six on one mount (Nos. 385–400).

385. The Duke of Cumberland and gentlemen in attendance.

Pencil and watercolour, 7.8 × 17.7 cm. (3⅛ × 7 in.) *No. 14351.*
PLATE 142

Letters A, C, B, D, under the principal figures from left to right are taken to indicate, perhaps from an inscription on the old mount, William Duke of Cumberland, in blue with the star of the Garter; Sir Thomas Rich, in green; Lord Albemarle, in pink with a star; and, standing somewhat apart and making a leg, Thomas Sandby in green.

This drawing and No. 386 are so close to the group in the centre of No. 102 (Plate 144) with its immediate accessories that they must be either copies from it or preliminary drawings, almost cartoons, for just those features in which that composition differs from No. 101. They are not fragments cut from still another unfinished version of the subject, for they have been coloured as independent sketches, and are without shadow. Moreover, not all the subsidiary figures have been introduced; the coach between the main group and the figure called Thomas Sandby and the horses' heads at the Duke's shoulder are not present here, nor is there any indication of the buildings beyond. The chief point in favour of their being copies is that there is much tentative pencil drawing around the figures in Nos. 101 and 102 and little or none in the small drawings. All traces of preliminary work may, however, have been erased from the latter, as seems to have occurred elsewhere, taking away at the same time the greater part of the leading rein between Barnard Smith and the colt's mouth and the whole of its coils in his hand. The pencil work would remain in the larger drawing since it is altogether unfinished. On the other hand, the figures in the small drawings do not show any of the careful miniature portraiture in pen which is a marked feature of the large drawings and the dress is far more detailed and careful in the latter. The Duke's star, for instance, is a mere patch left uncoloured in the sketch; in the larger drawing the cross is carefully picked out in red. The figures are of the same size, except the hussars in the background who are smaller in the sketch No. 387.

All the figures both in the small sketches and the larger drawings are by the same hand. They differ too much from the clumsy and wooden figures in the drawings in which the 'staffage' as well as the architecture may have been copied or provided by Thomas Sandby to allow them to be credited to him. Horses and men alike are completely in Paul Sandby's early and careful manner; it is not therefore necessary to suppose that Gilpin or another was called in to furnish them. (See on No. 388.)

George Keppel, 3rd Earl of Albemarle (1724-1772) was Lord of the Bedchamber to the Duke of Cumberland, K.G., 1765, installed 1771. Sir Thomas Rich of Sonning, who succeeded to the baronetcy in 1762, was an admiral and M.P. for Great Marlow, 1784-1790; he does not appear to have had any connection with the Duke; on the other hand,

Sir Robert Rich of Roos Hall, 5th baronet (1717-1785), who succeeded to the baronetcy in 1768, lost an arm at Culloden. Sir Thomas Rich is also supposed to be represented in the coloured print No. 179.

386. Barnard or Barney Smith, the Duke's stud-groom lunging a colt.

Pencil, pen and watercolour, 8 × 20 cm. (3⅛ × 7⅞ in.) *No. 14352.*
PLATE 143

See on the preceding. Both horse and man differ considerably from those in the large unfinished drawing of the new north face of Cumberland Lodge, No. 101, and correspond closely, as do the small background figures, with the version No. 102 in which the Duke, etc., appear. The profile of Barnard Smith is not outlined with the pen as in No. 102, and the greater part of the rein and its coil are lacking. As in Nos. 388, 389 and 391 the coat of the horse shows the trick of reflecting light which is a noticeable feature in the metal surfaces in the Sandpit Gate drawings, Nos. 245, *et seq*, and there are also the flicking notes with the brush and the sharp emphasis on the eye, which mark the horses in the drawings quoted.

387. A hussar and a servant of William Duke of Cumberland.

Pencil and watercolour, 5 × 2.5 cm. (2 × 1 in.) *No. 14350.*

See on No. 385. The group occurs, slightly smaller and outlined with pen in No. 102, replacing a similar pair of figures in No. 101. For the hussar on the right Sandby has returned to a sketch used on a larger scale in the foreground of the 'Ascot Race-meeting', No. 147.

388. 'The Dam of Gimcrack', facing half right, a groom and two horses indicated in the background.

Pencil, a little pen and watercolour, 7.7 × 11.8 cm. (3 × 4⅝ in.)
PLATE 151 *No. 14348.*

The title as given inscribed in pencil on the drawing in the artist's hand.

Gimcrack by Cripple–Miss Elliott was foaled in 1760 and bred by Mr. Gideon Elliott at Murrell Green, Hants. There is nothing to connect either Gimcrack or Miss Elliott with Windsor or the Duke of Cumberland's stud.

On the other hand, a mare, with a different head but also with a blaze-face, stands in precisely this position on the left of a picture by Sawrey Gilpin and G. Barret, which was bought for the Royal Collection (No. 2040) at Christie's on February 23rd, 1883, as 'The Long Walk, Windsor Great Park, with H.R.H. William Duke of Cumberland's Brood Mares and Colts', and was stated in the sale catalogue to have come with other pictures by Gilpin and Barret from Lord Albemarle's collection (Fig. 19). In this picture, too, a footman with two horses stands awaiting the Duke on a road to the left of the mare precisely as in the drawing except that they are slightly further away and the horses are attached to a carriage. Normally, such a juxtaposition would indicate that the drawing is a copy from the painting; but not only is it a habit of the Sandbys, from very early days (see on Nos. 154, 221 and 385-6), to repeat an incident with its accessories in small sketches and large drawings, but here the mare is of a different character. Further, the whole landscape is very similar to Sandby's view of the Castle and the Long Walk, No. 82. It is possible that the oil painting with its portraits of horses, being on a scale beyond Sandby's powers, was executed by another from a

FIG. 19. SAWREY GILPIN, R.A., AND (?) GEORGE BARRET, R.A.   THE DUKE OF CUMBERLAND INSPECTING HIS STUD (OIL PAINTING)

drawing by him. Indeed, Lot 62 on the 3rd day of his 1817 sale was a framed and glazed drawing, 'A Portrait of H.R.H. William Duke of Cumberland inspecting the mares and foals in His Royal Highness' racing stud, at Windsor Great Park—animals by Gilpin'. Whether Barret is rightly credited with the landscape in the oil painting is doubtful since Gilpin exhibited at Spring Gardens in 1771 (No. 44), 'H.R.H. the late Duke of Cumberland visiting his stud with a view of Windsor Castle from the Great Park, by Mr. Marlow'. Similarly the catalogue of the 1817 Sale may have been wrong in crediting Gilpin with the animals in Sandby's drawing of the subject. The mare in this drawing is clearly a pendant to the next and has the characteristics, the metallic sheen of the coat, the small head and the sparkling eye of all Sandby's horses. The compilers may have thought that the drawing of the horses showed more knowledge than could be expected from Sandby, a view which was not shared by Gilpin who, *ex hypothesi*, must have considered the prominent shoulder in this drawing incompatible with a racehorse and substituted in his picture a more nag-like head. Otherwise the blaze face shown both in drawing and picture might be taken to indicate another of the Duke's famous mares, Cypron, the dam of Herod. Certainly Sandby at the end of his life might easily have written 'Gimcrack' instead of 'Herod' when he wished to give a worthy pendant to 'the dam of Eclipse'.

389. 'The Dam of Eclipse'. Full length to left.
Pencil and watercolour, touches of pen, 7.7 × 9.9 cm. (3 × 3⅞ in.)
PLATE 152   *No. 14349.*
Companion to No. 388, the title, as given, inscribed on the drawing in the same hand. 'Spiletta' on the modern mount proclaims the erudition of the mounter but also affords insight into his methods.

Eclipse was foaled in 1764 by Marske out of Spiletta in the stud of the Duke of Cumberland. She is stated to have been a bay, as in this drawing (Theodore Cook, *Eclipse and O'Kelly*, 1907, p. 70). This drawing has no connection with any of the horses in the picture in the Royal Collection referred to above in which the white mare was, according to a label on the back, described by Gilpin to Lady Albemarle as the dam of Eclipse. It seems that equine iconography is as uncertain as human.

390. 'Barnard Smith's Pad', saddled and fastened by the bridle to a post.
Pencil, pen and watercolour, 9.9 × 11.8 cm. (3⅞ × 4⅝ in.)
                                                            No. 14353.
Inscribed on the modern mount 'Barnard Smith's pad, supposed to have been the fastest nag-horse ever known abt 1752'.

A similar drawing, but with cows and trees in the background, is in an album at the British Museum (L.B. 138, No. 68).

Without the precision of outline of the preceding.

391. Two mares with foals in a paddock; landscape background with a distant village and church, sunset sky.

Pen and watercolour, pencil and (?) some black chalk, 26.5 × 37.5 cm. (10⅜ × 14¾ in.) *No. 14347.*
PLATE 150

The mare and foal occur in the much earlier 'Windsor Castle from the S.E.' at Drumlanrig (Fig. 5).

There is nothing to show that this drawing was included in any of the books of sketches; it has the character of an independent watercolour, separately acquired. The loosely washed foliage with edges in pen would date it about 1780. The metallic sheen in the horses' coats is noticeable; the shadows on the white horse are blue, and there are sharp accents in black; the front legs of the white horse are left in pencil; one hind leg is also not finished.

Three on one mount (Nos. 392–394).

392. A coach with two horses and coachman on the box, facing right; the horses repeated below.

Pencil, 13 × 17.5 cm. (5⅛ × 6⅞ in.) *No. 14365.*
PLATE 147

Apparently used, with slight modifications, for the coach in No. 20.

393. A postilion travelling chariot, facing left. Detail of spring above in right corner.

Pencil, 14.7 × 22.2 cm. (5¾ × 8¾ in.) *No. 14366.*

Inscribed at foot in pencil, 'The travelling carriage of Wm. Duke of Cumberland'; W and crown on the door.

The wheels, two of which only are attempted, are noticeably roughly drawn.

394. A similar carriage, facing half left; details of springs and sections of mouldings above.

Pencil, 13.9 × 17.5 cm. (5½ × 6⅞ in.) *No. 14367.*
PLATE 148

Used for the carriage on the extreme left of No. 147 with the negro servant of No. 348 behind.

A colour indication 'red' in pencil in the (?) same writing as on Nos. 398 and 401; 'brass' written against the detail of a spring, and sections of the mouldings, named 'front' and 'door', separately shown. Crowned arms on the door.

More careful drawing, the wheels still somewhat uncertain.

395. The same or a similar carriage, facing half right, slight indication of a horse.

Pencil, 17.3 × 23.7 cm. (6¾ × 9⅜ in.) *No. 14368.*
Pencil F at foot. (See on No. 1.)

On a larger scale than the preceding and with less precision and detail; apparently much has been erased. The arms on the door do not appear to be those of William Duke of Cumberland.

Six on one mount (Nos. 396–401).

396. A similar carriage, without lamps, and two horses, facing right.

Pencil and grey wash, 7 × 12.2 cm. (2¾ × 4¾ in.) *No. 14355.*
Arms on the door, a separate note of a postilion in pencil above the horses.

397. A similar carriage, seen from behind, facing half left.
Pencil, 9.5 × 13.7 cm. (3¾ × 5⅜ in.) *No. 14358.*
Pencil F mark at foot. (See on No. 1.)

398. A two-wheeled carriage, without springs and with basket splashboards behind the seat, facing left.
Pencil, with indications of chalk at key points, 7 × 11.2 cm. (2¾ × 4⅜ in.) *No. 14356.*
Inscribed 'W Dk C' in pencil with the mark 'F' between 'Dk' and 'C'. The word 'green' in pencil on one of the splashboards, and 'black' on the front in the same handwriting as on No. 401 and (?) 394.

Used in the engraving 'The New Building on Shrub's Hill' by Canot after T. Sandby in the 'Eight Views' of 1754 and followed exactly except for two or three distortions, without which distinctive features would have been hidden by the personages introduced.

Drawn with an even, soft line and considerable precision, it may conceivably be by T. Sandby, in which case Nos. 401 and 394, which are similarly inscribed, must also be his. He, however, could scarcely have refrained from using the ruler for the spokes of the wheels and would have been unlikely to subordinate the ruled line to freehand where it has been employed as in the shafts. Carefully drawn carriages and carts, with similarly constructed wheels, are frequent in Paul's work. Moreover, in a drawing of this type, one brother may quite well have worked over the other's sketch.

399. Two sketches: a two-wheeled hooded carriage (? cabriolet) seen from behind, facing left; and the entrance to a coach-house.
Pencil, 9.5 × 15 cm. (3¾ × 5⅞ in.) *No. 14360.*
Pencil F mark under the carriage. (See on No. 1.)

The carriage on the right is apparently of a later type than the others of the series and more lightly sketched. The little scene of two men wheeling a carriage through the open door of a gabled coach-house is clearly a sketch from life unlike the pencil drawings of Windsor dated 1777 (No. 1, etc.), but the little figures are drawn in much the same rapid shorthand.

400. 'The Stables at the Great Lodge', a travelling chariot in the yard.
Pen and watercolour over very slight indications in pencil, 14.4 × 20.2 cm. (5⅝ × 8 in.) *No. 14359.*
PLATE 149
Inscribed 'W Dk C' at foot, right, in pencil.

A loose pen drawing with flat wash of the back of the stables at Cumberland Lodge, the front of which is shown in Nos. 99, *et seq.* The coach, which has arms and a crown on the panels, appears to have an open roof, but the details are not clear. Otherwise it is of much the same type as No. 392.

401. An open four-wheeled carriage, with coachman's box, and ornamented splashboard; facing half right.
Pencil, pen and grey wash over pencil, 9.7 × 13.7 cm. (3¾ × 5⅜ in.) *No. 14357.*
PLATE 145

Inscribed 'W Dk C' in pencil and with 'Brass', 'Yellow', 'Red', in the same handwriting as on Nos. 398 and (?) 394, and other indications of colour by initials in pencil against details of the drawing.

The carriage is of an earlier and heavier type dating from the first half of the century and possibly foreign. The line even and precise (see on No. 398).

Four on one mount (Nos. 402-405).

402. A tented wagon, from behind, facing half left, with indications of a coachman on the box and two horses.

Pen and grey wash over slight pencil, the driver and horses outlined with brush only, 6.8×12.6 cm. (2⅝×5 in.) *No. 14362.*

The group occurs in a 'Milkhouse Street' at Walker's Galleries in 1932, at a slightly different angle in the title print of the third set of Welsh views (1777) and no doubt elsewhere.

403. The same, front and side view, facing left. No horses.
Pen and grey wash over slight pencil, 6.6×12.8 cm. (2⅝×5 in.)
No. 14363.

404. A similar wagon belonging to Sir W. W. Wynn, facing right.

Pen, grey and blue washes, 12×22 cm. (4¾×8⅝ in.) *No. 14364.*
PLATE 146

Inscribed in the artist's hand in pencil at the top 'Belonging to Sr W W Wynn 1777'.

Careful and accurate penwork and delicate washes. The body of the cart is washed blue, which does not occur elsewhere in this series. There are more indications of the road and the verge. The very slight remains of pencil in the spokes of the back wheel, front springs, etc., suggest that more may have been erased here and elsewhere.

405. A two-wheeled covered cart with driver and a pair of horses, facing right.
Pencil and grey wash, discoloured, 10×16.5 cm. (3⅞×6½ in.)
No. 14361.
An offset, washed grey and yellow, the reins in the driver's right hand is at the British Museum (L.B. 98 (b)).
Clumsier in drawing than the preceding.
The construction of the cart is remarkable; it has heavy wheels, a short box body with a barrel top and wooden doors behind (one only shown in pencil, swinging open), the driver seated within a high semi-circular hood.

406. A high-seated two-wheeled carriage with one horse, driven by a man with a lady and child at his side, facing half right; the horse standing still.
Pencil, outlines gone over with pen, 12.5×16.5 cm. (4⅞×6½ in.)
A date 1768 in pencil at foot. *No. 14545.*
From the books bought by Sir T. Dyke Acland at the Sandby Sale in 1817, third day, Lots 39 and 44.
The study used, with variations, for the horse and cart in the drawings of Castle Hill, Nos. 23 and 24 q.v.

407. The Chinese Junk on Virginia Water.
Pencil, perhaps partly offset, 8×8.5 cm. (3⅛×3⅜ in.)
Inscribed below, in pencil, in the same hand as No. 1, etc., and with the F mark, 'Chinese Junk in Windsor Park lake'.
Verso. A minute sketch of an imposing façade.
Pencil, 7.8×8.7 cm. *No. 14643.*
See on No. 409.

408. The same.
Pen over slight pencil, 11.4×14.4 cm. (4½×5⅝ in.)
No. 14644. Fig. 20.

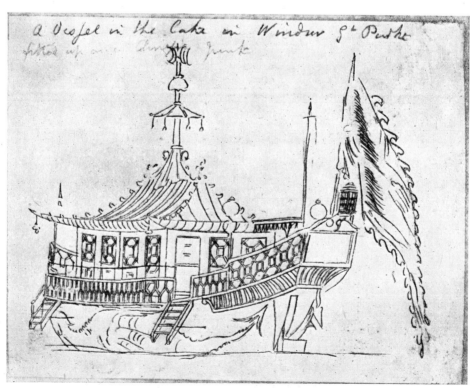

FIG. 20. THE CHINESE JUNK (CAT. NO. 408)

similarly inscribed, above, 'a Vessel in the lake in Windsor Gt Parke fitted up as a Chinese Junk'. On the reverse the beginning of an architectural sketch, a dome or arch surmounted by a pedestal and statue.

See on No. 409.

409. The same.

Pen and grey wash, partly over pencil, 10.5×13.5 cm. (4⅛×5⅜ in.) *No. 14645.*

Similarly inscribed, above, 'a vessel in the lake in Wr Gt Parke'. In both these inscriptions and in 78 and 118 the 'ss' of 'vessel' has the short 's' in front of the long, perhaps an idiosyncrasy of Paul Sandby's.

These three workshop scraps are not easy to explain. Nos. 408 and 409 do not appear to be tracings from each other but feeble and perfunctory enlargements of No. 407. They are not drawings for, nor copies from, the print in the 'Eight Views' of 1754; for, though the boat appears roughly in the same position in it and the associated drawings, No. 120 in this collection and at the British Museum (L. B. Thomas Sandby No. 7), the line of the stern is corrected in the print, the detail is also better understood, the gangways more complete, and the pennant is waving instead of hanging down as in all three drawings. The gangways differ in these three drawings, those of No. 408 being the more complete. The version at the British Museum has only one of them, an omission which, among others, shows that that watercolour is not quite finished.

Seven on one mount (Nos. 410–416).

410. Two brown and white spaniels, asleep, or the same dog from two points of view.

Pencil, pen and watercolour, 9×23.3 cm. (3½×9⅛ in.)
PLATE 153   *No. 14340.*

411. A black and white spaniel sitting up and two wolf-hounds.

Pencil, pen and watercolour, 8.8×9 cm. (3½×3½ in.)
PLATE 155   *No. 14342.*

412. A black and white spaniel asleep.

Pencil and watercolour, 4.3×7 cm. (1¾×2¾ in.) *No. 14343.*

413. Two brown and white spaniels asleep.

Pen and watercolour over slight pencil, 5×8.1 cm. (2×3¼ in.)
                                             No. 14344.

414. A spaniel.

Pencil, 3.5×5.5 cm. (1⅜×2⅛ in.) *No. 14345.*

415. A wolf-hound, chained, asleep.

Pencil and watercolour, 8.5×10.7 cm. (3⅜×4¼ in.) *No. 14341.*
PLATE 154

416. Composite study of dogs and cattle.

Pen and watercolour over pencil, 13.5×28.4 cm. (5⅜×11⅛ in.)
PLATE 156   *No. 14346.*

Inscribed in the artist's hand in pencil at foot 'favouraite [*sic*] Dogs belonging to Wm Dk of Cumberland'. Since one of the two books of drawings, lot 44, bought by Sir T. D. Acland at the Sandby sale in 1817 was described as containing 'favourite animals, etc., of William, Duke of Cumberland', these seven drawings were probably among those acquired from his descendant in 1930 (see Introd. p. 2).

The four spaniels and a greyhound in the foreground are elaborated and coloured as in the preceding drawings, and they are set on a green ground as in Nos. 413 and 415. The cattle are on a different scale; some are uncoloured.

XV. PORTRAIT SKETCHES AT PRINT SALES.

417. Sixty-two thumbnail portraits of artists, amateurs, etc., mostly drawn in pencil, pen or wash on the margin of catalogues of print sales; now placed in a modern album. *No. 14732.*

A print with the title 'Sketches taken at print sales' at the British Museum published Feb. 1st, 1798, by Silvester Harding, without name of artist, contains 54 heads of which 50 are identical (some in reverse) with these. Names are inscribed in pencil on the print, but as there is a note in the margin referring to the originals at Windsor Castle, it is probable that the names on the print have been taken from the inscriptions on the drawings and therefore afford no confirmation of the identifications. In some cases noted below the print appears to have been inscribed in error; in a few cases names are given in the print which are not now on, or with, the drawings. Those on the drawings do not appear to be in Paul Sandby's handwriting, and descriptions and initials have been added in yet another hand. These are indicated in the following list by square brackets [ ]; editorial comments by ( ).

Except in a few cases where, as mentioned below, the date of the sale (1783 or 1786) happens to occur on the portion of the catalogue cut out with the portrait, it has not been possible to date the sketches which are in a variety of techniques and may be spread over a number of years. A group of 14 similar heads was engraved by H. Adlard for Arnold's *Magazine of the Fine Arts*, VOL. II, 1833, p. 433, with the title 'Characters sketched by P. Sandby at Rysbrack's sale 1764'. The title and names under the sketches appear to be intended as facsimiles of Paul Sandby's handwriting. There is nothing inconsistent in this with the fact that one of the portraits is inscribed with the name of Mr. Pond. Arthur Pond died six years before the date of the sale.

The sketches are mentioned by W. Sandby, p. 216, as in the Royal Library and as all made on one sale catalogue. There is nothing to show when and whence they were obtained nor is the collection mentioned in the catalogues of the Paul Sandby sales in 1811, 1812 and 1817.

1. Capt. Baillie (named Dr. Hutchell in the print).
2. Rd. Collins, Min. painter (not on catalogue paper).
3. Dicky Cosway [Min. Painter].
4. Copley [J. S.]. *Fig. 21.*
5. Downman [J.] Painter. *Fig. 22.*
6. Val Green [Mez.].
7. Grozier [*sic*] [Joh] Mez: Scraper.
8. Hall Engraver (absent from the print).
9. Hall Engraver (a different head from No. 8).
10. Hone [N.] Painter. *Fig. 24.*
11. Howse [*sic*] Painter (? John Howes. In print wrongly inscribed 'Northcote'.)
12. [J.] Jones Mezzot Scraper (also inscribed at back).
13. Miles [Edward] Min. Painter.

FIG. 21. J. S. COPLEY, R.A.

FIG. 22. J. DOWNMAN, A.R.A.

FIG. 23. SIR JOSEPH BANKS, P.R.S.

FIG. 24. N. HONE, R.A.

FIG. 25. J. NORTHCOTE, R.A.

FIG. 26. BARBELL OF SPITALFIELDS

FIGS. 21-26. PORTRAITS FROM THE MARGINS OF SALE-CATALOGUES (CAT. NO. 417)

14. [J] Northcote [R.A.] (not on catalogue paper, name and dates also inscribed at back. In the print, the name is attached to an entirely different head, while a head somewhat similar to this is inscribed 'Phillippe'). *Fig. 25.*
15. J. R. Smith, Scraper.
16. Josh Strutt of Engravers.
17. Aug. Toussaint, Min. Painter.
18. (Reverse of No. 15) Anon. (absent from the print).
19. Sir Chas. Asgill [Bt. Lord Mayor 1757, Bt. 1761].
20. Austin [water colour painter] (? William Austin, caricaturist, engraver, etc., d. 1820).
21. Mr. Baker of St. Paul's Cross (inscription on mount).
22. Sir Jos. Bankes [*sic*] (Catalogue dated 1786. Not in print). *Fig. 23.*
23. Barbell of Spittle Fields [*sic*]. *Fig. 26.*
24. (*a*) J. Boydell.
    (*b*) Waldron [actor].
25. Mr. Combes (in ink) [numismatist].
26. Davenport of Strand.
27. Goodison. (With slight sketch of No. 2).
28. [Theodosius] Forrest cut his throat [author and lawyer].
29. Graves of Catherine St. (Incised with the stylus and the paper reddened at the back).
30. Gerard. (Apparently not from a catalogue, mounted, the name on the mount and, on a separate slip, in ink, 'Mr. Gerard auctioneer of Litchfeild [*sic*] St. Soho).
31. D. Graham (not in print).
32. Mitchell Banker.
33. Mr. Humphry [*sic*] ('Mr. Humphrys' on the back. Not from a catalogue; not in print; the drawing different from all others of series; the inscription perhaps in the same hand as the added descriptions on the others.'
34. Mr. Moore. (With pen inscription (as on No. 30) on a label 'Mr. Moore formerly linen draper in York St retired from business several years—a great collector of Rembrandst' [*sic*] prints and other Old Masters taken 1782'.'
35. Revd. Mr. Parsons, a collector.
36. Palmer of Strand at Rylands opposite the New Church in the Strand. (Absent from print).
    Nos. 35 and 36 are on the same fragment of a catalogue dated 1783. They are mounted similarly to No. 30 and inscribed in pencil on the border. No. 36 is also inscribed with the name Palmer in ink at the back of the mount.
37. Powel. Hogarth Collector.
38. Anon. (In print inscribed 'S. Harding'.)
39. Pillon [actor]. (Nos. 38 and 39 on one fragment.)
40. Justice Russell (not from a catalogue).
41. Richards of Boydells. (In print as Richards R.A.).
42. Lord Hertford. (Catalogue dated 1786. Not in print).

43. Anty Storer [collector] (the name attached to a different head in the print).
44. (*a*) Mr. Turvill.
    (*b*) Philippe Junr. (Absent from print).
45. Caleb Whitford ; (doubtful in print).
46. [Ralph] Willett the Collector.
47. Wilson gunsmith.
48. Woodhouse Clerk at Prescott.
49. Mr. Woodhall.
50. A boy, medallion, not of the series, pencil and wash.
51. 'Yorick'. Not of the series, soft pencil.
52. Medallion head in pen, pencil caricatures at back. Not of the series.
53. Anon. (Named Richardson in print).
54. Anon. also in print.
55. Anon. also in print. Not from a catalogue.
56. Anon. Not in print.
57-59. Anon. Also in print.
60. Anon. Not in print.
61. Anon. Also in print.
62. Anon. (Named Thane in print).

418. 'Mr. Smith, He composed the music for the Opera of the Duenna, at Mr. Sandby's house, Clay Hall in Berks.'

Pencil, 15.9 × 10.8 cm. (6¼ × 4¼ in.)

Inscribed as given above in pencil at foot of drawing in Paul Sandby's hand. (At end of volume No. 417).

The only example in this collection of Paul Sandby's loosest manner of pencil drawing from the life. The head is carefully drawn with sharp pencil and the body and arms roughly and summarily indicated, with some disproportion. The style is in strong contrast with the portrait studies of his earlier period. Similar drawings at the Victoria and Albert Museum are a sketch of a youth (D.93-1901) and studies for the watercolour of the artist's studio in St. George's Row (D.175, 188 and 196-1901) ; also the portrait of Francis Grose in Mr. I. A. Williams' collection referred to on No. 1. All of these have the 'F' mark.

There were three composers of the name Smith towards the end of the eighteenth century who might have composed the music for a performance at a private house, if that is the meaning intended by the words. The name of the most prominent of them, John Christopher Smith, occurs as that of the godfather of Thomas Sandby's fourth and fifth children in 1762 and 1763 (W. Sandby p.177). It is more likely that Sandby's memory played him false about the name of the opera than that one of the composers set out to rival the Linley's famous music to Sheridan's libretto.

There is no other record of a Mr. Sandby at Clay Hall, which is in Old Windsor, between Frogmore and the Great Park.

CONCORDANCE OF NUMBERS

Inventory	Catalogue	Inventory	Catalogue	Inventory	Catalogue	Inventory	Catalogue	Inventory	Catalogue	Inventory	Catalogue
13549	253	14384	266	14455	311	14526	5	14598	75	14670	146
13551	252	85	257	56	312	27	3	99	74	71	145
13552	251	86	264	57	313	28	6			73	200
13765	203	87	265	58	314	29	7	14600	76	74	201
		88	290	59	315			1	77	75	147
14318	254	89	289			14530	8	2	78	76	148
19	255			14460	331	31	10	3	79	77	149
		14390	296	61	332	32	9	4	80	78	169
14320	256	91	297	62	333	33	11	5	81	79	170
21	260	92	298	63	334	34	12	6	82		
22	261	93	299	64	335	35	13	7	83	14680	171
23	262	94	300	65	336	36	14	8	84	81	172
24	263	95	288	66	337	37	15	9	85	82	174
25	269	96	287	67	338	38	16			83	173
26	270	97	323	68	339	39	17	14610	86	84	176
27	271	98	324	69	222			12	87	85	175
28	249	99	322			14540	18	13	88	86	177
29	250			14470	223	41	19	14	89	87	178
		14400	326	71	224	42	21	15	90	88	179
14330	248	1	325	72	225	43	22	16	97	89	196
31	245	2	213	73	226	44	23	17	64		
32	247	3	214	74	227	45	406	18	92	14690	180
33	246	4	215	75	228	46	24	19	93	91	182
34	209	5	273	76	229	47	25			92	183
35	210	6	206	77	230	48	26	14620	94	93	184
36	211	7	207	78	340	49	27	21	91	94	181
37	212	8	208	79	341			22	96	95	185
38	321	9	275			14550	28	23	107	96	162
39	320			14480	342	51	29	24	108	97	161
		14410	276	81	343	52	30	25	98	98	163
14340	410	11	291	82	344	53	31	26	99	99	186
41	415	12	292	83	345	54	32	27	100		
42	411	13	293	84	346	55	33	28	102	14700	164
43	412	14	294	85	347	56	34	29	101	1	167
44	413	15	295	86	348	57	35			2	165
45	414	16	329	87	349	58	36	14630	103	3	166
46	416	17	330	88	350	59	37	31	104	4	190
47	391	18	327	89	351			32	105	5	168
48	388	19	328			14560	38	33	106	6	187
49	389			14490	352	61	39	34	109	7	188
		14420	301	91	354	62	40	35	110	8	189
14350	387	21	302	92	353	63	41	36	111	9	197
51	385	22	303	93	346	65	42	37	112		
52	386	23	304	94	358	66	43	38	113	14711	159
53	390	24	283	95	355	67	44	39	114	12	160
54	384	25	284	96	359	68	20			13	198
55	396	26	285	97	357	69	45	14640	115	15	142
56	398	27	286	98	360			41	117	16	143
57	401	28	308	99	361	14570	46	42	118	17	160(a)
58	397	29	309			71	47	43	407	18	199
59	400			14500	363	72	48	44	408	19	195
		14430	216	1	362	73	49	45	409		
14360	399	31	217	2	231	74	50	46	119	14720	191
61	405	32	218	3	232	75	51	47	120	21	192
62	402	33	277	4	233	76	52	48	121	22	151
63	403	34	278	5	234	77	53	49	122	23	153
64	404	35	279	6	235	78	54			24	152
65	392	36	272	7	236	79	55	14650	123	25	154
66	393	37	317	8	237			51	124	26	155
67	394	38	316	9	238	14580	56	52	125	27	157
68	395	39	305			81	57	53	126	28	156
69	378			14510	239	82	58	54	127	29	158
		14440	306	11	364	83	59	55	128		
14370	379	41	307	12	365	84	60	56	129	14730	204
71	377	42	202	13	366	85	61	57	130	31	205
72	380	43	376	14	367	86	62	58	133	32	{ 417 418 }
73	381	44	374	15	368	88	63	59	134		
74	382	45	375	16	369	89	65	14660	138	17152	193
75	383	46	240	17	370			61	139	53	194
76	258	47	241	18	371	14590	67	62	140		
77	259	48	242	19	372	91	66	63	131	17177	150
78	280	49	243			92	68	64	132		
79	281			14520	373	93	69	65	135	17308	95
		14450	244	21	318	94	70	66	136		
14380	282	51	221	22	319	95	71	67	137	17312	185(a)
81	274	52	219	23	1	96	72	68	141		
82	268	53	220	24	2	97	73	69	144		
83	267	54	310	25	4						

PLATES

LANDSCAPES : Nos. 1-72

FIGURE STUDIES : Nos. 73-141

COACHES, HORSES AND DOGS : Nos. 142-156

1. WINDSOR CASTLE: THE DEVIL'S TOWER FROM THE BLACK ROD (Cat. No. 39)

2. THE NORTH TERRACE LOOKING WEST (Cat. No. 3)

3. THE NORTH TERRACE LOOKING EAST . Pencil (Cat. No. 7)

4. THE NORTH TERRACE, THE WEST END (Cat. No. 6)

5. THE WEST APPROACH TO THE NORMAN GATE (Cat. No. 12)

6. THE NORMAN GATE AND DEPUTY GOVERNOR'S HOUSE (Cat. No. 13)

7. THE OLD SOUTH ENTRANCE WITH MOAT BRIDGE AND RUBBISH GATE FROM THE WEST
Pencil (Cat. No. 17)

8. THE KING'S GATE AND ENTRANCE TO THE SOUTH TERRACE FROM THE EAST (Cat. No. 16)

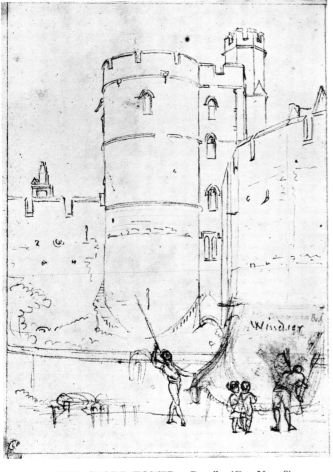

9. THE STORE TOWER . Pencil (Cat. No. 18)

10. ST. GEORGE'S CHAPEL WITH DENTON'S COMMONS . Pencil (Cat. No. 46)

11. THE STORE TOWER, ETC., FROM CASTLE HILL (Cat. No. 19)

12. THE DEVIL'S (MAIDS OF HONOUR) TOWER FROM THE CLERK OF THE WORKS' OFFICE
(Cat. No. 20)

13. VIEW THROUGH QUEEN ELIZABETH'S GATE LOOKING WEST (Cat. No. 24)

14. VIEW FROM QUEEN ELIZABETH'S GATE LOOKING EAST   (Cat. No. 22)

15. HENRY VIII GATEWAY FROM CASTLE HILL   (Cat. No. 25)

16. VIEW THROUGH THE NORMAN GATE (Cat. No. 14)

17. HENRY VIII GATEWAY FROM WITHIN. Monochrome (Cat. No. 27)

18. HENRY VIII GATEWAY FROM WITHIN (Cat. No. 28)

19. HENRY VIII GATEWAY FROM WITHOUT (Cat. No. 26)

20. HENRY VIII GATEWAY AND CHANCELLOR OF THE GARTER'S TOWER (Cat. No. 29)

21. THE GOVERNOR OF THE POOR KNIGHTS' TOWER AND THE GARTER CHAMBER (Cat. No. 30)

22. ST. GEORGE'S CHAPEL AND ENTRANCE TO SINGING MEN'S CLOISTER (Cat. No. 31)

23. THE ENTRANCE TO THE SINGING MEN'S CLOISTER AND CRANE'S BUILDING (Cat. No. 32)

24. SINGING MEN'S CLOISTER AND JULIUS CÆSAR'S TOWER (Cat. No. 33)

25. THE LOWER WARD LOOKING WEST (Cat. No. 37)

26. THE QUADRANGLE (Cat. No. 38)

27. SECRETARY OF STATE'S TOWER, ETC., FROM THE LITTLE PARK (Cat. No. 54)

28. VIEW FROM THE BLACK ROD WITH WINCHESTER AND STORE TOWERS, ETC. (Cat. No. 43)

29. VIEW FROM THE BLACK ROD WITH DEVIL'S TOWER, ETC. (Cat. No. 42)

30. VIEW FROM THE END OF THE NORTH TERRACE, LOOKING EAST (Cat. No. 52)

31. VIEW OF THE SEAT NEAR THE TERRACE AND OF THE ADJACENT COUNTRY (Cat. No. 51)

32. THE COMET OF 1783 (Cat. No. 53)

33. WINDSOR CASTLE FROM DATCHET LANE (Cat. No. 69)

34. WINDSOR CASTLE FROM THE MAESTRICHT POND (Cat. No. 58)

36. THE HUNDRED STEPS . Gouache   (Cat. No. 49)

37. WINCHESTER TOWER AND PART OF THE HUNDRED STEPS (Cat. No. 50)

38. WINDSOR CASTLE FROM DATCHET LANE ON A REJOICING NIGHT, 1768 . Gouache (Cat. No. 60)

39. THE ROUND TOWER . Monochrome   (Cat. No. 44)

40.   WINDSOR CASTLE FROM ISHERWOOD'S BREWHOUSE IN DATCHET LANE . Gouache   (Cat. No. 73)

41. DATCHET LANE WITH CASTLE AND TOWN (Cat. No. 70)

42. THE CASTLE FROM THE BACK FIELDS AT ETON . Gouache (Cat. No. 75)

43. THE CASTLE FROM THE LONG WALK (Cat. No. 82)

44. THE TOWN AND CASTLE FROM THE LOWER END OF SHEET STREET (Cat. No. 84)

45. THE BISHOPSGATE ENTRANCE TO WINDSOR GREAT PARK, 1801 . Gouache (Cat. No. 106)

46. WINDSOR CASTLE FROM BISHOPSGATE (Cat. No. 86)

47. THE OLD OAK IN THE WOODYARD, 1792 (Cat. No. 91)

48. THE WHEELWRIGHT'S SHOP IN THE WOODYARD (Cat. No. 92)

49. "IN OLD WINDSOR WOOD" (Cat. No. 89)

50. VIEW NEAR CRANBOURNE LODGE (Cat. No. 87)

51. THOMAS SANDBY: THE TERRACE AND BOWLING GREEN (?) AT CRANBOURNE LODGE, 1752 (Cat. No. 111)

52. THOMAS SANDBY: WINDSOR GREAT PARK FROM NEAR CRANBOURNE LODGE, 1752 (Cat. No. 114)

53. THOMAS SANDBY: VIEW IN WINDSOR GREAT PARK (Cat. No. 113)

54. THOMAS SANDBY: WINDSOR GREAT PARK WITH VIRGINIA WATER (Cat. No. 115)

55. DETAIL OF PLATE 54

56. THE REMOVAL FROM THE THAMES AT OUSELEY OF THE HULK WHICH BECAME THE CHINESE JUNK ON VIRGINIA WATER (Cat. No. 118)

57. THOMAS SANDBY : THE GREAT LODGE IN WINDSOR GREAT PARK (Cat. No. 100)

58. PAUL AND THOMAS SANDBY: THE GREAT BRIDGE OVER THE VIRGINIA RIVER (Cat. No. 120)

59. ASCOT HEATH RACES (Cat. No. 147)

60. DETAIL OF PLATE 59.

61. THE BACK OF PAUL SANDBY'S LODGING AT CHARLTON, KENT (Cat. No. 191)

62. THOMAS SANDBY: A ROUND BRICK TOWER IN COURSE OF CONSTRUCTION (Cat. No. 190)

63. THOMAS SANDBY: OLD SOMERSET HOUSE, THE GARDEN FRONT (Cat. No. 163)

64. THOMAS SANDBY: THE BRIDGE OF MAGNIFICENCE OVER THE THAMES AT SOMERSET HOUSE
(Cat. No. 186)

65. THOMAS SANDBY: ORMOND OR RICHMOND LODGE, KEW (Cat. No. 159)

66. THE PRINCE'S HOUSE AT KEW (KEW PALACE) (Cat. No. 160)

67. VIEW NEAR THE SERPENTINE RIVER DURING THE ENCAMPMENT 1780. (Cat. No. 171)

68. VIEW NEAR THE SERPENTINE RIVER DURING THE ENCAMPMENT, 1780,
FACING TO KNIGHTSBRIDGE (Cat. No. 172)

69. THE ROYAL MILITARY ACADEMY AT WOOLWICH (Cat. No. 192)

70. A PARK SCENE NEAR WOOLWICH, 1796 (Cat. No. 193)

71. THE CHEESE-CAKE HOUSE IN HYDE PARK . Gouache   (Cat. No. 183)

72. LANDSCAPE COMPOSITION WITH AN OLD BEECH TREE . Gouache   (Cat. No. 149)

73. " MR. FORD, DEPUTY RANGER WINDSOR
GREAT PARK " . Monochrome (Cat. No. 213)

74. A VIOLIN PLAYER . Watercolour
(Cat. No. 211)

75. " ALLAN RAMSAY " . Watercolour (Cat. No. 214)

76. AN OLD LADY PLAYING CARDS . Watercolour (Cat. No. 218)

77. IN SOMERSET HOUSE GARDENS . Watercolour (Cat. No. 240)

78. IN SOMERSET HOUSE GARDENS . Watercolour (Cat. No. 241)

79. A MINIATURE (Cat. No. 222)

80. IN THE GROUNDS OF HERIOT'S HOSPITAL, EDINBURGH (Cat. No. 219)

81. THE PARAPET OF SOMERSET HOUSE GARDENS (TWO WOMEN) . Watercolour
(Cat. No. 234)

82.   THE PARAPET OF SOMERSET HOUSE GARDENS (TWO MEN) . Watercolour
(Cat. No. 244)

83. AT SANDPIT GATE: WASHING CLOTHES
Watercolour (Cat. No. 248)

84. AT SANDPIT GATE: MAKING PIES
Watercolour (Cat. No. 246)

85. AT SANDPIT GATE: WASHING-DAY . Watercolour (Cat. No. 250)

86. A WINDSOR CHARACTER . Watercolour (Cat. No. 251)

87. "BOB DUNN" . Watercolour
(Cat. No. 254)

88. "A LONDON PIEMAN"
Watercolour (Cat. No. 341)

89. "VOULES, THE DUKE OF
CUMBERLAND'S BAILIFF" . Watercolour
(Cat. No. 255)

90. A SERVANT OF THE DUKE OF
CUMBERLAND . Watercolour
(Cat. No. 252)

91. A MAN IN A BUFF COAT AND CRIMSON
WAISTCOAT . Watercolour   (Cat. No. 344)

92. TWO LADIES . Red and black chalk   (Cat. No. 263)

93. "COLONEL DAVID WATSON". Red and black chalk (Cat. No. 273)

94. A LADY, PAINTING . Watercolour   (Cat. No. 259)

95. THE CELEBRATED KITTY FISHER AS A MILKMAID (Cat. No. 258)

96. MRS. LANE . Red and black chalk (Cat. No. 267)

97. A LADY IN A SHORT SKIRT . Red chalk (Cat. No. 260)

98. TWO LADIES FROM BEHIND, IN A HIGH WIND . Red chalk   (Cat. No. 262)

99. "COLONEL DEACON" . Watercolour
(Cat. No. 231)

100. TWO FIGURES CONVERSING
Watercolour (Cat. No. 360)

101. A LADY, STANDING . Pencil
(Cat. No. 264)

102. "LADY MAXWELL" . Watercolour
(Cat. No. 292)

103. TWO MEN STANDING AT A
RAIL . Watercolour (Cat. No. 227)

104. A GROUP . Pen and brown wash
(Cat. No. 312)

105. A GROUP OF MEN . Watercolour (Cat. No. 243)

106. A GROUP FOR THE "NORTH TERRACE LOOKING WEST"
Watercolour (Cat. No. 242)

107. A GIRL STANDING BY A CHAIR
Watercolour (Cat. No. 291)

108. "LADY LADD". Watercolour
(Cat. No. 301)

109. NEGRO SERVANT OF THE
DUKE OF CUMBERLAND
(Cat. No. 348)

110.   A LADY SEWING . Chalk and watercolour   (Cat. No. 282)

III. A GIRL, READING, BY A WINDOW . Watercolour (Cat. No. 286)

112. A LADY, SEATED . Chalk and wash
(Cat. No. 278)

113. TWO WOMEN AND TWO CHILDREN . Pen and wash   (Cat. No. 305)

114. "MISS ISHERWOODS THE BREWER'S DAUGHTERS" . Pencil and wash   (Cat. No. 300)

115.   A GIRL LEANING ON A BOY'S SHOULDER
Watercolour (Cat. No. 306)

116.   A GIRL SEATED AT A TABLE
Watercolour (Cat. No. 307)

117. A GIRL, SEEN FROM BEHIND
Pencil and brown wash (Cat. No. 311)

118. A YOUNG GIRL, SEATED . Chalk
(Cat. No. 299)

119. "THE LADIES WALDEGRAVE " . Pencil, pen and wash   (Cat. No. 296)

120.   A LADY CARRYING A KETTLE . Chalks and watercolour
(Cat. No. 289)

121. "MRS. EYRE" . Watercolour (Cat. No. 283)

122. A COUNTRY GIRL . Watercolour (Cat. No. 316)

123. "SAMUEL COTES, THE PAINTER" . Watercolour (Cat. No. 322)

124. "SIR HENRY ELWES, BART". Watercolour (Cat. No. 327)

125. A YOUNG MAN STANDING
Watercolour (Cat. No. 342)

126. A YOUNG OFFICER
Watercolour (Cat. No. 336)

127. A YOUNG MAN, ADVANCING
Watercolour (Cat. No. 340)

128. A YOUNG MAN TAKING SNUFF
Watercolour (Cat. No. 333)

129. "DAVID MORIER" . Watercolour (Cat. No. 326)

130. A MAN AT THE WATERGATE OF
SOMERSET HOUSE . Pen and wash (Cat. No. 339)

131. " MR. GANDON, ARCHITECT "
Watercolour (Cat. No. 323)

132. " JEFFERIES, MAP AND PRINT-SELLER OF
ST. MARTIN'S LANE " . Brown wash (Cat. No. 372)

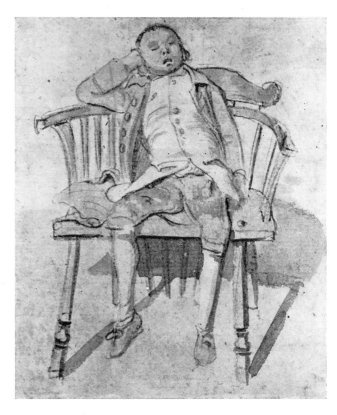

133. " GEORGE MORLAND, WHEN A BOY " . Brown and
grey wash (Cat. No. 373)

134. A HUNTSMAN . Brown wash (Cat. No. 369)

135. "MR. HOWSE" . Watercolour
(Cat. No. 329)

136. SIR WATKIN WILLIAMS WYNN . Brown wash
(Cat. No. 371)

137. TWO SOLDIERS SEATED . Pen and wash (Cat. No. 382)

138. A COACHMAN . Watercolour
(Cat. No. 354)

139. TWO COACHMEN . Grey wash
(Cat. No. 337)

140. "A STROLLING PLAYER AT LUTON AS MACBETH" . Watercolour
(Cat. No. 376)

141. "A STROLLING PLAYER AT LUTON AS HAMLET" . Watercolour (Cat. No. 375)

142. THE DUKE OF CUMBERLAND AND GENTLEMEN AT THE GREAT LODGE . Watercolour (Cat. No. 385)

143. BARNARD SMITH LUNGING A COLT AT THE GREAT LODGE . Watercolour (Cat. No. 386)

144. THE NEW NORTH FACE OF THE GREAT LODGE WITH BARNARD SMITH LUNGING A COLT, ETC. . Watercolour
(Detail of Cat. No. 102)

145. AN OPEN CARRIAGE, BELONGING TO THE DUKE OF CUMBERLAND
Grey wash (Cat. No. 401)

146.   A WAGGON BELONGING TO SIR W. W. WYNN . Watercolour (Cat. No. 404)

147. A COACH WITH TWO HORSES . Pencil
(Cat. No. 392)

148. A TRAVELLING CHARIOT OF THE DUKE OF
CUMBERLAND . Pencil (Cat. No. 394)

149. A CHARIOT IN THE YARD OF CUMBERLAND LODGE . Watercolour (Cat. No. 400)

150.   MARES IN A PADDOCK . Watercolour   (Cat. No. 391)

151.   "THE DAM OF GIMCRACK " . Watercolour
(Cat. No. 388)

152.   "THE DAM OF ECLIPSE " . Watercolour
(Cat. No. 389)

153. SPANIELS . Watercolour (Cat. No. 410)

154. A WOLF-HOUND . Watercolour (Cat. No. 415)

155. A SPANIEL AND TWO WOLF-HOUNDS
Watercolour (Cat. No. 411)

156. DOGS AND CATTLE . Watercolour (Cat. No. 416)

W. PARRY (1742-1791): PAUL SANDBY SKETCHING
Black chalk

INDEX

INDEX

Actors 375, 376
Adam, William 206
Albemarle, Lord . . . 102, 385
Arch, Triumphal 187
Architectural designs 121-146, 178, 186-190
Artists . . 230, 259, 339, 371, 417
Ascot Heath Races
      147; figure studies 251, 252
      King's Booth at . . . 148
Asgill, Sir Charles 417
Austin 417

Baillie, Captain 417
Baker, Mr. 417
Banks, Sir Joseph 417
      collection 12, 13, 16, 19, 20
      24, 25, 29-33, 37, 38, 41, 50, 51, 52
      54, 58, 59, 61, 72, References 1, 21
      42, 65, 83
Barbell, Mr. 417
Bateman, Hon. John (Richard) . 90
Baylis House 51
'Bell,' engraver . . . 208, 210
'Berry, Misses,' see Sandby, Misses of
      Norwich
'Boot and Blockhead,' The . . 204
Boydell 417
Bridge of Magnificence . . 186
      at Maidenhead . . . 197
      at Virginia Water . 115, 120
      at Windsor . 62-64, 76, 77, 200
Bridgnorth 199
British Museum (Montagu House) . 179
Buccleuch, Duke of, collection . 6, 58
'Buckhurst or Buckhorse' Welsh poet . 374

Camp scenes, including Encampments,
      see also Hyde Park 152-158, 169-185
Campaigns, Duke of Cumberland's 150-158
'Campbell, Capt. Archibald' . 243
Canterbury, The Great Gateway . 195
'Carrol, Susan' . . . 317
Cavallo, Dr. 53
'Chambers, Lady' . . 275-278
'Chambers, Sir Samuel' . . 208
Charlton, Kent, P. Sandby's house at . 191
Cheesecake House in Hyde Park 183, 184
Churchill, Lady Mary . . 13, 290
Clark, Miss 242
'Clarke, Sir John', see Clerk
'Clayton, Lady' . . . 265
Clerk, John, of Eldin . . 206
Coaches or carts 20, 23-25, 99, 100, 119
      392-406, 392-406, see also 20, 23-
      25, 99, 100, 119
Coachmen 337, 346, 349, 352, 353, 354, 356
      392
'Collins, Martha' . . . 320
Collins, Richard . . . 417
Combes, Mr. 417
Comet of 1783 53
Compositions . 87, 88, 97, 104, 112, 113, 149
Copley (J. S.) 417
Cosway, R. 417
'Cotes, Samuel' . . . 322
Covent Garden Piazza . . 164
'Cox Heath' 158
Cozens, J. R. 86
Culloden, Battle of, plan and sketch 150, 151
Cumberland, William Augustus Duke
      of . 98-102, 119, 120, 158, 204, 385
Cumberland livery . 252, 256, 348, 352

Davenport, Mr. 417
Davis the Smith . . . 243
'Deaken, Col.' (Deacon) . . 231
'Deley, Brig.-Gen. B.' . . 215

Diest 155
'Dineley, Sir John' . . 179, 236
Dogs . 410-416, see also 369-371
Donelly, see Dineley
Downman (J.) 417
Dun, see Nunn

Edward Augustus Duke of York, see
      York
Edinburgh . . 207, 219, 232
Elliott, Gideon 388
'Elliott, Miss,' see 'Lady Chambers'
'Elwes, Sir Henry' . . . 327
Encampments, 1780 . . 169-179
'Eyre, Mrs.' . . . 280, 283

F. Mark 1, 17, 21, 117, 220, 269, 271, 297
      384, 395, 397, 399, 407, see also 272
Fisher, Dr. John 39
'Fisher, Kitty' 258
Flitcroft, Henry . . . 120
Ford, Mr. 'Deputy Ranger' . 213
Forrest, T. 417
Fort Augustus . . . 152-154
Francklin or Franklin . . 209
Frederick, Duke of York, see York
Freemasons' Hall . . . 168

'Gandon, Mr.' . . 179, 323, 380
'Gandon, Mrs.' 287
George II 119
Gerard 417
Goodison 417
Gordon, Duchess of, see Maxwell
Graham, D. 417
Green, V. 417
Grimm, S. H. . . . 200-201
Grozier, (J.) 417

Hall, Engraver 417
'Harcourt, Lady Elizabeth' . 315
Hayman, F. . . 272, 274
Heriot's Hospital, Edinburgh . 219
Hertford, Lord 417
'Hervey, Mr.' 242
Holbein Gate, Whitehall . 165, 166
      — proposed adaptation . 167
Hone (N.) 417
Horses 385-392, see also 28, 52, 54, 57, 58
      59, 70-73, 101, 102, 147, 152, 153
'Howse, Mr.' . . 242, 329, 366
Humphry, Mr. 417
Huntsman and dog . . . 369
Hyde Park . . . 169-185(a)

Ingram, Capt. Bruce, collection . 288
Isherwood, Henry . 71, 106, 243, 300
      — Misses . . . 300

'Jefferies, Map & Printseller' . 372
Jones (J.) 417
Junk, Chinese . 117-119, 407-409

'Kenilworth' . . . 156, 157
Keppel, Laura 296
Kew Palace 160
Kirkcudbright, Lord . . . 205

'Ladd, Lady' 301
Lane, Mrs. 267
'Levison, J. W.' . . 324, 325
Lind, Dr. 53
Lockman, Dr. 53

London: see Somerset House, Whitehall,
      Covent Garden, Freemasons' Hall,
      Encampments, Leicester Square,
      Richmond, etc.

Magnificence, Bridge of . . . 186
Maidenhead Bridge . . . 197
'Marsden, Miss' 272
'Maxwell, Lady' 292
Meldart 155
'Mercier, Mrs.,' and sons . 257, 266
Middleton, see Myddleton
Miles (E.) 417
Military Knights of Windsor . 236
Molyneux, Hon. Sir R., collection 1, 21, 83
Montagu House 179
Moore, Mr. 417
'Morier, David' 326
'Morland, George' . . . 373
Munn, see Nunn
Myddleton, Miss . . . 205

Negro servant . . . 348
Netherlands, camps . 156, 157
Nine holes, game of . . 152
Nocturne . 36, 53, 60, 61
Northcote (J.) . . . 417
Norwich, Girl from . . 269-271
'Nunn, Robert' . . 212, 254

Officers . . . 332, 336
'Ord, Mr.' 328
Ormonde Lodge, Richmond . 159
Ostriches, Duke of Cumberland's . 99

Palmer, Mr. 417
Parsons, Rev. 417
Piazza, Covent Garden . . 164
Pillon, Mr. 417
Philippe 417
Poor Knights, see Military Knights of
      Windsor
Portarlington, Lord, House in Ireland 189
Powder Magazine, Hyde Park . 180, 181
Powel, Mr. 417
'Powell, Mr.' 229
Powney, Mr. 106
Princes and Princesses, drawings by . 79
Princess Royal, H.R.H., collection
      4, 8, 13, 31, 51
Prison scene 203

'Ramsay, Allan' . . . 214
Ratcatcher . . 36, 239
'Reynolds, Sir Joshua' . . 253
Rich, Sir Thomas . 102, 179, 385
Richards, Mr. 417
Richmond Lodge, see Ormonde
Rooker, M. A. . . 8, 116
Ruins in Windsor Park . 121 et seq.
Russell, Mr. Justice . . . 417

SANDBY family history 109, 189, 245, 274
      322, 371
      — Paul, his house at Charlton 191
      — Mrs. Paul . 191, 274
      — Misses, of Norwich . 288
Sandby, Thomas, drawings by 66-68, 78
      98-103, 109-115, 119, 121-141, 145
      148, 150-158, 163, 165-168, 186-190
      — and Paul, drawings by 120, 160, 164
      — drawings attributed to 142-144
      — supposed portraits of 102, 253, 385
      — his house in Windsor Great
      Park . . . 109

Sandpit Gate   212, 245, 246, 248, 249, 250
St. James's Park, encampment in .   178
Seabrook, W.   .   .   .   13, 61, 72
Servants and retainers: *see also* coach-
    men 237, 252, 254-256, 317, 318, 320
    348, 350, 351, 352, 369, 387
Slough   51
Smith, Barnard, or Barney
    101, 102, 385, 386
Smith, Mr.   418
Smith, J. R.   417
Soldiers: *see also* Camp scenes 20, 377-383
Somerset House and Gardens 161-163, 186
    figure studies   234, 240, 241, 244, 339
Stoke Place   51
Storer, A.   417
Strutt, J.   417
Sutler's Tent, Hyde Park.   .   .   169
Syon House   .   .   .   160, 160(a)

Terrace and Bowling Green   111, figure
    studies 231
Theatre in Leicester Square   .   .   188
Toussaint, A.   417
Tower in Course of Construction   .   190
Triumphal Arch   .   .   .   187
Turvill, Mr.   417

'Undertaker, An'   .   .   .   335

Venables, Miss   .   .   .   209
Violin player .   .   .   211, 220
'Voules, Bailiff'   .   .   .   255

'Waldegrave, the Ladies'   .   .   296
Waldron   417
Wales, Prince of   .   .   159, 160
'Wallace, Lady'   .   .   .   308
'Watson, Colonel David' .   .   242, 273
Whitbread, Mr., his gardener's wife .   321
Whitehall   .   .   .   165, 166
Whitford, Caleb   .   .   .   417
'Wild, Jonathan'   .   .   .   202
Willett (R.)   417
William Augustus Duke of Cumber-
    land, *see* Cumberland
Williams, I. A., collection   .   1, 51, 418
Wilson, Mr.   417

WINDSOR CASTLE

General Views

    Distant View   .   .   .   201
    North front .   .   62, 67, 68
    from Bishopsgate   .   .   86
        the Brocas   .   .   80
        Cranbourne Lodge   .   114
        Datchet Lane   .   60, 61, 69

WINDSOR CASTLE (*contd.*)

General views (*contd.*)

    from Eton   .   .   63-65, 74, 75
        the Goswells .   .   78, 79
        the Great Park   .   .   85
        the Home or Little Park
            52, 54-59
        Isherwoods Brewery   70-73
        the Long Walk   .   .   82
        Maestricht Pond   .   58
        Sheet Street   .   .   83,84
        the Slopes   .   .   56
        Spital Hill   .   .   81
        the Thames   .   .   62

Details

    GATES

    King's Gate *see* Rubbish Gate
    Henry VIII Gateway   .   23-29
    Norman Gate   .   .   11-14
    Queen Elizabeth's Gate .   21-24
    Rubbish Gate   .   16, 17, 38
    South Entrance   .   .   17
    Town Gate .   .   .   21-24

    TERRACES

    North Terrace looking West
        1-6, 53, 66-68; figure studies 221
        242
    North Terrace looking East
        7-10; figure studies 243
    Seat and View from the Terrace   51
    South Terrace   .   .   16

    TOWERS

    from Black Rod   .   .   39-44
        Curfew Tower   .   31-33
        Devil's *see* Maids of Honour
        Garter Tower   .   .   29
        Governor's Tower .   .   19 30
        Henry III Tower 18, 19, 34-37
            41, 43
        Julius Cæsar's, *see* Curfew
        Magazine Tower   .   11, 12
        Maids of Honour Tower 20, 39
            42
        Round Tower 10, 15, 34-36, 38
            40-44
        Salisbury Tower   .   23-25
        Store Tower, *see* Henry III
        Unidentified Tower   .   45
        Victoria Tower   .   54, 55
        Winchester Tower 1-6, 14, 43
            48-50
    Black Rod   .   .   .   39-44
    Canons' Houses   .   .   1-6
    Castle Hill   .   .   .   16
    Crane's Building   .   .   32
    Debtors' Prison   .   .   28
    Denton's Commons   .   .   46

WINDSOR CASTLE (*contd.*)

Details (*contd.*)

    Deputy Governor's House   .   11-13
    Engine House   .   .   .   60-64
    Equerries' Stables   .   .   49
    Garter Chamber   .   .   30
    Great Court, *see* Quadrangle
    Guard Room   .   .   .   34, 37
    Horseshoe Cloister   .   26, 31-33
    Hundred Steps .   .   .   47-50
    Lower Ward .   .   .   34-37
    Picture Gallery (project)   .   66-68
    Quadrangle   .   .   .   38, 42
    Queen Elizabeth's Gallery   1-5, 8, 9, 14
    — projected addition   .   66-68
    Queen's Lodge   .   16, 54, 55, 81, 82
    St. George's Chapel 26, 30-32, 37, 46, 76
    Singing Men's Cloister, *see* Horseshoe
    Star Chamber   .   .   .   7
    Tennis Court   .   .   .   54, 55

WINDSOR PARK

    Belvedere .   .   .   116, 120
    Bishopsgate   .   .   89, 106-108
    Cranbourne Lodge   .   87, 110-115
    Cumberland Lodge 98-103, 190, 400
    'Gamekeeper's Lodge'   .   .   105
    Great Lodge, *see* Cumberland Lodge
    Home Park   .   .   .   51, 52
    Manor Cottage .   .   .   90
    Manor Lodge   .   .   .   119
    Royal Lodge   .   .   95, 109
    Summerhouse   .   .   51, 59
    Virginia Water .   .   115-120
    Woodyard   .   .   .   91-96

WINDSOR TOWN

    Isherwood's Brewery .   .   71-73
    Windsor Bridge   .   62-64, 76, 77
    Windsor Poor Knights
        see Military Knights
    Windsor Uniform   .   2, 87, 159, 242
    Witt, Sir Robert, collection   .   272, 274
    Woodhall, Mr.   .   .   .   417
    Woodhouse, Mr.   .   .   .   417
    Woodland scenes and compositions 87, 88
        97, 104, 112, 113, 149
    Woolwich, Royal Military Academy .   192
        Park scenes   .   .   193, 194
    Wrexham, Gresford Lodge, near   .   198
    Wynn, Sir Watkin Williams   .   196, 371
    Wynnstay   196, 319, 371, 374, 404

    Yeoman, Mr.   .   .   .   242
    York, Edward Augustus Duke of   .   204
    York, Frederick Duke of .   .   159, 160
    'Yorick'   417

The numbers in this Index refer to the Catalogue and not to the Plates

THOMAS SANDBY, R.A., SILHOUETTE, JAMES LIND, M.P.